The World As I See It

Out of My Later Years

ALBERT EINSTEIN

The World As I See It

Translated by Alan Harris

Out of My Later Years

Quality Paperback Books   New York

THE WORLD AS I SEE IT

PREFACE TO ORIGINAL EDITION

Only individuals have a sense of responsibility.—NIETZSCHE.

THIS book does not represent a complete collection of the articles, addresses, and pronouncements of Albert Einstein; it is a selection made with a definite object—namely, to give a picture of a man. To-day this man is being drawn, contrary to his own intention, into the whirlpool of political passions and contemporary history. As a result, Einstein is experiencing the fate that so many of the great men of history experienced : his character and opinions are being exhibited to the world in an utterly distorted form.

To forestall this fate is the real object of this book. It meets a wish that has constantly been expressed both by Einstein's friends and by the wider public. It contains work belonging to the most various dates—the article on " The International of Science " dates from the year 1922, the address on " The Principles of Scientific Research " from 1923, the " Letter to an Arab " from 1930— and the most various spheres, held together by the unity of the personality which stands behind all these utterances. Albert Einstein believes in humanity, in a peaceful world of mutual helpfulness, and in the high mission of science. This book is intended as a plea for this belief at a time which compels every one of us to overhaul his mental attitude and his ideas.

J. H.

INTRODUCTION TO ABRIDGED EDITION

IN his biography of Einstein Mr. H. Gordon
Garbedian relates that an American newspaper man
asked the great physicist for a definition of his theory
of relativity in one sentence. Einstein replied that
it would take him three days to give a short
definition of relativity. He might well have added
that unless his questioner had an intimate acquaintance with mathematics and physics, the definition
would be incomprehensible.

To the majority of people Einstein's theory is a
complete mystery. Their attitude towards Einstein
is like that of Mark Twain towards the writer of a
work on mathematics : here was a man who had
written an entire book of which Mark could not
understand a single sentence. Einstein, therefore, is
great in the public eye partly because he has made
revolutionary discoveries which cannot be translated
into the common tongue. We stand in proper awe
of a man whose thoughts move on heights far beyond
our range, whose achievements can be measured only
by the few who are able to follow his reasoning and
challenge his conclusions.

There is, however, another side to his personality.
It is revealed in the addresses, letters, and occasional
writings brought together in this book. These frag-
ments form a mosaic portrait of Einstein the man.
Each one is, in a sense, complete in itself; it presents
his views on some aspect of progress, education,

peace, war, liberty, or other problems of universal interest. Their combined effect is to demonstrate that the Einstein we can all understand is no less great than the Einstein we take on trust.

Einstein has asked nothing more from life than the freedom to pursue his researches into the mechanism of the universe. His nature is of rare simplicity and sincerity; he always has been, and he remains, genuinely indifferent to wealth and fame and the other prizes so dear to ambition. At the same time he is no recluse, shutting himself off from the sorrows and agitations of the world around him. Himself familiar from early years with the handicap of poverty and with some of the worst forms of man's inhumanity to man, he has never spared himself in defence of the weak and the oppressed. Nothing could be more unwelcome to his sensitive and retiring character than the glare of the platform and the heat of public controversy, yet he has never hesitated when he felt that his voice or influence would help to redress a wrong. History, surely, has few parallels with this introspective mathematical genius who laboured unceasingly as an eager champion of the rights of man.

Albert Einstein was born in 1879 at Ulm. When he was four years old his father, who owned an electrochemical works, moved to Munich, and two years later the boy went to school, experiencing a rigid, almost military, type of discipline and also the isolation of a shy and contemplative Jewish child among Roman Catholics—factors which made a deep and enduring impression. From the point of view of his teachers he was an unsatisfactory pupil, apparently incapable of progress in languages, history, geography, and other primary subjects. His interest in mathematics was roused, not by his instructors, but by a Jewish medical student, Max Talmey, who gave him a book on geometry, and so set him upon a course of enthusiastic study which made him, at the age of fourteen, a better mathematician than his masters. At this stage also he began the study of philosophy, reading and re-reading the words of Kant and other metaphysicians.

Business reverses led the elder Einstein to make a fresh start in Milan, thus introducing Albert to the joys of a freer, sunnier life than had been possible in Germany. Necessity, however, made this holiday a brief one, and after a few months of freedom the preparation for a career began. It opened with an effort, backed by a certificate of mathematical proficiency given by a teacher in the Gymnasium at Munich, to obtain admission to the Polytechnic Academy at Zurich. A year passed in the study of necessary subjects which he had neglected for mathematics, but once admitted, the young Einstein became absorbed in the pursuit of science and philosophy and made astonishing progress. After five distinguished years at the Polytechnic he hoped to step into the post of assistant professor, but found that the kindly words of the professors who had stimulated the hope did not materialize.

Then followed a weary search for work, two brief interludes of teaching, and a stable appointment as examiner at the Confederate Patent Office at Berne. Humdrum as the work was, it had the double advantage of providing a competence and of leaving his mind free for the mathematical speculations which were then taking shape in the theory of relativity. In 1905 his first monograph on the theory was published in a Swiss scientific journal, the *Annalen der Physik*. Zurich awoke to the fact that it possessed a genius in the form of a patent office clerk, promoted him to be a lecturer at the University and four years later—in 1909—installed him as Professor.

His next appointment was (in 1911) at the University of Prague, where he remained for eighteen months. Following a brief return to Zurich, he went, early in 1914, to Berlin as a professor in the Prussian Academy of Sciences and director of the Kaiser Wilhelm Institute for Theoretical Physics. The period of the Great War was a trying time for Einstein, who could not conceal his ardent pacifism, but he found what solace he could in his studies. Later events brought him into the open and into many parts of the world, as an exponent not only of pacifism but also of world-disarmament and the cause of Jewry. To a man of such views, as passionately held as they were by Einstein, Germany under the Nazis was patently impossible. In 1933 Einstein made his famous declaration : " As long as I have any choice, I will stay only in a country where political liberty, toleration, and equality of all citizens before the law are the rule." For a time he was a homeless exile; after offers had come to him from Spain and France and Britain, he settled in Princeton as Professor of Mathematical and Theoretical Physics, happy in his work, rejoicing in a free environment, but haunted always by the tragedy of war and oppression.

The World As I See It, in its original form, includes essays by Einstein on relativity and cognate subjects. For reasons indicated above, these have been omitted in the present edition; the object of this reprint is simply to reveal to the general reader the human side of one of the most dominating figures of our day.

CONTENTS

PART I

THE WORLD AS I SEE IT

xi

PART II
POLITICS AND PACIFISM

CONTENTS

PART III

GERMANY 1933

PART IV

THE JEWS

I
The World As I See It

The Meaning of Life

WHAT is the meaning of human life, or of organic life altogether? To answer this question at all implies a religion. Is there any sense then, you ask, in putting it? I answer, the man who regards his own life and that of his fellow-creatures as meaningless is not merely unfortunate but almost disqualified for life.

The World as I see it

What an extraordinary situation is that of us mortals! Each of us is here for a brief sojourn; for what purpose he knows not, though he sometimes thinks he feels it. But from the point of view of daily life, without going deeper, we exist for our fellow-men—in the first place for those on whose smiles and welfare all our happiness depends, and next for all those unknown to us personally with whose destinies we are bound up by the tie of sympathy. A hundred times every day I remind myself that my inner and outer life depend on the labours of other men, living and dead, and that I must exert myself in order to give in the same measure as I have received and am still receiving. I am strongly drawn to the simple life and am often oppressed by the feeling that I am engrossing an unnecessary amount of the labour of my fellow-men. I regard class differences as contrary to justice and, in the last resort, based on force.   I also consider that plain living is good for everybody, physically and mentally.

In human freedom in the philosophical sense I am definitely a disbeliever.   Everybody acts not only under external compulsion but also in accordance with inner necessity.   Schopenhauer's saying, that " a man can do as he will, but not will as he will," has been an inspiration to me since my youth up, and a continual consolation and unfailing well-spring of patience in the face of the hardships of life, my own and others'.   This feeling mercifully mitigates the sense of responsibility which so easily becomes paralysing, and it prevents us from taking ourselves and other people too seriously; it conduces to a view of life in which humour, above all, has its due place.

To inquire after the meaning or object of one's own existence or of creation generally has always seemed to me absurd from an objective point of view.   And yet everybody has certain ideals which determine the direction of his endeavours and his judgments.   In this sense I have never looked upon ease and happiness as ends in themselves—such an ethical basis I call more proper for a herd of swine.   The ideals which have lighted me on my way and time after time given me new courage to face life cheerfully, have been Truth, Goodness, and Beauty.   Without the sense of fellowship with men of like mind, of preoccupation with the objective, the eternally unattainable in the field of art and scientific research, life would have seemed to me empty.   The ordinary objects of human endeavour—property, outward success, luxury— have always seemed to me contemptible.

My passionate sense of social justice and social

responsibility has always contrasted oddly with
my pronounced freedom from the need for direct
contact with other human beings and human communities. I gang my own gait and have never belonged to my country, my home, my friends, or
even my immediate family, with my whole heart;
in the face of all these ties I have never lost an
obstinate sense of detachment, of the need for
solitude—a feeling which increases with the years.
One is sharply conscious, yet without regret, of the
limits to the possibility of mutual understanding
and sympathy with one's fellow-creatures. Such
a person no doubt loses something in the way of
geniality and light-heartedness; on the other
hand, he is largely independent of the opinions,
habits, and judgments of his fellows and avoids the
temptation to take his stand on such insecure
foundations.

My political ideal is that of democracy. Let
every man be respected as an individual and no
man idolized. It is an irony of fate that I myself
have been the recipient of excessive admiration
and respect from my fellows through no fault, and
no merit, of my own. The cause of this may well
be the desire, unattainable for many, to understand the one or two ideas to which I have with
my feeble powers attained through ceaseless
struggle. I am quite aware that it is necessary
for the success of any complex undertaking that
one man should do the thinking and directing and
in general bear the responsibility. But the led
must not be compelled, they must be able to choose
their leader. An autocratic system of coercion, in
my opinion, soon degenerates. For force always
attracts men of low morality, and I believe it to be
an invariable rule that tyrants of genius are suc-

ceeded by scoundrels. For this reason I have always been passionately opposed to systems such as we see in Italy and Russia to-day. The thing that has brought discredit upon the prevailing form of democracy in Europe to-day is not to be laid to the door of the democratic idea as such, but to lack of stability on the part of the heads of governments and to the impersonal character of the electoral system. I believe that in this respect the United States of America have found the right way. They have a responsible President who is elected for a sufficiently long period and has sufficient powers to be really responsible. On the other hand, what I value in our political system is the more extensive provision that it makes for the individual in case of illness or need. The really valuable thing in the pageant of human life seems to me not the State but the creative, sentient individual, the personality; it alone creates the noble and the sublime, while the herd as such remains dull in thought and dull in feeling.

This topic brings me to that worst outcrop of the herd nature, the military system, which I abhor. That a man can take pleasure in marching in formation to the strains of a band is enough to make me despise him. He has only been given his big brain by mistake; a backbone was all he needed. This plague-spot of civilization ought to be abolished with all possible speed. Heroism by order, senseless violence, and all the pestilent nonsense that goes by the name of patriotism—how I hate them! War seems to me a mean, contemptible thing: I would rather be hacked in pieces than take part in such an abominable business. And yet so high, in spite of everything, is my opinion of the human race that I believe this

bogey would have disappeared long ago, had the
sound sense of the nations not been systematically
corrupted by commercial and political interests
acting through the schools and the Press.

The fairest thing we can experience is the mysterious. It is the fundamental emotion which
stands at the cradle of true art and true science.
He who knows it not and can no longer wonder, no
longer feel amazement, is as good as dead, a
snuffed-out candle. It was the experience of
mystery—even if mixed with fear—that engendered religion. A knowledge of the existence
of something we cannot penetrate, of the manifestations of the profoundest reason and the most
radiant beauty, which are only accessible to our
reason in their most elementary forms—it is this
knowledge and this emotion that constitute the
truly religious attitude; in this sense, and in this
alone, I am a deeply religious man. I cannot conceive of a God who rewards and punishes his
creatures, or has a will of the type of which we are
conscious in ourselves. An individual who should
survive his physical death is also beyond my comprehension, nor do I wish it otherwise; such
notions are for the fears or absurd egoism of feeble
souls. Enough for me the mystery of the eternity
of life, and the inkling of the marvellous structure
of reality, together with the single-hearted endeavour to comprehend a portion, be it never so
tiny, of the reason that manifests itself in nature.

The Liberty of Doctrine—à propos of the Gumbel Case

Academic chairs are many, but wise and noble
teachers are few; lecture-rooms are numerous and
large, but the number of young people who
genuinely thirst after truth and justice is small.

Nature scatters her common wares with a lavish hand, but the choice sort she produces but seldom.

We all know that, so why complain? Was it not ever thus and will it not ever thus remain? Certainly, and one must take what Nature gives as one finds it. But there is also such a thing as a spirit of the times, an attitude of mind character-istic of a particular generation, which is passed on from individual to individual and gives a society its particular tone. Each of us has to do his little bit towards transforming this spirit of the times.

Compare the spirit which animated the youth in our universities a hundred years ago with that prevailing to-day. They had faith in the ameli-oration of human society, respect for every honest opinion, the tolerance for which our classics had lived and fought. In those days men strove for a larger political unity, which at that time was called Germany. It was the students and the teachers at the universities who kept these ideals alive.

To-day also there is an urge towards social progress, towards tolerance and freedom of thought, towards a larger political unity, which we to-day call Europe. But the students at our universities have ceased as completely as their teachers to enshrine the hopes and ideals of the nation. Anyone who looks at our times coolly and dispassionately must admit this.

We are assembled to-day to take stock of our-selves. The external reason for this meeting is the Gumbel case. This apostle of justice has written about unexpiated political crimes with devoted industry, high courage, and exemplary fairness, and has done the community a signal service by his books. And this is the man whom

the students, and a good many of the staff, of his
university are to-day doing their best to expel.

Political passion cannot be allowed to go to
such lengths. I am convinced that every man
who reads Herr Gumbel's books with an open
mind will get the same impression from them as
I have. Men like him are needed if we are ever to
build up a healthy political society.

Let every man judge according to his own
standards, by what he has himself read, not by
what others tell him.

If that happens, this Gumbel case, after an
unedifying beginning, may still do good.

Good and Evil

It is right in principle that those should be the
best loved who have contributed most to the
elevation of the human race and human life.
But, if one goes on to ask who they are, one finds
oneself in no inconsiderable difficulties. In the
case of political, and even of religious, leaders, it
is often very doubtful whether they have done
more good or harm. Hence I most seriously
believe that one does people the best service by
giving them some elevating work to do and thus
indirectly elevating them. This applies most of
all to the great artist, but also in a lesser degree
to the scientist. To be sure, it is not the fruits of
scientific research that elevate a man and enrich
his nature, but the urge to understand, the intellectual work, creative or receptive. It would
surely be absurd to judge the value of the Talmud,
for instance, by its intellectual fruits.

The true value of a human being is determined
primarily by the measure and the sense in

which he has attained to liberation from the
self.

Society and Personality

When we survey our lives and endeavours we
soon observe that almost the whole of our actions
and desires are bound up with the existence of
other human beings. We see that our whole
nature resembles that of the social animals. We
eat food that others have grown, wear clothes that
others have made, live in houses that others have
built. The greater part of our knowledge and
beliefs has been communicated to us by other
people through the medium of a language which
others have created. Without language our
mental capacities would be poor indeed, comparable to those of the higher animals; we have,
therefore, to admit that we owe our principal
advantage over the beasts to the fact of living in
human society. The individual, if left alone
from birth, would remain primitive and beast-like
in his thoughts and feelings to a degree that we
can hardly conceive. The individual is what he
is and has the significance that he has not so much
in virtue of his individuality, but rather as a
member of a great human society, which directs
his material and spiritual existence from the
cradle to the grave.

A man's value to the community depends primarily on how far his feelings, thoughts, and
actions are directed towards promoting the good
of his fellows. We call him good or bad according to how he stands in this matter. It looks
at first sight as if our estimate of a man depended
entirely on his social qualities.

And yet such an attitude would be wrong. It

is clear that all the valuable things, material, spiritual, and moral, which we receive from society can be traced back through countless generations to certain creative individuals. The use of fire, the cultivation of edible plants, the steam engine—each was discovered by one man.

Only the individual can think, and thereby create new values for society—nay, even set up new moral standards to which the life of the community conforms. Without creative, independently thinking and judging personalities the upward development of society is as unthinkable as the development of the individual personality without the nourishing soil of the community.

The health of society thus depends quite as much on the independence of the individuals composing it as on their close political cohesion. It has been said very justly that Græco-Europeo-American culture as a whole, and in particular its brilliant flowering in the Italian Renaissance, which put an end to the stagnation of mediæval Europe, is based on the liberation and comparative isolation of the individual.

Let us now consider the times in which we live. How does society fare, how the individual? The population of the civilized countries is extremely dense as compared with former times; Europe to-day contains about three times as many people as it did a hundred years ago. But the number of great men has decreased out of all proportion. Only a few individuals are known to the masses as personalities, through their creative achievements. Organization has to some extent taken the place of the great man, particularly in the technical sphere, but also to a very perceptible extent in the scientific.

The lack of outstanding figures is particularly striking in the domain of art. Painting and music have definitely degenerated and largely lost their popular appeal. In politics not only are leaders lacking, but the independence of spirit and the sense of justice of the citizen have to a great extent declined. The democratic, parliamentarian regime, which is based on such independence, has in many places been shaken, dictatorships have sprung up and are tolerated, because men's sense of the dignity and the rights of the individual is no longer strong enough. In two weeks the sheep-like masses can be worked up by the newspapers into such a state of excited fury that the men are prepared to put on uniform and kill and be killed, for the sake of the worthless aims of a few interested parties. Compulsory military service seems to me the most disgraceful symptom of that deficiency in personal dignity from which civilized mankind is suffering to-day. No wonder there is no lack of prophets who prophesy the early eclipse of our civilization. I am not one of these pessimists; I believe that better times are coming. Let me shortly state my reasons for such confidence.

In my opinion, the present symptoms of decadence are explained by the fact that the development of industry and machinery has made the struggle for existence very much more severe, greatly to the detriment of the free development of the individual. But the development of machinery means that less and less work is needed from the individual for the satisfaction of the community's needs. A planned division of labour is becoming more and more of a crying necessity, and this division will lead to the material security of the individual. This security and the spare time and energy which the individual will have at his command can be made to further his development. In this way the community may regain its health, and we will hope that future historians will explain the morbid symptoms of present-day society as the childhood ailments of an aspiring humanity, due entirely to the excessive speed at which civilization was advancing.

Address at the Grave of H. A. Lorentz

It is as the representative of the German-speaking academic world, and in particular the Prussian Academy of Sciences, but above all as a pupil and affectionate admirer that I stand at the grave of the greatest and noblest man of our times. His genius was the torch which lighted the way from the teachings of Clerk Maxwell to the achievements of contemporary physics, to the fabric of which he contributed valuable materials and methods.

His life was ordered like a work of art down to the smallest detail. His never-failing kindness and magnanimity and his sense of justice, coupled with an intuitive understanding of people and things, made him a leader in any sphere he entered. Everyone followed him gladly, for they felt that he never set out to dominate but always simply to be of use. His work and his example will live on as an inspiration and guide to future generations.

H. A. Lorentz's work in the cause of International Co-operation

With the extensive specialization of scientific research which the nineteenth century brought about, it has become rare for a man occupying a leading position in one of the sciences to manage at the same time to do valuable service to the community in the sphere of international organization and international politics. Such service demands not only energy, insight, and a reputation based on solid achievements, but also a freedom from national prejudice and a devotion to the common ends of all, which have become rare in our times. I have met no one who combined all these qualities in himself so perfectly as H. A. Lorentz. The marvellous thing about the effect of his personality was this : Independent and headstrong natures, such as are particularly common among men of learning, do not readily bow to another's will and for the most part only accept his leadership grudgingly. But, when Lorentz is in the presidential chair, an atmosphere of happy co-operation is invariably created, however much those present may differ in their aims and habits of thought. The secret of this success lies not only in his swift comprehension of people and things and his marvellous command of language, but above all in this, that one feels that his whole heart is in the business in hand, and that, when he is at work, he has room for nothing else in his mind. Nothing disarms the recalcitrant so much as this.

Before the war Lorentz's activities in the cause of international relations were confined to presiding at congresses of physicists. Particularly noteworthy among these were the Solvay Congresses, the first two of which were held at Brussels in 1909 and 1912. Then came the European war, which was a crushing blow to all who had the improvement of human relations in general at heart. Even before the war was over, and still more after its end, Lorentz devoted himself to the work of reconciliation. His efforts were especially directed towards the re-establishment of fruitful and friendly co-operation between men of learning and scientific societies. An outsider can hardly conceive what uphill work this is. The accumulated resentment of the war period has not yet died down, and many influential men persist in the irreconcilable attitude into which they allowed themselves to be driven by the pressure of circumstances. Hence Lorentz's efforts resemble those of a doctor with a recalcitrant patient who refuses to take the medicines carefully prepared for his benefit.

But Lorentz is not to be deterred, once he has recognized a course of action as the right one. The moment the war was over, he joined the governing body of the " Conseil de recherche," which was founded by the savants of the victorious countries, and from which the savants and learned societies of the Central Powers were excluded. His object in taking this step, which caused great offence to the academic world of the Central Powers, was to influence this institution in such a way that it could be expanded into something truly international. He and other right-minded men succeeded, after repeated efforts, in securing the removal of the offensive exclusion-clause from the statutes of the " Conseil." The goal, which is the restoration of normal and fruitful co-operation between learned societies, is, however, not yet attained, because the academic world of the Central Powers, exasperated by nearly ten years of exclusion from practically all international gatherings, has got into a habit of keeping itself to itself. Now, however, there are good grounds for hoping that the ice will soon be broken, thanks to the tactful efforts of Lorentz, prompted by pure enthusiasm for the good cause.

Lorentz has also devoted his energies to the service of international cultural ends in another way, by consenting to serve on the League of Nations Commission for international intellectual co-operation, which was called into existence some five years ago with Bergson as chairman. For the last year Lorentz has presided over the Commission, which, with the active support of its subordinate, the Paris Institute, is to act as a go-between in the domain of intellectual and artistic work among the various spheres of culture. There too the beneficent influence of this intelligent, humane, and modest personality, whose unspoken but faithfully followed advice is, " Not mastery but service," will lead people in the right way.

May his example contribute to the triumph of that spirit !

In Honour of Arnold Berliner's Seventieth Birthday

(Arnold Berliner is the editor of the periodical *Die Naturwissenschaften*.)

I should like to take this opportunity of telling my friend Berliner and the readers of this paper why I rate him and his work so highly. It has to be done here because it is one's only chance of getting such things said; since our training in objectivity has led to a taboo on everything personal, which we mortals may transgress only on quite exceptional occasions such as the present one.

And now, after this dash for liberty, back to the objective! The province of scientifically determined fact has been enormously extended, theoretical knowledge has become vastly more profound in every department of science. But the assimilative power of the human intellect is and remains strictly limited. Hence it was inevitable that the activity of the individual investigator should be confined to a smaller and smaller section of human knowledge. Worse still, as a result of this specialization, it is becoming increasingly difficult for even a rough general grasp of science as a whole, without which the true spirit of research is inevitably handicapped, to keep pace with progress. A situation is developing similar to the one symbolically represented in the Bible by the story of the Tower of Babel. Every serious scientific worker is painfully conscious of this involuntary relegation to an ever-narrowing sphere of knowledge, which is threatening to deprive the investigator of his broad horizon and degrade him to the level of a mechanic.

We have all suffered under this evil, without making any effort to mitigate it. But Berliner has come to the rescue, as far as the German-speaking world is concerned, in the most admirable way. He saw that the existing popular periodicals were sufficient to instruct and stimulate the layman; but he also saw that a first-class, well-edited organ was needed for the guidance of the scientific worker who desired to be put sufficiently *au courant* of developments in scientific problems, methods, and results to be able to form a judgment of his own. Through many years of hard work he has devoted himself to this object with great intelligence and no less great determination, and done us all, and science, a service for which we cannot be too grateful.

It was necessary for him to secure the co-operation of successful scientific writers and induce them to say what they had to say in a form as far as possible intelligible to non-specialists. He has often told me of the fights he had in pursuing this object, the difficulties of which he once described to me in the following riddle : Question : What is a scientific author? Answer : A cross between a mimosa and a porcupine.[1] Berliner's achievement would have been impossible but for the peculiar intensity of his longing for a clear, comprehensive view of the largest possible area of scientific country. This feeling also drove him to produce a text-book of physics, the fruit of many years of strenuous work, of which a medical student said to me the other day : " I don't know how I should ever have got a clear idea of the principles of modern physics in the time at my disposal without this book."

Berliner's fight for clarity and comprehensiveness of outlook has done a great deal to bring the problems, methods, and results of science home to many people's minds. The scientific life of our time is simply inconceivable without his paper. It is just as important to make knowledge live and to keep it alive as to solve specific problems. We are all conscious of what we owe to Arnold Berliner.

Popper-Lynkæus was more than a brilliant engineer and writer. He was one of the few out-

---

[1] Do not be angry with me for this indiscretion, my dear Berliner. A serious-minded man enjoys a good laugh now and then.

standing personalities who embody the conscience of a generation. He has drummed it into us that society is responsible for the fate of every individual and shown us a way to translate the consequent obligation of the community into fact. The community or State was no fetish to him; he based its right to demand sacrifices of the individual entirely on its duty to give the individual personality a chance of harmonious development.

Obituary of the Surgeon, M. Katzenstein

During the eighteen years I spent in Berlin I had few close friends, and the closest was Professor Katzenstein. For more than ten years I spent my leisure hours during the summer months with him, mostly on his delightful yacht. There we confided our experiences, ambitions, emotions to each other. We both felt that this friendship was not only a blessing because each understood the other, was enriched by him, and found in him that responsive echo so essential to anybody who is truly alive; it also helped to make both of us more independent of external experience, to objectivize it more easily.

I was a free man, bound neither by many duties nor by harassing responsibilities; my friend, on the contrary, was never free from the grip of urgent duties and anxious fears for the fate of those in peril. If, as was invariably the case, he had performed some dangerous operations in the morning, he would ring up on the telephone, immediately before we got into the boat, to en-quire after the condition of the patients about whom he was worried; I could see how deeply concerned he was for the lives entrusted to his care. It was marvellous that this shackled outward existence did not clip the wings of his soul; his imagination and his sense of humour were irrepressible. He never became the typical conscientious North German, whom the Italians in the days of their freedom used to call *bestia seriosa*. He was sensitive as a youth to the tonic beauty of the lakes and woods of Brandenburg, and as he sailed the boat with an expert hand through these beloved and familiar surroundings he opened the secret treasure-chamber of his heart to me—he spoke of his experiments, scientific ideas, and ambitions. How he found time and energy for them was always a mystery to me; but the passion for scientific enquiry is not to be crushed by any burdens. The man who is possessed with it perishes sooner than it does.

There were two types of problems that engaged his attention. The first forced itself on him out of the necessities of his practice. Thus he was always thinking out new ways of inducing healthy muscles to take the place of lost ones, by ingenious transplantation of tendons. He found this remarkably easy, as he possessed an uncommonly strong spatial imagination and a remarkably sure feeling for mechanism. How happy he was when he had succeeded in making somebody fit for normal life by putting right the muscular system of his face, foot, or arm! And the same when he avoided an operation, even in cases which had been sent to him by physicians for surgical treatment (in cases of gastric ulcer by neutralizing the pepsin). He also set great store by the treatment of peritonitis by an anti-toxic coli-serum which he discovered, and rejoiced in the successes he achieved with it. In talking of it he often lamented the fact that this method of treatment was not endorsed by his colleagues.

The second group of problems had to do with the common conception of an antagonism between different sorts of tissue. He believed that he was here on the track of a general biological principle of widest application, whose implications he followed out with admirable boldness and persistence. Starting out from this basic notion he discovered that osteomyelon and periosteum prevent each other's growth if they are not separated from each other by bone. In this way he succeeded in explaining hitherto inexplicable cases of wounds failing to heal, and in bringing about a cure.

This general notion of the antagonism of the tissues, especially of epithelium and connective tissue, was the subject to which he devoted his scientific energies, especially in the last ten years of his life. Experiments on animals and a systematic investigation of the growth of tissues in a nutrient fluid were carried out side by side. How thankful he was, with his hands tied as they were by his duties, to have found such an admirable and infinitely enthusiastic fellow-worker in Fräulein Knake! He succeeded in securing wonderful results bearing on the factors which favour the growth of epithelium at the expense of that of connective tissue, results which may well be of decisive importance for the study of cancer. He also had the pleasure of inspiring his own son to become his intelligent and independent fellow-worker, and of exciting the warm interest and co-operation of Sauerbruch just in the last years of his life, so that he was able to die with the consoling thought that his life's work would not perish, but would be vigorously continued on the lines he had laid down.

I for my part am grateful to fate for having given me this man, with his inexhaustible goodness and high creative gifts, for a friend.

Congratulations to Dr. Solf

I am delighted to be able to offer you, Dr. Solf, the heartiest congratulations, the congratulations of Lessing College, of which you have become an indispensable pillar, and the congratulations of all who are convinced of the need for close contact between science and art and the public which is hungry for spiritual nourishment.

You have not hesitated to apply your energies to a field where there are no laurels to be won, but quiet, loyal work to be done in the interests of the general standard of intellectual and spiritual life, which is in peculiar danger to-day owing to a variety of circumstances. Exaggerated respect for athletics, an excess of coarse impressions which the complications of life through the technical discoveries of recent years has brought with it, the increased severity of the struggle for existence due to the economic crisis, the brutalization of political life—all these factors are hostile to the ripening of the character and the desire for real culture, and stamp our age as barbarous, materialistic, and superficial. Specialization in every sphere of intellectual work is producing an ever-widening gulf between the intellectual worker and the non-specialist, which makes it more difficult for the life of the nation to be fertilized and enriched by the achievements of art and science.

But contact between the intellectual and the masses must not be lost. It is necessary for the elevation of society and no less so for renewing the strength of the intellectual worker; for the flower of science does not grow in the desert. For this reason you, Herr Solf, have devoted a portion of your energies to Lessing College, and we are grateful to you for doing so. And we wish you further success and happiness in your work for this noble cause.

Of Wealth

I am absolutely convinced that no wealth in the world can help humanity forward, even in the hands of the most devoted worker in this cause. The example of great and pure characters is the only thing that can produce fine ideas and noble deeds. Money only appeals to selfishness and always tempts its owners irresistibly to abuse it.

Can anyone imagine Moses, Jesus, or Gandhi armed with the money-bags of Carnegie?

Education and Educators

A letter.

Dear Miss——,

I have read about sixteen pages of your manuscript and it made me—smile. It is clever, well observed, honest, it stands on its own feet up to a point, and yet it is so typically feminine, by which I mean derivative and vitiated by personal rancour. I suffered exactly the same treatment at the hands of my teachers, who disliked me for my independence and passed me over when they wanted assistants (I must admit that I was somewhat less of a model student than you). But it would not have been worth my while to write anything about my school life, still less would I have liked to be responsible for anyone's printing or actually reading it. Besides, one always cuts a poor figure if one complains about others who are struggling for their place in the sun too after their own fashion.

Therefore pocket your temperament and keep your manuscript for your sons and daughters, in order that they may derive consolation from it and—not give a damn for what their teachers tell them or think of them.

Incidentally I am only coming to Princeton to research, not to teach. There is too much education altogether, especially in American schools. The only rational way of educating is to be an example—of what to avoid, if one can't be the other sort.

With best wishes.

To the Schoolchildren of Japan

In sending this greeting to you Japanese school-children, I can lay claim to a special right to do so. For I have myself visited your beautiful country, seen its cities and houses, its mountains and woods, and in them Japanese boys who had learnt from them to love their country. A big fat book full of coloured drawings by Japanese children lies always on my table.

If you get my message of greeting from all this distance, bethink you that ours is the first age in history to bring about friendly and under-standing intercourse between people of different countries; in former times nations passed their lives in mutual ignorance, and in fact hated or feared one another. May the spirit of brotherly understanding gain ground more and more among them. With this in mind I, an old man, greet you Japanese schoolchildren from afar and hope that your generation may some day put mine to shame.

Teachers and Pupils

An address to children

(The principal art of the teacher is to awaken the joy in creation and knowledge.)

My dear Children,

I rejoice to see you before me to-day, happy youth of a sunny and fortunate land.

Bear in mind that the wonderful things you learn in your schools are the work of many generations, produced by enthusiastic effort and infinite labour in every country of the world. All this is put into your hands as your inheritance in order that you may receive it, honour it, add to it, and one day faithfully hand it on to your children. Thus do we mortals achieve immortality in the permanent things which we create in common.

If you always keep that in mind you will find a meaning in life and work and acquire the right attitude towards other nations and ages.

Paradise Lost

As late as the seventeenth century the savants and artists of all Europe were so closely united by the bond of a common ideal that co-operation between them was scarcely affected by political events. This unity was further strengthened by the general use of the Latin language.

To-day we look back at this state of affairs as at a lost paradise. The passions of nationalism have destroyed this community of the intellect, and the Latin language, which once united the whole world, is dead. The men of learning have become the chief mouthpieces of national tradition and lost their sense of an intellectual commonwealth.

Nowadays we are faced with the curious fact that the politicians, the practical men of affairs, have become the exponents of international ideas. It is they who have created the League of Nations.

Religion and Science

Everything that the human race has done and thought is concerned with the satisfaction of felt needs and the assuagement of pain. One has to keep this constantly in mind if one wishes to understand spiritual movements and their development. Feeling and desire are the motive forces behind all human endeavour and human creation, in however exalted a guise the latter may present itself to us. Now what are the feelings and needs that have led men to religious thought and belief in the widest sense of the words? A little consideration will suffice to show us that the most varying emotions preside over the birth of religious thought and experience. With primitive man it is above all fear that evokes religious notions—fear of hunger, wild beasts, sickness, death. Since at this stage of existence understanding of causal connexions is usually poorly developed, the human mind creates for itself more or less analogous beings on whose wills and actions these fearful happenings depend. One's object now is to secure the favour of these beings by carrying out actions and offering sacrifices which, according to the tradition handed down from generation to generation, propitiate them or make them well disposed towards a mortal. I am speaking now

of the religion of fear. This, though not created,
is in an important degree stabilized by the formation of a special priestly caste which sets up
as a mediator between the people and the beings
they fear, and erects a hegemony on this basis.
In many cases the leader or ruler whose position
depends on other factors, or a privileged class,
combines priestly functions with its secular
authority in order to make the latter more secure;
or the political rulers and the priestly caste make
common cause in their own interests.

The social feelings are another source of the
crystallization of religion. Fathers and mothers
and the leaders of larger human communities are
mortal and fallible. The desire for guidance, love,
and support prompts men to form the social or
moral conception of God. This is the God of
Providence who protects, disposes, rewards, and
punishes, the God who, according to the width
of the believer's outlook, loves and cherishes the
life of the tribe or of the human race, or even life
as such, the comforter in sorrow and unsatisfied
longing, who preserves the souls of the dead.
This is the social or moral conception of God.

The Jewish scriptures admirably illustrate the
development from the religion of fear to moral
religion, which is continued in the New Testament.
The religions of all civilized peoples, especially
the peoples of the Orient, are primarily moral
religions. The development from a religion of
fear to moral religion is a great step in a nation's
life. That primitive religions are based entirely
on fear and the religions of civilized peoples purely
on morality is a prejudice against which we must
be on our guard. The truth is that they are all
intermediate types, with this reservation, that on

the higher levels of social life the religion of morality predominates.

Common to all these types is the anthropomorphic character of their conception of God. Only individuals of exceptional endowments and exceptionally high-minded communities, as a general rule, get in any real sense beyond this level. But there is a third state of religious experience which belongs to all of them, even though it is rarely found in a pure form, and which I will call cosmic religious feeling. It is very difficult to explain this feeling to anyone who is entirely without it, especially as there is no anthropomorphic conception of God corresponding to it.

The individual feels the nothingness of human desires and aims and the sublimity and marvellous order which reveal themselves both in nature and in the world of thought. He looks upon individual existence as a sort of prison and wants to experience the universe as a single significant whole. The beginnings of cosmic religious feeling already appear in earlier stages of development— e.g., in many of the Psalms of David and in some of the Prophets. Buddhism, as we have learnt from the wonderful writings of Schopenhauer especially, contains a much stronger element of it.

The religious geniuses of all ages have been distinguished by this kind of religious feeling, which knows no dogma and no God conceived in man's image; so that there can be no Church whose central teachings are based on it. Hence it is precisely among the heretics of every age that we find men who were filled with the highest kind of religious feeling and were in many cases regarded by their contemporaries as Atheists,

sometimes also as saints. Looked at in this
light, men like Democritus, Francis of Assisi,
and Spinoza are closely akin to one another.

How can cosmic religious feeling be communicated from one person to another, if it can
give rise to no definite notion of a God and no
theology? In my view, it is the most important
function of art and science to awaken this feeling
and keep it alive in those who are capable of it.

We thus arrive at a conception of the relation of
science to religion very different from the usual
one. When one views the matter historically
one is inclined to look upon science and religion
as irreconcilable antagonists, and for a very
obvious reason. The man who is thoroughly
convinced of the universal operation of the law
of causation cannot for a moment entertain the
idea of a being who interferes in the course of
events—that is, if he takes the hypothesis of
causality really seriously. He has no use for the
religion of fear and equally little for social or
moral religion. A God who rewards and punishes
is inconceivable to him for the simple reason that
a man's actions are determined by necessity,
external and internal, so that in God's eyes
he cannot be responsible, any more than an
inanimate object is responsible for the motions it
goes through. Hence science has been charged
with undermining morality, but the charge is
unjust. A man's ethical behaviour should be
based effectually on sympathy, education, and
social ties; no religious basis is necessary. Man
would indeed be in a poor way if he had to be
restrained by fear and punishment and hope of
reward after death.

It is therefore easy to see why the Churches have

always fought science and persecuted its devotees. On the other hand, I maintain that cosmic religious feeling is the strongest and noblest incitement to scientific research. Only those who realize the immense efforts and, above all, the devotion which pioneer work in theoretical science demands, can grasp the strength of the emotion out of which alone such work, remote as it is from the immediate realities of life, can issue. What a deep conviction of the rationality of the universe and what a yearning to understand, were it but a feeble reflection of the mind revealed in this world, Kepler and Newton must have had to enable them to spend years of solitary labour in disentangling the principles of celestial mechanics ! Those whose acquaintance with scientific research is derived chiefly from its practical results easily develop a completely false notion of the mentality of the men who, surrounded by a sceptical world, have shown the way to those like-minded with themselves, scattered through the earth and the centuries. Only one who has devoted his life to similar ends can have a vivid realization of what has inspired these men and given them the strength to remain true to their purpose in spite of countless failures. It is cosmic religious feeling that gives a man strength of this sort. A contemporary has said, not unjustly, that in this materialistic age of ours the serious scientific workers are the only profoundly religious people.

The Religiousness of Science

You will hardly find one among the profounder sort of scientific minds without a peculiar religious feeling of his own. But it is different from the

religion of the naïve man.   For the latter God is
a being from whose care one hopes to benefit and
whose punishment one fears; a sublimation of a
feeling similar to that of a child for its father, a
being to whom one stands to some extent in a
personal relation, however deeply it may be tinged
with awe.

But the scientist is possessed by the sense of
universal causation.   The future, to him, is every
whit as necessary and determined as the past.
There is nothing divine about morality, it is a
purely human affair.   His religious feeling takes
the form of a rapturous amazement at the harmony
of natural law, which reveals an intelligence of
such superiority that, compared with it, all the
systematic thinking and acting of human beings
is an utterly insignificant reflection.   This feeling
is the guiding principle of his life and work, in so
far as he succeeds in keeping himself from the
shackles of selfish desire.   It is beyond question
closely akin to that which has possessed the
religious geniuses of all ages.

The Plight of Science

The German-speaking countries are menaced
by a danger to which those in the know are in
duty bound to call attention in the most emphatic
terms.   The economic stress which political events
bring in their train does not hit everybody equally
hard.   Among the hardest hit are the institutions
and individuals whose material existence depends
directly on the State.   To this category belong the
scientific institutions and workers on whose
work not merely the well-being of science but also
the position occupied by Germany and Austria
in the scale of culture very largely depends.

To grasp the full gravity of the situation it is necessary to bear in mind the following consideration. In times of crisis people are generally blind to everything outside their immediate necessities. For work which is directly productive of material wealth they will pay. But science, if it is to flourish, must have no practical end in view. As a general rule, the knowledge and the methods which it creates only subserve practical ends indirectly and, in many cases, not till after the lapse of several generations. Neglect of science leads to a subsequent dearth of intellectual workers able, in virtue of their independent outlook and judgment, to blaze new trails for industry or adapt themselves to new situations. Where scientific enquiry is stunted the intellectual life of the nation dries up, which means the withering of many possibilities of future development. This is what we have to prevent. Now that the State has been weakened as a result of non-political causes, it is up to the economically stronger members of the community to come to the rescue directly, and prevent the decay of scientific life.

Far-sighted men with a clear understanding of the situation have set up institutions by which scientific work of every sort is to be kept going in Germany and Austria. Help to make these efforts a real success. In my teaching work I see with admiration that economic troubles have not yet succeeded in stifling the will and the enthusiasm for scientific research. Far from it! Indeed, it looks as if our disasters had actually quickened the devotion to non-material goods. Everywhere people are working with burning enthusiasm in the most difficult circumstances.

See to it that the will-power and the talents of the
youth of to-day do not perish to the grievous hurt
of the community as a whole.

Fascism and Science

A letter to Signor Rocco, Minister of State, Rome.

My dear Sir,

Two of the most eminent and respected men of
science in Italy have applied to me in their
difficulties of conscience and requested me to
write to you with the object of preventing, if
possible, a piece of cruel persecution with which
men of learning are threatened in Italy. I refer
to a form of oath in which fidelity to the Fascist
system is to be promised. The burden of my
request is that you should please advise Signor
Mussolini to spare the flower of Italy's intellect
this humiliation.

However much our political convictions may
differ, I know that we agree on one point : in the
progressive achievements of the European mind
both of us see and love our highest good. Those
achievements are based on the freedom of thought
and of teaching, on the principle that the desire
for truth must take precedence of all other desires.
It was this basis alone that enabled our civilization
to take its rise in Greece and to celebrate its
rebirth in Italy at the Renaissance. This
supreme good has been paid for by the martyr's
blood of pure and great men, for whose sake
Italy is still loved and reverenced to-day.

Far be it from me to argue with you about
what inroads on human liberty may be justified
by reasons of State. But the pursuit of scientific
truth, detached from the practical interests of

everyday life, ought to be treated as sacred by every Government, and it is in the highest interests of all that honest servants of truth should be left in peace.   This is also undoubtedly in the interests of the Italian State and its prestige in the eyes of the world.

Hoping that my request will not fall on deaf ears, I am, etc.   A. E.

Interviewers

To be called to account publicly for everything one has said, even in jest, an excess of high spirits, or momentary anger, fatal as it must be in the end, is yet up to a point reasonable and natural. But to be called to account publicly for what others have said in one's name, when one cannot defend oneself, is indeed a sad predicament. " But who suffers such a dreadful fate ? " you will ask. Well, everyone who is of sufficient interest to the public to be pursued by interviewers. You smile incredulously, but I have had plenty of direct experience and will tell you about it.

Imagine the following situation.   One morning a reporter comes to you and asks you in a friendly way to tell him something about your friend N. At first you no doubt feel something approaching indignation at such a proposal. But you soon discover that there is no escape. If you refuse to say anything, the man writes : " I asked one of N.'s supposedly best friends about him. But he prudently avoided my questions. This in itself enables the reader to draw the inevitable conclusions." There is, therefore, no escape, and you give the following information : " Mr. N. is a cheerful, straightforward man, much liked by all his friends. He can find a bright side to any situation. His enterprise and industry know no bounds; his job takes up his entire energies. He is devoted to his family and lays everything he possesses at his wife's feet. . . ."

Now for the reporter's version : " Mr. N. takes nothing very seriously and has a gift for making himself liked, particularly as he carefully cultivates a hearty and ingratiating manner. He is so completely a slave to his job that he has no time for the considerations of any non-personal subject or for any mental activity outside it. He spoils his wife unbelievably and is utterly under her thumb. . . ."

A real reporter would make it much more spicy, but I expect this will be enough for you and your friend N. He reads this, and some more like it, in the paper next morning, and his rage against you knows no bounds, however cheerful and benevolent his natural disposition may be. The injury done to him gives you untold pain, especially as you are really fond of him.

What's your next step, my friend? If you know, tell me quickly, so that I may adopt your method with all speed.

Thanks to America

Mr. Mayor, Ladies, and Gentlemen,

The splendid reception which you have accorded to me to-day puts me to the blush in so far as it is meant for me personally, but it gives me all the more pleasure in so far as it is meant for me as a representative of pure science. For this gathering is an outward and visible sign that the world is no longer prone to regard material power and wealth as the highest goods. It is gratifying that men should feel an urge to proclaim this in an official way.

In the wonderful two months which I have been privileged to spend in your midst in this fortunate land, I have had many opportunities of observing what a high value men of action and of practical life attach to the efforts of science; a good few of them have placed a considerable proportion of their fortunes and their energies at the service of scientific enterprises and thereby contributed to the prosperity and prestige of this country.

I cannot let this occasion pass without referring in a spirit of thankfulness to the fact that American patronage of science is not limited by national frontiers. Scientific enterprises all over the civilized world rejoice in the liberal support of American institutions and individuals—a fact which is, I am sure, a source of pride and gratification to all of you.

These tokens of an international way of thinking and feeling are particularly welcome; for the world is to-day more than ever in need of international thinking and feeling by its leading nations and personalities, if it is to progress towards a better and more worthy future. I may be permitted to express the hope that this internationalism of the American nation, which proceeds from a high sense of responsibility, will very soon extend itself to the sphere of politics. For without the active co-operation of the great country of the United States in the business of regulating international relations, all efforts directed towards this important end are bound to remain more or less ineffectual.

I thank you most heartily for this magnificent

reception and, in particular, the men of learning
in this country for the cordial and friendly
welcome I have received from them. I shall
always look back on these two months with
pleasure and gratitude.

The University Course at Davos

Senatores boni viri, senatus autem bestia. So a
friend of mine, a Swiss professor, once wrote in
his irritable way to a university faculty which
had annoyed him. Communities tend to be less
guided than individuals by conscience and a
sense of responsibility. What a fruitful source
of suffering to mankind this fact is! It is the
cause of wars and every kind of oppression, which
fill the earth with pain, sighs, and bitterness.

And yet nothing truly valuable can be achieved
except by the unselfish co-operation of many
individuals. Hence the man of good will is never
happier than when some communal enterprise is
afoot and is launched at the cost of heavy sacrifices,
with the single object of promoting life and culture.

Such pure joy was mine when I heard about the
university courses at Davos. A work of rescue
is being carried out there, with intelligence and a
wise moderation, which is based on a grave need,
though it may not be a need that is immediately
obvious to everyone. Many a young man goes to
this valley with his hopes fixed on the healing
power of its sunny mountains and regains his
bodily health. But thus withdrawn for long
periods from the will-hardening discipline of
normal work and a prey to morbid reflection on
his physical condition, he easily loses the power
of mental effort and the sense of being able to hold
his own in the struggle for existence. He becomes

a sort of hot-house plant and, when his body is cured, often finds it difficult to get back to normal life. Interruption of intellectual training in the formative period of youth is very apt to leave a gap which can hardly be filled later.

Yet, as a general rule, intellectual work in moderation, so far from retarding cure, indirectly helps it forward, just as moderate physical work does. It is in this knowledge that the university courses are being instituted, with the object not merely of preparing these young people for a profession but of stimulating them to intellectual activity as such. They are to provide work, training, and hygiene in the sphere of the mind.

Let us not forget that this enterprise is admirably calculated to establish such relations between members of different nations as are favourable to the growth of a common European feeling. The effects of the new institution in this direction are likely to be all the more advantageous from the fact that the circumstances of its birth rule out every sort of political purpose. The best way to serve the cause of internationalism is by co-operating in some life-giving work.

From all these points of view I rejoice that the energy and intelligence of the founders of the university courses at Davos have already attained such a measure of success that the enterprise has outgrown the troubles of infancy. May it prosper, enriching the inner lives of numbers of admirable human beings and rescuing many from the poverty of sanatorium life !

Congratulations to a Critic

To see with one's own eyes, to feel and judge without succumbing to the suggestive power of the fashion of the day, to be able to express what one has seen and felt in a snappy sentence or even in a cunningly wrought word—is that not glorious? Is it not a proper subject for congratulation?

Greeting to G. Bernard Shaw

There are few enough people with sufficient independence to see the weaknesses and follies of their contemporaries and remain themselves untouched by them. And these isolated few usually soon lose their zeal for putting things to rights when they have come face to face with human obduracy. Only to a tiny minority is it given to fascinate their generation by subtle humour and grace and to hold the mirror up to it by the impersonal agency of art. To-day I salute with sincere emotion the supreme master of this method, who has delighted—and educated—us all.

Some Notes on my American Impressions

I must redeem my promise to say something about my impressions of this country. That is not altogether easy for me. For it is not easy to take up the attitude of an impartial observer when one is received with such kindness and undeserved respect as I have been in America. First of all let me say something on this head.

The cult of individual personalities is always, in my view, unjustified. To be sure, nature distributes her gifts variously among her children. But there are plenty of the well-endowed ones too, thank God, and I am firmly convinced that most of them live quiet, unregarded lives. It strikes me as unfair, and even in bad taste, to select a few of them for boundless admiration, attributing superhuman powers of mind and character to them. This has been my fate, and the contrast between the popular estimate of my powers and achievements and the reality is simply grotesque. The consciousness of this extraordinary state of affairs would be unbearable but for one great consoling thought : it is a welcome symptom in an age which is commonly denounced as materialistic, that it makes heroes of men whose ambitions lie wholly in the intellectual and moral sphere. This proves that knowledge and justice are ranked above wealth and power by a large section of the human race. My experience teaches me that this idealistic outlook is particularly prevalent in America, which is usually decried as a particularly materialistic country. After this digression I come to my proper theme, in the hope that no more weight will be attached to my modest remarks than they deserve.

What first strikes the visitor with amazement is the superiority of this country in matters of technics and organization. Objects of everyday use are more solid than in Europe, houses infinitely more convenient in arrangement. Everything is designed to save human labour. Labour is expensive, because the country is sparsely inhabited in comparison with its natural resources. The high price of labour was the stimulus which evoked the marvellous development of technical devices and methods of work. The opposite extreme is illustrated by over-populated China or India, where the low price of labour has stood in the way of the development of machinery. Europe is half-way between the two. Once the machine is sufficiently highly developed it becomes cheaper in the end than the cheapest labour. Let the Fascists in Europe, who desire on narrow-

minded political grounds to see their own particular countries more densely populated, take
heed of this. The anxious care with which the
United States keep out foreign goods by means of
prohibitive tariffs certainly contrasts oddly with
this notion. . . . But an innocent visitor must
not be expected to rack his brains too much, and,
when all is said and done, it is not absolutely
certain that every question admits of a rational
answer.

The second thing that strikes a visitor is the
joyous, positive attitude to life. The smile on
the faces of the people in photographs is symbolical
of one of the American's greatest assets. He is
friendly, confident, optimistic, and—without envy.
The European finds intercourse with Americans
easy and agreeable.

Compared with the American, the European is
more critical, more self-conscious, less good-
hearted and helpful, more isolated, more fastidious
in his amusements and his reading, generally
more or less of a pessimist.

Great importance attaches to the material
comforts of life, and peace, freedom from care,
security are all sacrificed to them. The American
lives for ambition, the future, more than the
European. Life for him is always becoming,
never being. In this respect he is even further
removed from the Russian and the Asiatic than
the European is. But there is another respect in
which he resembles the Asiatic more than the
European does : he is less of an individualist than
the European—that is, from the psychological,
not the economic, point of view.

More emphasis is laid on the " we " than the
" I." As a natural corollary of this, custom and

convention are very powerful, and there is much more uniformity both in outlook on life and in moral and æsthetic ideas among Americans than among Europeans. This fact is chiefly responsible for America's economic superiority over Europe. Co-operation and the division of labour are carried through more easily and with less friction than in Europe, whether in the factory or the university or in private good works. This social sense may be partly due to the English tradition.

In apparent contradiction to this stands the fact that the activities of the State are comparatively restricted as compared with Europe. The European is surprised to find the telegraph, the telephone, the railways, and the schools predominantly in private hands. The more social attitude of the individual, which I mentioned just now, makes this possible here. Another consequence of this attitude is that the extremely unequal distribution of property leads to no intolerable hardships. The social conscience of the rich man is much more highly developed than in Europe. He considers himself obliged as a matter of course to place a large portion of his wealth, and often of his own energies too, at the disposal of the community, and public opinion, that allpowerful force, imperiously demands it of him. Hence the most important cultural functions can be left to private enterprise, and the part played by the State in this country is, comparatively, a very restricted one.

The prestige of government has undoubtedly been lowered considerably by the Prohibitior laws. For nothing is more destructive of respect for the government and the law of the land than passing laws which cannot be enforced. It is an open secret that the dangerous increase of crime in this country is closely connected with this.

There is also another way in which Prohibition, in my opinion, has led to the enfeeblement of the State. The public-house is a place which gives people a chance to exchange views and ideas on public affairs. As far as I can see, people here have no chance of doing this, the result being that the Press, which is mostly controlled by definite interests, has an excessive influence over public opinion.

The over-estimation of money is still greater in this country than in Europe, but appears to me to be on the decrease. It is at last beginning to be realized that great wealth is not necessary for a happy and satisfactory life.

As regards artistic matters, I have been genuinely impressed by the good taste displayed in the modern buildings and in articles of common use; on the other hand, the visual arts and music have little place in the life of the nation as compared with Europe.

I have a warm admiration for the achievements of American institutes of scientific research. We are unjust in attempting to ascribe the increasing superiority of American research-work exclusively to superior wealth; zeal, patience, a spirit of comradeship, and a talent for co-operation play an important part in its successes. One more observation to finish up with. The United States is the most powerful technically advanced country in the world to-day. Its influence on the shaping of international relations is absolutely incalculable. But America is a large country and its people have so far not shown much interest in great international problems, among which the

problem of disarmament occupies first place to-
day. This must be changed, if only in the
essential interests of the Americans. The last
war has shown that there are no longer any
barriers between the continents and that the
destinies of all countries are closely interwoven.
The people of this country must realize that they
have a great responsibility in the sphere of international politics. The part of passive spectator
is unworthy of this country and is bound in the
end to lead to disaster all round.

Reply to the Women of America

An American Women's League felt called upon to
protest against Einstein's visit to their country. They
received the following answer.

Never yet have I experienced from the fair sex
such energetic rejection of all advances; or, if I
have, never from so many at once.

But are they not quite right, these watchful
citizenesses? Why should one open one's doors
to a person who devours hard-boiled capitalists
with as much appetite and gusto as the Cretan
Minotaur in days gone by devoured luscious Greek
maidens, and on top of that is low-down enough
to reject every sort of war, except the unavoidable
war with one's own wife? Therefore give heed
to your clever and patriotic women-folk and
remember that the Capitol of mighty Rome was
once saved by the cackling of its faithful geese.

II
Politics and Pacifism

Peace

THE importance of securing international peace was recognized by the really great men of former generations. But the technical advances of our times have turned this ethical postulate into a matter of life and death for civilized mankind to-day, and made the taking of an active part in the solution of the problem of peace a moral duty which no conscientious man can shirk.

One has to realize that the powerful industrial groups concerned in the manufacture of arms are doing their best in all countries to prevent the peaceful settlement of international disputes, and that rulers can achieve this great end only if they are sure of the vigorous support of the majority of their peoples. In these days of democratic government the fate of the nations hangs on themselves; each individual must always bear that in mind.

The Pacifist Problem

Ladies and Gentlemen,

I am very glad of this opportunity of saying a few words to you about the problem of pacificism. The course of events in the last few years has once more shown us how little we are justified in leaving the struggle against armaments and against the war spirit to the Governments. On the other hand, the formation of large organizations with a large membership can of itself bring us very little nearer to our goal. In my opinion, the best method in this case is the violent one of conscientious objection, with the aid of organizations for giving moral and material support to the courageous conscientious objectors in each country. In this way we may succeed in making the problem of pacificism an acute one, a real struggle which attracts forceful natures. It is an illegal struggle, but a struggle for people's real rights against their governments in so far as the latter demand criminal acts of the citizen.

Many who think themselves good pacifists will jib at this out-and-out pacifism, on patriotic grounds. Such people are not to be relied on in the hour of crisis, as the World War amply proved.

I am most grateful to you for according me an opportunity to give you my views in person.

Address to the Students' Disarmament Meeting

Preceding generations have presented us, in a highly developed science and mechanical knowledge, with a most valuable gift which carries with it possibilities of making our life free and beautiful such as no previous generation has enjoyed. But this gift also brings with it dangers to our existence as great as any that have ever threatened it.

The destiny of civilized humanity depends more than ever on the moral forces it is capable of generating. Hence the task that confronts our age is certainly no easier than the tasks our immediate predecessors successfully performed.

The foodstuffs and other goods which the world needs can be produced in far fewer hours of work than formerly. But this has made the problem of the division of labour and the distribution of the goods produced far more difficult. We all feel that the free play of economic forces, the unregulated and unrestrained pursuit of wealth and power by the individual, no longer leads automatically to a tolerable solution of these problems. Production, labour, and distribution need to be organized on a definite plan, in order to prevent valuable productive energies from being thrown away and sections of the population from becoming impoverished and relapsing into savagery. If unrestricted *sacro egoismo* leads to disastrous consequences in economic life, it is a still worse guide in international relations. The development of mechanical methods of warfare is such that human life will become intolerable if people do not before long discover a way of preventing war. The importance of this object is only equalled by the inadequacy of the attempts hitherto made to attain it.

People seek to minimize the danger by limitation of armaments and restrictive rules for the conduct of war. But war is not like a parlour-game in which the players loyally stick to the rules. Where life and death are at stake, rules and obligations go by the board. Only the absolute repudiation of all war is of any use here. The creation of an international court of arbitration is not enough. There must be treaties guaranteeing that the decisions of this court shall be made effective by all the nations acting in concert. Without such a guarantee the nations will never have the courage to disarm seriously.

Suppose, for example, that the American, English, German, and French Governments insisted on the Japanese Government's putting an immediate stop to their warlike operations in China, under pain of a complete economic boycott. Do you suppose that any Japanese Government would be found ready to take the responsibility of plunging its country into such a perilous adventure? Then why is it not done? Why must every individual and every nation tremble for their existence? Because each seeks his own wretched momentary advantage and refuses to subordinate it to the welfare and prosperity of the community.

That is why I began by telling you that the fate of the human race was more than ever dependent on its moral strength to-day. The way to a joyful and happy state is through renunciation and self-limitation everywhere.

Where can the strength for such a process come from? Only from those who have had the chance in their early years to fortify their minds and broaden their outlook through study. Thus we of the older generation look to you and hope that you will strive with all your might to achieve what was denied to us.

To Sigmund Freud

Dear Professor Freud,

It is admirable the way the longing to perceive the truth has overcome every other desire in you. You have shown with irresistible clearness how inseparably the combative and destructive instincts are bound up with the amative and vital ones in the human psyche. At the same time a deep yearning for that great consummation, the internal and external liberation of mankind from war, shines out from the ruthless logic of your expositions. This has been the declared aim of all those who have been honoured as moral and spiritual leaders beyond the limits of their own time and country without exception, from Jesus Christ to Goethe and Kant. Is it not significant that such men have been universally accepted as leaders, in spite of the fact that their efforts to mould the course of human affairs were attended with but small success?

I am convinced that the great men—those whose achievements, even though in a restricted sphere, set them above their fellows—are animated to an overwhelming extent by the same ideals. But they have little influence on the course of political events. It almost looks as if this domain, on which the fate of nations depends, had inevitably to be given over to violence and irresponsibility.

Political leaders or governments owe their position partly to force and partly to popular election. They cannot be regarded as representative of the best elements, morally and intellectually, in their respective nations. The intellectual *élite* have no direct influence on the history of nations in these days; their lack of cohesion prevents them from taking a direct part in the solution of contemporary problems. Don't you think that a change might be brought about in this respect by a free association of people whose work and achievements up to date constitute a guarantee of their ability and purity of aim? This international association, whose members would need to keep in touch with each other by a constant interchange of opinions, might, by defining its attitude in the Press—responsibility always resting with the signatories on any given occasion—acquire a considerable and salutary moral influence over the settlement of political questions. Such an association would, of course, be a prey to all the ills which so often lead to degeneration in learned societies, dangers which are inseparably bound up with the imperfection of human nature. But should not an effort in this direction be risked in spite of this? I look upon the attempt as nothing less than an imperative duty.

If an intellectual association of standing, such as I have described, could be formed, it would no doubt have to try to mobilize the religious organizations for the fight against war. It would give countenance to many whose good intentions are paralysed to-day by a melancholy resignation. Finally, I believe that an association formed of persons such as I have described, each highly esteemed in his own line, would be just the thing to give valuable moral support to those elements in the League of Nations which are really working for the great object for which that institution exists.

I had rather put these proposals to you than to anyone else in the world, because you are least of all men the dupe of your desires and because your critical judgment is supported by a most earnest sense of responsibility.

Compulsory Service
From a letter

Instead of permission being given to Germany to introduce compulsory service it ought to be taken away from everybody else : in future none but mercenary armies should be permitted, the size and equipment of which should be discussed at Geneva. This would be better for France than to have to permit compulsory service in Germany. The fatal psychological effect of the military education of the people and the violation of the individual's rights which it involves would thus be avoided.

Moreover, it would be much easier for two countries which had agreed to compulsory arbitration for the settlement of all disputes arising out of their mutual relations to combine their military establishments of mercenaries into a single organization with a mixed staff. This would mean a financial relief and increased security for both of them. Such a process of amalgamation might extend to larger and larger combinations, and finally lead to an " international police," which would be bound gradually to degenerate as international security increased.

Will you discuss this proposal with our friends by way of setting the ball rolling? Of course I do not in the least insist on this particular proposal. But I do think it essential that we should come forward with a positive programme; a merely negative policy is unlikely to produce any practical results.

Germany and France

Mutual trust and co-operation between France and Germany can come about only if the French demand for security against military attack is satisfied. But should France frame demands in accordance with this, such a step would certainly be taken very ill in Germany.

A procedure something like the following seems, however, to be possible. Let the German Government of its own free will propose to the French that they should jointly make representations to the League of Nations that it should suggest to all member States to bind themselves to the following :—

(1) To submit to every decision of the international court of arbitration.

(2) To proceed with all its economic and military force, in concert with the other members of the League, against any State which breaks the peace or resists an international decision made in the interests of world peace.

Arbitration

Systematic disarmament within a short period. This is possible only in combination with the guarantee of all for the security of each separate nation, based on a permanent court of arbitration independent of governments.

Unconditional obligation of all countries not merely to accept the decisions of the court of arbitration but also to give effect to them.

Separate courts of arbitration for Europe with Africa, America, and Asia (Australia to be apportioned to one of these). A joint court of arbitration for questions involving issues that cannot be settled within the limits of any one of these three regions.

The International of Science

At a sitting of the Academy during the War, at the time when national and political infatuation had reached its height, Emil Fischer spoke the following emphatic words : " It's no use, Gentlemen, science is and remains international." The really great scientists have always known this and felt it passionately, even though in times of political confusion they may have remained isolated among their colleagues of inferior calibre. In every camp during the War this mass of voters betrayed their sacred trust. The international society of the academies was broken up. Congresses were and still are held from which colleagues from ex-enemy countries are excluded. Political considerations, advanced with much solemnity, prevent the triumph of purely objective ways of thinking without which our great aims must necessarily be frustrated.

What can right-minded people, people who are proof against the emotional temptations of the moment, do to repair the damage? With the majority of intellectual workers still so excited, truly international congresses on the grand scale cannot yet be held. The psychological obstacles to the restoration of the international associations of scientific workers are still too formidable to be overcome by the minority whose ideas and feelings are of a more comprehensive kind. These last can aid in the great work of restoring the international societies to health by keeping in close touch with like-minded people all over the world and resolutely championing the international cause in their own spheres. Success on a large scale will take time, but it will undoubtedly come. I cannot let this opportunity pass without paying a tribute to the way in which the desire to preserve the confraternity of the intellect has remained alive through all these difficult years in the breasts of a large number of our English colleagues especially.

The disposition of the individual is everywhere better than the official pronouncements. Right-minded people should bear this in mind and not allow themselves to be misled and get angry: *senatores boni viri, senatus autem bestia.*

If I am full of confident hope concerning the progress of international organization in general, that feeling is based not so much on my confidence in the intelligence and high-mindedness of my fellows, but rather on the irresistible pressure of economic developments. And since these depend largely on the work even of reactionary scientists, they too will help to create the international organization against their wills.

The Institute for Intellectual Co-operation

During this year the leading politicians of Europe have for the first time drawn the logical conclusion from the truth that our portion of the globe can only regain its prosperity if the underground struggle between the traditional political units ceases. The political organization of Europe must be strengthened, and a gradual attempt made to abolish tariff barriers. This great end cannot be achieved by treaties alone. People's minds must, above all, be prepared for it. We must try gradually to awaken in them a sense of solidarity which does not, as hitherto, stop at frontiers. It is with this in mind that the League of Nations has created the *Commission de co-opération intellectuelle.* This Commission is to be an absolutely international and entirely non-political authority, whose business it is to put the intellectuals of all the nations, who were isolated by the war, into touch with each other. It is a difficult task; for it has, alas, to be admitted that—at least in the countries with which I am most closely acquainted—the artists and men of learning are governed by narrowly nationalist feelings to a far greater extent than the men of affairs.

Hitherto this Commission has met twice a year. To make its efforts more effective, the French Government has decided to create and maintain a permanent Institute for intellectual co-operation, which is just now to be opened. It is a generous act on the part of the French nation and deserves the thanks of all.

It is an easy and grateful task to rejoice and praise and say nothing about the things one regrets or disapproves of. But honesty alone can help our work forward, so I will not shrink from combining criticism with this greeting to the new-born child.

I have daily occasion for observing that the greatest obstacle which the work of our Commission has to encounter is the lack of confidence in its political impartiality. Everything must be done to strengthen that confidence and everything avoided that might harm it.

When, therefore, the French Government sets up and maintains an Institute out of public funds in Paris as a permanent organ of the Commission, with a Frenchman as its Director, the outside observer can hardly avoid the impression that French influence predominates in the Commission. This impression is further strengthened by the fact that so far a Frenchman has also been chairman of the Commission itself. Although the individuals in question are men of the highest reputation, liked and respected everywhere, nevertheless the impression remains.

Dixi et salvavi animam meam. I hope with all my heart that the new Institute, by constant interaction with the Commission, will succeed in promoting their common ends and winning the confidence and recognition of intellectual workers all over the world.

A Farewell

A letter to the German Secretary of the League of Nations

Dear Herr Dufour-Feronce,

Your kind letter must not go unanswered, otherwise you may get a mistaken notion of my attitude. The grounds for my resolve to go to Geneva no more are as follows : Experience has, unhappily, taught me that the Commission, taken as a whole, stands for no serious determination to make real progress with the task of improving international relations. It looks to me far more like an embodiment of the principle *ut aliquid fieri videatur*. The Commission seems to me even worse in this respect than the League taken as a whole.

It is precisely because I desire to work with all my might for the establishment of an international arbitrating and regulative authority *superior to the State*, and because I have this object so very much at heart, that I feel compelled to leave the Commission.

The Commission has given its blessing to the oppression of the cultural minorities in all countries by causing a National Commission to be set up in each of them, which is to form the only channel of communication between the intellectuals of a country and the Commission. It has thereby deliberately abandoned its function of giving moral support to the national minorities in their struggle against cultural oppression.

Further, the attitude of the Commission in the matter of combating the chauvinistic and militaristic tendencies of education in the various countries has been so lukewarm that no serious efforts in this fundamentally important sphere can be hoped for from it.

The Commission has invariably failed to give moral support to those individuals and associations who have thrown themselves without reserve into the business of working for an international order and against the military system.

The Commission has never made any attempt to resist the appointment of members whom it knew to stand for tendencies the very reverse of those it is bound in duty to foster.

I will not worry you with any further arguments, since you will understand my resolve well enough from these few hints. It is not my business to draw up an indictment, but merely to explain my position. If I nourished any hope whatever I should act differently—of that you may be sure.

The Question of Disarmament

The greatest obstacle to the success of the disarmament plan was the fact that people in general left out of account the chief difficulties of the problem. Most objects are gained by gradual steps : for example, the supersession of absolute monarchy by democracy. Here, however, we are concerned with an objective which cannot be reached step by step.

As long as the possibility of war remains, nations will insist on being as perfectly prepared militarily as they can, in order to emerge triumphant from the next war. It will also be impossible to avoid educating the youth in warlike traditions and cultivating narrow national vanity joined to the glorification of the warlike spirit, as long as people have to be prepared for occasions when such a spirit will be needed in the citizens for the purpose of war. To arm is to give one's voice and make one's preparations not for peace but for war. Therefore people will not disarm step by step; they will disarm at one blow or not at all.

The accomplishment of such a far-reaching change in the life of nations presupposes a mighty moral effort, a deliberate departure from deeply ingrained tradition. Anyone who is not prepared to make the fate of his country in case of a dispute depend entirely on the decisions of an international court of arbitration, and to enter into a treaty to this effect without reserve, is not really resolved to avoid war. It is a case of all or nothing.

It is undeniable that previous attempts to ensure peace have failed through aiming at inadequate compromises.

Disarmament and security are only to be had in combination. The one guarantee of security is an undertaking by all nations to give effect to the decisions of the international authority.

We stand, therefore, at the parting of the ways. Whether we find the way of peace or continue along the old road of brute force, so unworthy of our civilization, depends on ourselves. On the one side the freedom of the individual and the security of society beckon to us, on the other slavery for the individual and the annihilation of our civilization threaten us. Our fate will be according to our deserts.

The Disarmament Conference of 1932

I

May I begin with an article of political faith? It runs as follows : The State is made for man, not man for the State. And in this respect science resembles the State. These are old sayings, coined by men for whom human personality was the highest human good. I should shrink from repeating them, were it not that they are for ever threatening to fall into oblivion, particularly in these days of organization and mechanization. I regard it as the chief duty of the State to protect the individual and give him the opportunity to develop into a creative personality.

That is to say, the State should be our servant and not we its slaves. The State transgresses this commandment when it compels us by force to engage in military and war service, the more so since the object and the effect of this slavish service is to kill people belonging to other countries or interfere with their freedom of development. We are only to make such sacrifices to the State as will promote the free development of individual human beings. To any American all this may be a platitude, but not to any European. Hence we may hope that the fight against war will find strong support among Americans.

And now for the Disarmament Conference. Ought one to laugh, weep, or hope when one thinks of it? Imagine a city inhabited by fiery-tempered, dishonest, and quarrelsome citizens. The constant danger to life there is felt as a serious handicap which makes all healthy development impossible. The magistrate desires to remedy this abominable state of affairs, although all his counsellors and the rest of the citizens insist on continuing to carry a dagger in their girdles. After years of preparation the magistrate determines to compromise and raises the question, how long and how sharp the dagger is allowed to be which anyone may carry in his belt when he goes out. As long as the cunning citizens do not suppress knifing by legislation, the courts, and the police, things go on in the old way, of course. A definition of the length and sharpness of the permitted dagger will help only the strongest and most turbulent and leave the weaker at their mercy. You will all understand the meaning of this parable. It is true that we have a League of Nations and a Court of Arbitration. But the League is not much more than a meeting-hall, and the Court has no means of enforcing its decisions. These institutions provide no security for any country in case of an attack on it. If you bear this in mind, you will judge the attitude of the French, their refusal to disarm without security, less harshly than it is usually judged at present.

Unless we can agree to limit the sovereignty of the individual State by all binding ourselves to take joint action against any country which openly or secretly resists a judgment of the Court of Arbitration, we shall never get out of a state of universal anarchy and terror. No sleight of hand can reconcile the unlimited sovereignty of the individual country with security against attack. Will it need new disasters to induce the countries to undertake to enforce every decision of the recognized international court? The progress of events so far scarcely justifies us in hoping for anything better in the near future. But everyone who cares for civilization and justice must exert all his strength to convince his fellows of the necessity for laying all countries under an international obligation of this kind.

It will be urged against this notion, not without a certain justification, that it over-estimates the efficacy of machinery, and neglects the psychological, or rather the moral, factor. Spiritual disarmament, people insist, must precede material disarmament. They say further, and truly, that the greatest obstacle to international order is that monstrously exaggerated spirit of nationalism which also goes by the fair-sounding but misused name of patriotism. During the last century and a half this idol has acquired an uncanny and exceedingly pernicious power everywhere.

To estimate this objection at its proper worth, one must realize that a *reciprocal* relation exists between external machinery and internal states of mind. Not only does the machinery depend on traditional modes of feeling and owe its origin and its survival to them, but the existing machinery in its turn exercises a powerful influence on national modes of feeling.

The present deplorably high development of nationalism everywhere is, in my opinion, intimately connected with the institution of compulsory military service or, to call it by its less offensive name, national armies. A country which demands military service of its inhabitants is compelled to cultivate a nationalistic spirit in them, which provides the psychological foundation of military efficiency. Along with this religion it has to hold up its instrument, brute force, to the admiration of the youth in its schools.

The introduction of compulsory service is therefore, to my mind, the prime cause of the moral collapse of the white race, which seriously threatens not merely the survival of our civilization but our very existence. This curse, along with great social blessings, started with the French Revolution, and before long dragged all the other nations in its train.

Therefore those who desire to encourage the growth of an international spirit and to combat chauvinism must take their stand against compulsory service. Is the severe persecution to which conscientious objectors to military service are subjected to-day a whit less disgraceful to the community than those to which the martyrs of religion were exposed in former centuries? Can you, as the Kellogg Pact does, condemn war and at the same time leave the individual to the tender mercies of the war machine in each country?

If, in view of the Disarmament Conference, we are not to restrict ourselves to the technical problems of organization involved but also to tackle the psychological question more directly from educational motives, we must try on international lines to invent some legal way by which the individual can refuse to serve in the army. Such a regulation would undoubtedly produce a great moral effect.

This is my position in a nutshell: Mere agreements to limit armaments furnish no sort of security. Compulsory arbitration must be supported by an executive force, guaranteed by all the participating countries, which is ready to proceed against the disturber of the peace with economic and military sanctions. Compulsory service, as the bulwark of unhealthy nationalism, must be combated; most important of all, conscientious objectors must be protected on an international basis.

Finally, I would draw your attention to a book, *War again To-morrow*, by Ludwig Bauer, which discusses the issues here involved in an acute and unprejudiced manner and with great psychological insight.

II

The benefits that the inventive genius of man has conferred on us in the last hundred years could make life happy and care-free if organization had been able to keep pace with technical progress. As it is, these hard-won achievements in the hands of our generation are like a razor in the hands of a child of three. The possession of marvellous means of production has brought care and hunger instead of freedom.

The results of technical progress are most baleful where they furnish means for the destruction of human life and the hard-won fruits of toil, as we of the older generation experienced to our horror in the Great War. More dreadful even than the destruction, in my opinion, is the humiliating slavery into which war plunges the individual. Is it not a terrible thing to be forced by the community to do things which every individual regards as abominable crimes? Only a few had the moral greatness to resist; them I regard as the real heroes of the Great War.

There is one ray of hope. I believe that the responsible leaders of the nations do, in the main, honestly desire to abolish war. The resistance to this essential step forward comes from those unfortunate national traditions which are handed on like a hereditary disease from generation to generation through the workings of the educational system. The principal vehicle of this tradition is military training and its glorification, and, equally, that portion of the Press which is controlled by heavy industry and the soldiers. Without disarmament there can be no lasting peace. Conversely, the continuation of military preparations on the present scale will inevitably lead to new catastrophes.

That is why the Disarmament Conference of 1932 will decide the fate of this generation and the next. When one thinks how pitiable, taken as a whole, have been the results of former conferences, it becomes clear that it is the duty of all intelligent and responsible people to exert their full powers to remind public opinion again and again of the importance of the 1932 Conference. Only if the statesmen have behind them the will to peace of a decisive majority in their own countries can they attain their great end, and for the formation of this public opinion each one of us is responsible in every word and deed.

The doom of the Conference would be sealed if the delegates came to it with ready-made instructions, the carrying out of which would soon become a matter of prestige. This seems to be generally realized. For meetings between the statesmen of two nations at a time, which have become very frequent of late, have been used to prepare the ground for the Conference by conversations about the disarmament problem. This seems to me a very happy device, for two men or groups of men can usually discuss things together most reasonably, honestly, and dispassionately when there is no third person present in front of whom they think they must be careful what they say. Only if exhaustive preparations of this kind are made for the Conference, if surprises are thereby ruled out, and an atmosphere of confidence is created by genuine good will, can we hope for a happy issue.

In these great matters success is not a matter of cleverness, still less of cunning, but of honesty and confidence. The moral element cannot be displaced by reason, thank heaven! It is not the individual spectator's duty merely to wait and criticize. He must serve the cause by all means in his power. The fate of the world will be such as the world deserves.

America and the Disarmament Conference

The Americans of to-day are filled with the cares arising out of economic conditions in their own country. The efforts of their responsible leaders are directed primarily to remedying the serious unemployment at home. The sense of being involved in the destiny of the rest of the world, and in particular of the mother country of Europe, is even less strong than in normal times.

But the free play of economic forces will not by itself automatically overcome these difficulties. Regulative measures by the community are needed to bring about a sound distribution of labour and consumption-goods among mankind; without them even the people of the richest country suffocate. The fact is that since the amount of work needed to supply everybody's needs has been reduced through the improvement of technical methods, the free play of economic forces no longer produces a state of affairs in which all the available labour can find employment. Deliberate regulation and organization are becoming necessary to make the results of technical progress beneficial to all.

If the economic situation cannot be cleared up
without systematic regulation, how much more
necessary is such regulation for dealing with the
problems of international politics ! Few people
still cling to the notion that acts of violence in the
shape of wars are either advantageous or worthy
of humanity as a method of solving international
problems. But they are not logical enough to
make vigorous efforts on behalf of the measures
which might prevent war, that savage and
unworthy relic of the age of barbarism. It
requires some power of reflection to see the issue
clearly and a certain courage to serve this great
cause resolutely and effectively.

Anybody who really wants to abolish war must
resolutely declare himself in favour of his own
country's resigning a portion of its sovereignty in
favour of international institutions : he must be
ready to make his own country amenable, in case
of a dispute, to the award of an international
court. He must in the most uncompromising
fashion support disarmament all round, which is
actually envisaged in the unfortunate Treaty of
Versailles; unless military and aggressively patriotic education is abolished, we can hope for no
progress.

No event of the last few years reflects such disgrace on the leading civilized countries of the
world as the failure of all disarmament conferences
so far; for this failure is due not only to the
intrigues of ambitious and unscrupulous politicians,
but also to the indifference and slackness of the
public in all countries. Unless this is changed we
shall destroy all the really valuable achievements
of our predecessors.

I believe that the American nation is only

imperfectly aware of the responsibility which
rests with it in this matter. People in America
no doubt think as follows : " Let Europe go to
the dogs, if it is destroyed by the quarrelsomeness
and wickedness of its inhabitants. The good seed
of our Wilson has produced a mighty poor crop in
the stony ground of Europe. We are strong and
safe and in no hurry to mix ourselves up in other
people's affairs."

Such an attitude is at once base and shortsighted. America is partly to blame for the
difficulties of Europe. By ruthlessly pressing her
claims she is hastening the economic and therewith
the moral collapse of Europe; she has helped to
Balkanize Europe, and therefore shares the responsibility for the breakdown of political morality
and the growth of that spirit of revenge which
feeds on despair. This spirit will not stop short of
the gates of America—I had almost said, has not
stopped short. Look around, and look forward.

The truth can be briefly stated : The Disarmament Conference comes as a final chance, to you
no less than to us, of preserving the best that civilized humanity has produced. And it is on you, as
the strongest and comparatively soundest among
us, that the eyes and hopes of all are focused.

Active Pacifism

I consider myself lucky in witnessing the great
peace demonstration organized by the Flemish
people. To all concerned in it I feel impelled to
call out in the name of men of good will with a
care for the future : " In this hour of opened eyes
and awakening conscience we feel ourselves united
with you by the deepest ties."

We must not conceal from ourselves that an

improvement in the present depressing situation is impossible without a severe struggle; for the handful of those who are really determined to do something is minute in comparison with the mass of the lukewarm and the misguided. And those who have an interest in keeping the machinery of war going are a very powerful body; they will stop at nothing to make public opinion subservient to their murderous ends.

It looks as if the ruling statesmen of to-day were really trying to secure permanent peace. But the ceaseless piling-up of armaments shows only too clearly that they are unequal to coping with the hostile forces which are preparing for war. In my opinion, deliverance can only come from the peoples themselves. If they wish to avoid the degrading slavery of war-service, they must declare with no uncertain voice for complete disarmament. As long as armies exist, any serious quarrel will lead to war. A pacifism which does not actually try to prevent the nations from arming is and must remain impotent.

May the conscience and the common sense of the peoples be awakened, so that we may reach a new stage in the life of nations, where people will look back on war as an incomprehensible aberration of their forefathers !

Letter to a Friend of Peace

It has come to my ears that in your great-heartedness you are quietly accomplishing a splendid work, impelled by solicitude for humanity and its fate. Small is the number of them that see with their own eyes and feel with their own hearts. But it is their strength that will decide whether the human race must relapse into that hopeless condition which a blind multitude appears to-day to regard as the ideal.

O that the nations might see, before it is too late, how much of their self-determination they have got to sacrifice in order to avoid the struggle of all against all ! The power of conscience and the international spirit has proved itself inadequate. At present it is being so weak as to tolerate parleying with the worst enemies of civilization. There is a kind of conciliation which is a crime against humanity, and it passes for political wisdom.

We cannot despair of humanity, since we are ourselves human beings. And it is a comfort that there still exist individuals like yourself, whom one knows to be alive and undismayed.

Another ditto

Dear friend and spiritual brother,

To be quite frank, a declaration like the one before me in a country which submits to conscription in peace-time seems to me valueless. What you must fight for is liberation from universal military service. Verily the French nation has had to pay heavily for the victory of 1918; for that victory has been largely responsible for holding it down in the most degrading of all forms of slavery. Let your efforts in this struggle be unceasing. You have a mighty ally in the German reactionaries and militarists. If France clings to universal military service, it will be impossible in the long run to prevent its introduction into Germany. For the demand of the Germans for equal rights will succeed in the end; and then there will be two German military slaves to every French one, which would certainly not be in the interests of France.

Only if we succeed in abolishing compulsory service altogether will it be possible to educate the youth in the spirit of reconciliation, joy in life, and love towards all living creatures.

I believe that a refusal on conscientious grounds to serve in the army when called up, if carried out by 50,000 men at the same moment, would be irresistible. The individual can accomplish little here, nor can one wish to see the best among us devoted to destruction through the machinery behind which stand the three great powers of stupidity, fear, and greed.

A third ditto

Dear Sir,

The point with which you deal in your letter is one of prime importance. The armament industry is, as you say, one of the greatest dangers that beset mankind. It is the hidden evil power behind the nationalism which is rampant everywhere. . . .

Possibly something might be gained by nationalization. But it is extremely hard to determine exactly what industries should be included. Should the aircraft industry? And how much of the metal industry and the chemical industry?

As regards the munitions industry and the export of war material, the League of Nations has busied itself for years with efforts to get this horrible traffic controlled—with what little success, we all know. Last year I asked a well-known American diplomat why Japan was not forced by a commercial boycott to desist from her policy of force. "Our commercial interests are too strong," was the answer. How can one help people who rest satisfied with a statement like that?

You believe that a word from me would suffice to get something done in this sphere? What an illusion! People flatter me as long as I do not get in their way. But if I direct my efforts towards objects which do not suit them, they immediately turn to abuse and calumny in defence of their interests. And the onlookers mostly keep out of the light, the cowards! Have you ever tested the civil courage of your countrymen? The silently accepted motto is "Leave it alone and don't speak of it." You may be sure that I shall do everything in my power along the lines you indicate, but nothing can be achieved as directly as you think.

Women and War

In my opinion, the patriotic women ought to be sent to the front in the next war instead of the men. It would at least be a novelty in this dreary sphere of infinite confusion, and besides— why should not such heroic feelings on the part of the fair sex find a more picturesque outlet than in attacks on a defenceless civilian?

Thoughts on the World Economic Crisis

If there is one thing that can give a layman in the sphere of economics the courage to express an opinion on the nature of the alarming economic difficulties of the present day, it is the hopeless confusion of opinions among the experts. What I have to say is nothing new and does not pretend to be anything more than the opinion of an independent and honest man who, unburdened by class or national prejudices, desires nothing but the good of humanity and the most harmonious possible scheme of human existence. If in what follows I write as if I were clear about certain things and sure of the truth of what I am saying, this is done merely for the sake of an easier mode of expression; it does not proceed from unwarranted self-confidence or a belief in the infallibility of my somewhat simple intellectual conception of problems which are in reality uncommonly complex.

As I see it, this crisis differs in character from past crises in that it is based on an entirely new set of conditions, due to rapid progress in methods of production. Only a fraction of the available human labour in the world is needed for the production of the total amount of consumption-goods necessary to life. Under a completely free economic system this fact is bound to lead to unemployment. For reasons which I do not propose to analyse here, the majority of people are compelled to work for the minimum wage on which life can be supported. If two factories produce the same sort of goods, other things being equal, that one will be able to produce them more cheaply which employs less workmen—i.e., makes the individual worker work as long and as hard as human nature permits. From this it follows inevitably that, with methods of production what they are to-day, only a portion of the available labour can be used. While unreasonable demands are made on this portion, the remainder is automatically excluded from the process of production. This leads to a fall in sales and profits. Businesses go smash, which further increases unemployment and diminishes confidence in industrial concerns and therewith public participation in these mediating banks; finally the banks become insolvent through the sudden withdrawal of deposits and the wheels of industry therewith come to a complete standstill.

The crisis has also been attributed to other causes which we will now consider.

(1) *Over-production.* We have to distinguish between two things here—real over-production and apparent over-production. By real over-production I mean a production so great that it exceeds the demand. This may perhaps apply to motor-cars and wheat in the United States at the present moment, although even that is doubtful. By "over-production" people usually mean a condition of things in which more of one particular article is produced than can, in existing circumstances, be sold, in spite of a shortage of consumption-goods among consumers. This condition of things I call apparent over-production. In this case it is not the demand that is lacking but the consumers' purchasing-power. Such apparent over-production is only another word for a crisis, and therefore cannot serve as an explanation of the latter; hence people who try to make over-production responsible for the crisis are merely juggling with words.

(2) *Reparations.* The obligation to pay reparations lies heavy on the debtor nations and their industries, compels them to go in for dumping, and so harms the creditor nations too. This is beyond dispute. But the appearance of the crisis in the United States, in spite of the high tariff-wall protecting them, proves that this cannot be the principal cause of the world crisis. The shortage of gold in the debtor countries due to reparations can at most serve as an argument for putting an end to these payments; it cannot

be dragged in as an explanation of the world crisis.

(3) *Erection of new tariff-walls. Increase in the unproductive burden of armaments. Political insecurity owing to latent danger of war.* All these things add considerably to the troubles of Europe, but do not materially affect America. The appearance of the crisis in America shows that they cannot be its principal causes.

(4) *The dropping-out of the two Powers, China and Russia.* This blow to world trade also does not touch America very nearly, and therefore cannot be a principal cause of the crisis.

(5) *The economic rise of the lower classes since the War.* This, supposing it to be a reality, could only produce a scarcity of goods, not an excessive supply.

I will not weary the reader by enumerating further contentions which do not seem to me to get to the heart of the matter. Of one thing I feel certain : this same technical progress which, in itself, might relieve mankind of a great part of the labour necessary to its subsistence, is the main cause of our present troubles. Hence there are those who would in all seriousness forbid the introduction of technical improvements. This is obviously absurd. But how can we find a more rational way out of our dilemma?

If we could somehow manage to prevent the purchasing-power of the masses, measured in terms of goods, from sinking below a certain minimum, stoppages in the industrial cycle such as we are experiencing to-day would be rendered impossible.

The logically simplest but also most daring

method of achieving this is a completely planned economy, in which consumption-goods are produced and distributed by the community. That, in essentials, is what is being attempted in Russia to-day. Much will depend on what results this mighty experiment produces. To hazard a prophecy here would be presumption. Can goods be produced as economically under such a system as under one which leaves more freedom to individual enterprise? Can this system maintain itself at all without the terror that has so far accompanied it, which none of us " westerners " would care to let himself in for? Does not such a rigid, centralized system tend towards protection and hostility to advantageous innovations? We must take care, however, not to allow these suspicions to become prejudices which prevent us from forming an objective judgment.

My personal opinion is that those methods are preferable which respect existing traditions and habits so far as that is in any way compatible with the end in view. Nor do I believe that a sudden transference of the control of industry to the hands of the public would be beneficial from the point of view of production; private enterprise should be left its sphere of activity, in so far as it has not already been eliminated by industry itself in the form of cartelization.

There are, however, two respects in which this economic freedom ought to be limited. In each branch of industry the number of working hours per week ought so to be reduced by law that unemployment is systematically abolished. At the same time minimum wages must be fixed in such a way that the purchasing power of the workers keeps pace with production.

Further, in those industries which have become monopolistic in character through organization on the part of the producers, prices must be controlled by the State in order to keep the creation of new capital within reasonable bounds and prevent the artificial strangling of production and consumption.

In this way it might perhaps be possible to establish a proper balance between production and consumption without too great a limitation of free enterprise, and at the same time to stop the intolerable tyranny of the owners of the means of production (land, machinery) over the wage-earners, in the widest sense of the term.

Culture and Prosperity

If one would estimate the damage done by the great political catastrophe to the development of human civilization, one must remember that culture in its higher forms is a delicate plant which depends on a complicated set of conditions and is wont to flourish only in a few places at any given time. For it to blossom there is needed, first of all, a certain degree of prosperity, which enables a fraction of the population to work at things not directly necessary to the maintenance of life; secondly, a moral tradition of respect for cultural values and achievements, in virtue of which this class is provided with the means of living by the other classes, those who provide the immediate necessities of life.

During the past century Germany has been one of the countries in which both conditions were fulfilled. The prosperity was, taken as a whole, modest but sufficient; the tradition of respect for culture vigorous. On this basis the German nation has brought forth fruits of culture which form an integral part of the development of the modern world. The tradition, in the main, still stands; the prosperity is gone. The industries of the country have been cut off almost completely from the sources of raw materials on which the existence of the industrial part of the population was based. The surplus necessary to support the intellectual worker has suddenly ceased to exist. With it the tradition which depends on it will inevitably collapse also, and a fruitful nursery of culture turn to wilderness.

The human race, in so far as it sets a value on culture, has an interest in preventing such impoverishment. It will give what help it can in the immediate crisis and reawaken that higher community of feeling, now thrust into the background by national egotism, for which human values have a validity independent of politics and frontiers. It will then procure for every nation conditions of work under which it can exist and under which it can bring forth fruits of culture.

Production and Purchasing Power

I do not believe that the remedy for our present difficulties lies in a knowledge of productive capacity and consumption, because this knowledge is likely, in the main, to come too late. Moreover the trouble in Germany seems to me to be not hypertrophy of the machinery of production but deficient purchasing power in a large section of the population, which has been cast out of the productive process through rationalization.

The gold standard has, in my opinion, the serious disadvantage that a shortage in the supply of gold automatically leads to a contraction of credit and also of the amount of currency in circulation, to which contraction prices and wages cannot adjust themselves sufficiently quickly. The natural remedies for our troubles are, in my opinion, as follows :—

(1) A statutory reduction of working hours, graduated for each department of industry, in order to get rid of unemployment, combined with the fixing of minimum wages for the purpose of adjusting the purchasing-power of the masses to the amount of goods available.

(2) Control of the amount of money in circulation and of the volume of credit in such a way as to keep the price-level steady, all special protection being abolished.

(3) Statutory limitation of prices for such articles as have been practically withdrawn from free competition by monopolies or the formation of cartels.

Production and Work

An answer to Cederström

Dear Herr Cederström,

Thank you for sending me your proposals, which interest me very much. Having myself given so much thought to this subject I feel that it is right that I should give you my perfectly frank opinion on them.

The fundamental trouble seems to me to be the almost unlimited freedom of the labour market combined with extraordinary progress in the methods of production. To satisfy the needs of the world to-day nothing like all the available labour is wanted. The result is unemployment and excessive competition among the workers, both of which reduce purchasing power and put the whole economic system intolerably out of gear.

I know Liberal economists maintain that every economy in labour is counterbalanced by an increase in demand. But, to begin with, I don't believe it, and even if it were true, the abovementioned factors would always operate to force the standard of living of a large portion of the human race down to an unnaturally low level.

I also share your conviction that steps absolutely must be taken to make it possible and necessary for the younger people to take part in the productive process. Further, that the older people ought to be excluded from certain sorts of work (which I call " unqualified " work), receiving instead a certain income, as having by that time done enough work of a kind accepted by society as productive.

I too am in favour of abolishing large cities, but not of settling people of a particular type— e.g., old people—in particular towns. Frankly, the idea strikes me as horrible. I am also of opinion that fluctuations in the value of money must be avoided, by substituting for the gold standard a standard based on certain classes of goods selected according to the conditions of consumption—as Keynes, if I am not mistaken, long ago proposed. With the introduction of this system one might consent to a certain amount of " inflation," as compared with the present monetary situation, if one could believe that the State would really make a rational use of the windfall thus accruing to it.

The weaknesses of your plan lie, so it seems to me, in the sphere of psychology, or rather, in your neglect of it. It is no accident that capitalism has brought with it progress not merely in production but also in knowledge. Egoism and competition are, alas, stronger forces than public spirit and sense of duty. In Russia, they say, it is impossible to get a decent piece of bread. . . . Perhaps I am over-pessimistic concerning State and other forms of communal enterprise, but I expect little good from them. Bureaucracy is the death of all sound work. I have seen and experienced too many dreadful warnings, even in comparatively model Switzerland.

I am inclined to the view that the State can only be of real use to industry as a limiting and regulative force. It must see to it that competition among the workers is kept within healthy limits, that all children are given a chance to develop soundly, and that wages are high enough for the goods produced to be consumed. But it can exert a decisive influence through its regulative function if—and there again you are right— its measures are framed in an objective spirit by independent experts.

I would like to write to you at greater length, but cannot find the time.

Minorities

It seems to be a universal fact that minorities —especially when the individuals composing them are distinguished by physical peculiarities—are treated by the majorities among whom they live as an inferior order of beings. The tragedy of such a fate lies not merely in the unfair treatment to which these minorities are automatically subjected in social and economic matters, but also in the fact that under the suggestive influence of the majority most of the victims themselves succumb to the same prejudice and regard their brethren as inferior beings.   This second and greater part of the evil can be overcome by closer combination and by deliberate education of the minority, whose spiritual liberation can thus be accomplished.

The efforts of the American negroes in this direction are deserving of all commendation and assistance.

Observations on the Present Situation in Europe

The distinguishing feature of the present political situation of the world, and in particular of Europe, seems to me to be this, that political development has failed, both materially and intellectually, to keep pace with economic necessity, which has changed its character in a comparatively short time.   The interests of each country must be subordinated to the interests of the wider community.   The struggle for this new orientation of political thought and feeling is a severe one, because it has the tradition of centuries against it.   But the survival of Europe depends on its successful issue.   It is my firm conviction that once the psychological impediments are overcome the solution of the real problems will not be such a terribly difficult matter.   In order to create the right atmosphere, the most essential thing is personal co-operation between men of like mind. May our united efforts succeed in building a bridge of mutual trust between the nations !

The Heirs of the Ages

Previous generations were able to look upon intellectual and cultural progress as simply the inherited fruits of their forebears' labours, which made life easier and more beautiful for them.

But the calamities of our times show us that this was a fatal illusion.

We see now that the greatest efforts are needed if this legacy of humanity's is to prove a blessing and not a curse. For whereas formerly it was enough for a man to have freed himself to some extent from personal egotism to make him a valuable member of society, to-day he must also be required to overcome national and class egotism. Only if he reaches those heights can he contribute towards improving the lot of humanity.

As regards this most important need of the age the inhabitants of a small State are better placed than those of a great Power, since the latter are exposed, both in politics and economics, to the temptation to gain their ends by brute force. The agreement between Holland and Belgium, which is the only bright spot in European affairs during the last few years, encourages one to hope that the small nations will play a leading part in the attempt to liberate the world from the degrading yoke of militarism through the renunciation of the individual country's unlimited right of self-determination.

III
Germany 1933

Manifesto

As long as I have any choice, I will only stay in a country where political liberty, toleration, and equality of all citizens before the law are the rule. Political liberty implies liberty to express one's political views orally and in writing, toleration, respect for any and every individual opinion.

These conditions do not obtain in Germany at the present time. Those who have done most for the cause of international understanding, among them some of the leading artists, are being persecuted there.

Any social organism can become psychically distempered just as any individual can, especially in times of difficulty. Nations usually survive these distempers. I hope that healthy conditions will soon supervene in Germany, and that in future her great men like Kant and Goethe will not merely be commemorated from time to time, but that the principles which they inculcated will also prevail in public life and in the general consciousness.

March, 1933.

Correspondence with the Prussian Academy of Sciences

The following correspondence is here published for the first time in its authentic and complete form. The version published in German newspapers was for the most part incorrect, important sentences being omitted.

The Academy's declaration of April 1, 1933, against Einstein.

The Prussian Academy of Sciences heard with indignation from the newspapers of Albert Einstein's participation in atrocity-mongering in France and America. It immediately demanded an explanation. In the meantime Einstein has announced his withdrawal from the Academy, giving as his reason that he cannot continue to serve the Prussian State under its present Government. Being a Swiss citizen, he also, it seems, intends to resign the Prussian nationality which he acquired in 1913 simply by becoming a full member of the Academy.

The Prussian Academy of Sciences is particularly distressed by Einstein's activities as an agitator in foreign countries, as it and its members have always felt themselves bound by the closest ties to the Prussian State and, while abstaining strictly from all political partisanship, have always stressed and remained faithful to the national idea. It has, therefore, no reason to regret Einstein's withdrawal.

Prof. Dr. Ernst Heymann,
Perpetual Secretary.

Le Coq, near Ostende, April 5, 1933

To the Prussian Academy of Sciences,

I have received information from a thoroughly reliable source that the Academy of Sciences has spoken in an official statement of " Einstein's participation in atrocity-mongering in America and France."

I hereby declare that I have never taken any part in atrocity-mongering, and I must add that I have seen nothing of any such mongering any-

where. In general people have contented themselves with reproducing and commenting on the
official statements and orders of responsible
members of the German Government, together
with the programme for the annihilation of the
German Jews by economic methods.

The statements I have issued to the Press were
concerned with my intention to resign my position
in the Academy and renounce my Prussian
citizenship; I gave as my reason for these steps
that I did not wish to live in a country where
the individual does not enjoy equality before
the law and freedom to say and teach what he
likes.

Further, I described the present state of affairs
in Germany as a state of psychic distemper in the
masses and also made some remarks about its
causes.

In a written document which I allowed the
International League for combating Anti-Semitism
to make use of for the purpose of enlisting support,
and which was not intended for the Press at all,
I also called upon all sensible people, who are still
faithful to the ideals of a civilization in peril, to
do their utmost to prevent this mass-psychosis,
which is exhibiting itself in such terrible symptoms
in Germany to-day, from spreading further.

It would have been an easy matter for the
Academy to get hold of a correct version of my
words before issuing the sort of statement about
me that it has. The German Press has repro-
duced a deliberately distorted version of my words,
as indeed was only to be expected with the Press
muzzled as it is to-day.

I am ready to stand by every word I have
published. In return, I expect the Academy to

communicate this statement of mine to its members and also to the German public before which I have been slandered, especially as it has itself had a hand in slandering me before that public.

The Academy's Answer of April 11, 1933

The Academy would like to point out that its statement of April 1, 1933, was based not merely on German but principally on foreign, particularly French and Belgian, newspaper reports which Herr Einstein has not contradicted; in addition, it had before it his much-canvassed statement to the League for combating anti-Semitism, in which he deplores Germany's relapse into the barbarism of long-passed ages. Moreover, the Academy has reason to know that Herr Einstein, who according to his own statement has taken no part in atrocity-mongering, has at least done nothing to counter-act unjust suspicions and slanders, which, in the opinion of the Academy, it was his duty as one of its senior members to do. Instead of that Herr Einstein has made statements, and in foreign countries at that, such as, coming from a man of world-wide reputation, were bound to be exploited and abused by the enemies not merely of the present German Government but of the whole German people.

For the Prussian Academy of Sciences,
(Signed) H. von Ficker,
E. Heymann,
Perpetual Secretaries.

Berlin, *April 7*, 1933
The Prussian Academy of Sciences.

Professor Albert Einstein, Leyden,
c/o Prof. Ehrenfest, Witte Rosenstr.

Dear Sir,

As the present Principal Secretary of the Prussian Academy I beg to acknowledge the receipt of your communication dated March 28 announcing your resignation of your membership of the Academy. The Academy took cognizance of your resignation in its plenary session of March 30, 1933.

While the Academy profoundly regrets the turn events have taken, this regret is inspired by the thought that a man of the highest scientific authority, whom many years of work among Germans and many years of membership of our society must have made familiar with the German character and German habits of thought, should have chosen this moment to associate himself with a body of people abroad who—partly no doubt through ignorance of actual conditions and events—have done much damage to our German people by disseminating erroneous views and unfounded rumours. We had confidently expected that one who had belonged to our Academy for so long would have ranged himself, irrespective of his own political sympathies, on the side of the defenders of our nation against the flood of lies which has been let loose upon it. In these days of mud-slinging, some of it vile, some of it ridiculous, a good word for the German people from you in particular might have produced a great effect, especially abroad. Instead of which your testimony has served as a handle to the enemies not merely of the present Government but of the German people. This has come as a bitter and grievous disappointment to us, which would no doubt have led inevitably to a parting of the ways even if we had not received your resignation.

Yours faithfully,
(signed) von Ficker.

Le Coq-sur-Mer, Belgium,
April 12, 1933

To the Prussian Academy of Sciences, Berlin.

I have received your communication of the seventh instant and deeply deplore the mental attitude displayed in it.

As regards the fact, I can only reply as follows : What you say about my behaviour is, at bottom, merely another form of the statement you have already published, in which you accuse me of having taken part in atrocity-mongering against the German nation. I have already, in my last letter, characterized this accusation as slanderous.

You have also remarked that a " good word " on my part for " the German people " would have produced a great effect abroad. To this I must reply that such a testimony as you suggest would have been equivalent to a repudiation of all those notions of justice and liberty for which I have all my life stood. Such a testimony would not be, as you put it, a good word for the German nation; on the contrary, it would only have helped the cause of those who are seeking to undermine the ideas and principles which have won for the German nation a place of honour in the civilized world. By giving such a testimony in the present circumstances I should have been contributing, even if only indirectly, to the barbarization of manners and the destruction of all existing cultural values.

It was for this reason that I felt compelled to resign from the Academy, and your letter only shows me how right I was to do so.

Munich, *April* 8, 1933

From the Bavarian Academy of Sciences
    to Professor Albert Einstein.

Sir,

In your letter to the Prussian Academy of Sciences you have given the present state of affairs in Germany as the reason for your resignation. The Bavarian Academy of Sciences, which some years ago elected you a corresponding member, is also a German Academy, closely allied to the Prussian and other German Academies; hence your withdrawal from the Prussian Academy of Sciences is bound to affect your relations with our Academy.

We must therefore ask you how you envisage your relations with our Academy after what has passed between yourself and the Prussian Academy.

The President of the Bavarian Academy of Sciences.

Le Coq-sur-Mer, *April* 21, 1933

To the Bavarian Academy of Sciences, Munich.

I have given it as the reason for my resignation from the Prussian Academy that in the present circumstances I have no wish either to be a German citizen or to remain in a position of quasi-dependence on the Prussian Ministry of Education.

These reasons would not, in themselves, involve the severing of my relations with the Bavarian Academy. If I nevertheless desire my name to be removed from the list of members, it is for a different reason.

The primary duty of an Academy is to encourage and protect the scientific life of a country. The learned societies of Germany have, however —to the best of knowledge—stood by and said nothing while a not inconsiderable proportion of German savants and students, and also of professional men of university education, have been deprived of all chance of getting employment or earning their livings in Germany. I would rather not belong to any society which behaves in such a manner, even if it does so under external pressure.

A Reply

The following lines are Einstein's answer to an invitation to associate himself with a French manifesto against Anti-Semitism in Germany.

I have considered this most important proposal, which has a bearing on several things that I have nearly at heart, carefully from every angle. As a result I have come to the conclusion that I cannot take a personal part in this extremely important affair, for two reasons :—

In the first place I am, after all, still a German citizen, and in the second I am a Jew. As regards the first point I must add that I have worked in German institutions and have always been treated with full confidence in Germany. However deeply I may regret the things that are being done there, however strongly I am bound to condemn the terrible mistakes that are being made with the approval of the Government; it is impossible for me to take part personally in an enterprise set on foot by responsible members of a foreign Government. In order that you may appreciate this fully, suppose that a French citizen in a more or less analogous situation had got up a protest against the French Government's action in conjunction with prominent German statesmen. Even if you fully admitted that the protest was amply warranted by the facts, you would still, I expect, regard the behaviour of your fellow-citizen as an act of treachery. If Zola had felt it necessary to leave France at the time of the Dreyfus case, he would still certainly not have associated himself with a protest by German official personages, however much he might have approved of their action. He would have confined himself to—blushing for his countrymen. In the second place, a protest against injustice and violence is incomparably more valuable if it comes entirely from people who have been prompted to it purely by sentiments of humanity and a love of justice. This cannot be said of a man like me, a Jew who regards other Jews as his brothers. For him, an injustice done to the Jews is the same as an injustice done to himself. He must not be the judge in his own case, but wait for the judgment of impartial outsiders.

These are my reasons. But I should like to add that I have always honoured and admired that highly developed sense of justice which is one of the noblest features of the French tradition

IV
The Jews

Jewish Ideals

THE pursuit of knowledge for its own sake, an almost fanatical love of justice, and the desire for personal independence—these are the features of the Jewish tradition which make me thank my stars that I belong to it.

Those who are raging to-day against the ideals of reason and individual liberty and are trying to establish a spiritless State-slavery by brute force rightly see in us their irreconcilable foes. History has given us a difficult row to hoe; but so long as we remain devoted servants of truth, justice, and liberty, we shall continue not merely to survive as the oldest of living peoples, but by creative work to bring forth fruits which contribute to the ennoblement of the human race, as heretofore.

Is there a Jewish Point of View?

In the philosophical sense there is, in my opinion, no specifically Jewish outlook. Judaism seems to me to be concerned almost exclusively with the moral attitude in life and to life. I look upon it as the essence of an attitude to life which is incarnate in the Jewish people rather than the essence of the laws laid down in the Thora and interpreted in the Talmud. To me, the Thora and the Talmud are merely the most important evidence for the manner in which the Jewish conception of life held sway in earlier times.

The essence of that conception seems to me to lie in an affirmative attitude to the life of all creation. The life of the individual has meaning only in so far as it aids in making the life of every living thing nobler and more beautiful. Life is sacred—that is to say, it is the supreme value, to which all other values are subordinate. The hallowing of the supra-individual life brings in its train a reverence for everything spiritual—a particularly characteristic feature of the Jewish tradition.

Judaism is not a creed: the Jewish God is simply a negation of superstition, an imaginary result of its elimination. It is also an attempt to base the moral law on fear, a regrettable and discreditable attempt. Yet it seems to me that the strong moral tradition of the Jewish nation has to a large extent shaken itself free from this fear. It is clear also that " serving God " was equated with " serving the living." The best of the Jewish people, especially the Prophets and Jesus, contended tirelessly for this.

Judaism is thus no transcendental religion; it is concerned with life as we live it and can up to a point grasp it, and nothing else. It seems to me, therefore, doubtful whether it can be called a religion in the accepted sense of the word, particularly as no " faith " but the sanctification of life in a supra-personal sense is demanded of the Jew.

But the Jewish tradition also contains something else, something which finds splendid expression in many of the Psalms—namely, a sort of intoxicated joy and amazement at the beauty and grandeur of this world, of which man can just form a faint notion. It is the feeling from which true scientific research draws its spiritual sustenance, but which also seems to find expression in the song of birds. To tack this on to the idea of God seems mere childish absurdity.

Is what I have described a distinguishing mark of Judaism? Is it to be found anywhere else under another name? In its pure form, nowhere, not even in Judaism, where the pure doctrine is obscured by much worship of the letter. Yet Judaism seems to me one of its purest and most vigorous manifestations. This applies particularly to the fundamental principle of the sanctification of life.

It is characteristic that the animals were expressly included in the command to keep holy the Sabbath day, so strong was the feeling that the ideal demands the solidarity of all living things. The insistence on the solidarity of all human beings finds still stronger expression, and it is no mere chance that the demands of Socialism were for the most part first raised by Jews.

How strongly developed this sense of the sanctity of life is in the Jewish people is admirably illustrated by a little remark which Walter Rathenau once made to me in conversation : " When a Jew says that he's going hunting to amuse himself, he lies." The Jewish sense of the sanctity of life could not be more simply expressed.

Jewish Youth

An Answer to a Questionnaire

It is important that the young should be induced to take an interest in Jewish questions and difficulties, and you deserve gratitude for devoting yourself to this task in your paper. This is of moment not merely for the destiny of the Jews,

whose welfare depends on their sticking together
and helping each other, but, over and above that,
for the cultivation of the international spirit,
which is in danger everywhere to-day from a
narrow-minded nationalism. Here, since the days
of the Prophets, one of the fairest fields of activity
has lain open to our nation, scattered as it is over
the earth and united only by a common tradition.

Addresses on Reconstruction in Palestine

I

Ten years ago, when I first had the pleasure of
addressing you on behalf of the Zionist cause,
almost all our hopes were still fixed on the future.
To-day we can look back on these ten years with
joy; for in that time the united energies of the
Jewish people have accomplished a splendid piece
of successful constructive work in Palestine,
which certainly exceeds anything that we dared
to hope then.

We have also successfully stood the severe test
to which the events of the last few years have
subjected us. Ceaseless work, supported by a
noble purpose, is leading slowly but surely to
success. The latest pronouncements of the
British Government indicate a return to a juster
judgment of our case; this we recognize with
gratitude.

But we must never forget what this crisis has
taught us—namely, that the establishment of
satisfactory relations between the Jews and the
Arabs is not England's affair but ours. We—that
is to say, the Arabs and ourselves—have got to
agree on the main outlines of an advantageous
partnership which shall satisfy the needs of both

nations. A just solution of this problem and one
worthy of both nations is an end no less important
and no less worthy of our efforts than the promotion of the work of construction itself. Remember
that Switzerland represents a higher stage of
political development than any national state,
precisely because of the greater political problems
which had to be solved before a stable community
could be built up out of groups of different
nationality.

Much remains to be done, but one at least of
Herzl's aims has already been realized : its task
in Palestine has given the Jewish people an
astonishing degree of solidarity and the optimism
without which no organism can lead a healthy life.

Anything we may do for the common purpose
is done not merely for our brothers in Palestine,
but for the well-being and honour of the whole
Jewish people.

II

We are assembled to-day for the purpose of
calling to mind our age-old community, its destiny,
and its problems. It is a community of moral
tradition, which has always shown its strength
and vitality in times of stress. In all ages it has
produced men who embodied the conscience of
the Western world, defenders of human dignity
and justice.

So long as we ourselves care about this community it will continue to exist to the benefit of mankind, in spite of the fact that it possesses no
self-contained organization. A decade or two ago
a group of far-sighted men, among whom Herzl of
immortal memory stood out above the rest, came
to the conclusion that we needed a spiritual centre

in order to preserve our sense of solidarity in difficult times. Thus arose the idea of Zionism and the work of settlement in Palestine, the successful realization of which we have been permitted to witness, at least in its highly promising beginnings.

I have had the privilege of seeing, to my great joy and satisfaction, how much this achievement has contributed to the recovery of the Jewish people, which is exposed, as a minority among the nations, not merely to external dangers, but also to internal ones of a psychological nature.

The crisis which the work of construction has had to face in the last few years has lain heavy upon us and is not yet completely surmounted. But the most recent reports show that the world, and especially the British Government, is disposed to recognize the great things which lie behind our struggle for the Zionist ideal. Let us at this moment remember with gratitude our leader Weizmann, whose zeal and circumspection have helped the good cause to success.

The difficulties we have been through have also brought some good in their train. They have shown us once more how strong the bond is which unites the Jews of all countries in a common destiny. The crisis has also purified our attitude to the question of Palestine, purged it of the dross of nationalism. It has been clearly proclaimed that we are not seeking to create a political society, but that our aim is, in accordance with the old tradition of Jewry, a cultural one in the widest sense of the word. That being so, it is for us to solve the problem of living side by side with our brother the Arab in an open, generous, and worthy manner. We have here an opportunity of showing what we have learnt in the thousands of years of our martyrdom. If we choose the right path we shall succeed and give the rest of the world a fine example.

Whatever we do for Palestine we do it for the honour and well-being of the whole Jewish people.

III

I am delighted to have the opportunity of addressing a few words to the youth of this country which is faithful to the common aims of Jewry. Do not be discouraged by the difficulties which confront us in Palestine. Such things serve to test the will to live of our community.

Certain proceedings and pronouncements of the English administration have been justly criticized. We must not, however, leave it at that but learn by experience.

We need to pay great attention to our relations with the Arabs. By cultivating these carefully we shall be able in future to prevent things from becoming so dangerously strained that people can take advantage of them to provoke acts of hostility. This goal is perfectly within our reach, because our work of construction has been, and must continue to be, carried out in such a manner as to serve the real interests of the Arab population also.

In this way we shall be able to avoid getting ourselves quite so often into the position, disagreeable for Jews and Arabs alike, of having to call in the mandatory Power as arbitrator. We shall thereby be following not merely the dictates of Providence but also our traditions, which alone give the Jewish community meaning and stability.

For that community is not, and must never become, a political one; this is the only permanent source whence it can draw new strength and the only ground on which its existence can be justified.

IV

For the last two thousand years the common property of the Jewish people has consisted entirely of its past. Scattered over the wide world, our nation possessed nothing in common except its carefully guarded tradition. Individual Jews no doubt produced great work, but it seemed as if the Jewish people as a whole had not the strength left for great collective achievements.

Now all that is changed. History has set us a great and noble task in the shape of active co-operation in the building up of Palestine. Eminent members of our race are already at work with all their might on the realization of this aim. The opportunity is presented to us of setting up centres of civilization which the whole Jewish people can regard as its work. We nurse the hope of erecting in Palestine a home of our own national culture which shall help to awaken the near East to new economic and spiritual life.

The object which the leaders of Zionism have in view is not a political but a social and cultural one. The community in Palestine must approach the social ideal of our forefathers as it is laid down in the Bible, and at the same time become a seat of modern intellectual life, a spiritual centre for the Jews of the whole world. In accordance with this notion, the establishment of a Jewish university in Jerusalem constitutes one of the most important aims of the Zionist organization.

During the last few months I have been to America in order to help to raise the material basis for this university there. The success of this enterprise was quite natural. Thanks to the untiring energy and splendid self-sacrificing spirit of the Jewish doctors in America, we have succeeded in collecting enough money for the creation of a medical faculty, and the preliminary work is being started at once. After this success I have no doubt that the material basis for the other faculties will soon be forthcoming. The medical faculty is first of all to be developed as a research institute and to concentrate on making the country healthy, a most important item in the work of development. Teaching on a large scale will only become important later on. As a number of highly competent scientific workers have already signified their readiness to take up appointments at the university, the establishment of a medical faculty seems to be placed beyond all doubt. I may add that a special fund for the university, entirely distinct from the general fund for the development of the country, has been opened. For the latter considerable sums have been collected during these months in America, thanks to the indefatigable labours of Professor Weizmann and other Zionist leaders, chiefly through the self-sacrificing spirit of the middle classes. I conclude with a warm appeal to the Jews in Germany to contribute all they can, in spite of the present economic difficulties, for the building up of the Jewish home in Palestine. This is not a matter of charity, but an enterprise which concerns all Jews and the success of which promises to be a source of the highest satisfaction to all.

V

For us Jews Palestine is not just a charitable or colonial enterprise, but a problem of central importance for the Jewish people. Palestine is not primarily a place of refuge for the Jews of Eastern Europe, but the embodiment of the re-awakening corporate spirit of the whole Jewish nation. Is it the right moment for this corporate sense to be awakened and strengthened? This is a question to which I feel compelled, not merely by my spontaneous feelings but on rational grounds, to return an unqualified " yes."

Let us just cast our eyes over the history of the Jews in Germany during the past hundred years. A century ago our forefathers, with few exceptions, lived in the ghetto. They were poor, without political rights, separated from the Gentiles by a barrier of religious traditions, habits of life, and legal restrictions; their intellectual development was restricted to their own literature, and they had remained almost unaffected by the mighty advance of the European intellect which dates from the Renaissance. And yet these obscure, humble people had one great advantage over us : each of them belonged in every fibre of his being to a community in which he was completely absorbed, in which he felt himself a fully privileged member, and which demanded nothing of him that was contrary to his natural habits of thought. Our forefathers in those days were pretty poor specimens intellectually and physically, but socially speaking they enjoyed an enviable spiritual equilibrium.

Then came emancipation, which suddenly opened up undreamed-of possibilities to the in-

dividual. Some few rapidly made a position for
themselves in the higher walks of business and
social life. They greedily lapped up the splendid
triumphs which the art and science of the Western
world had achieved. They joined in the process
with burning enthusiasm, themselves making
contributions of lasting value. At the same time
they imitated the external forms of Gentile life,
departed more and more from their religious and
social traditions, and adopted Gentile customs,
manners, and habits of thought. It seemed as
though they were completely losing their identity
in the superior numbers and more highly organized culture of the nations among whom they
lived, so that in a few generations there would be
no trace of them left. A complete disappearance
of Jewish nationality in Central and Western
Europe seemed inevitable.

But events turned out otherwise. Nationalities of different race seem to have an instinct
which prevents them from fusing. However
much the Jews adapted themselves, in language,
manners, and to a great extent even in the forms
of religion, to the European peoples among whom
they lived, the feeling of strangeness between the
Jews and their hosts never disappeared. This
spontaneous feeling is the ultimate cause of anti-
Semitism, which is therefore not to be got rid of
by well-meaning propaganda. Nationalities want
to pursue their own path, not to blend. A
satisfactory state of affairs can be brought about
only by mutual toleration and respect.

The first step in that direction is that we Jews
should once more become conscious of our existence
as a nationality and regain the self-respect that is
necessary to a healthy existence. We must learn

once more to glory in our ancestors and our history and once again take upon ourselves, as a nation, cultural tasks of a sort calculated to strengthen our sense of the community. It is not enough for us to play a part as individuals in the cultural development of the human race, we must also tackle tasks which only nations as a whole can perform. Only so can the Jews regain social health.

It is from this point of view that I would have you look at the Zionist movement. To-day history has assigned to us the task of taking an active part in the economic and cultural reconstruction of our native land. Enthusiasts, men of brilliant gifts, have cleared the way, and many excellent members of our race are prepared to devote themselves heart and soul to the cause. May every one of them fully realize the importance of this work and contribute, according to his powers, to its success!

The Jewish Community

A speech in London

Ladies and Gentlemen,

It is no easy matter for me to overcome my natural inclination to a life of quiet contemplation. But I could not remain deaf to the appeal of the O.R.T. and O.Z.E. societies[1]; for in responding to it I am responding, as it were, to the appeal of our sorely oppressed Jewish nation.

The position of our scattered Jewish community is a moral barometer for the political world. For what surer index of political morality and respect for justice can there be than the attitude of the

---

[1] Jewish charitable associations.

nations towards a defenceless minority, whose peculiarity lies in their preservation of an ancient cultural tradition?

This barometer is low at the present moment, as we are painfully aware from the way we are treated. But it is this very lowness that confirms me in the conviction that it is our duty to preserve and consolidate our community. Embedded in the tradition of the Jewish people there is a love of justice and reason which must continue to work for the good of all nations now and in the future. In modern times this tradition has produced Spinoza and Karl Marx.

Those who would preserve the spirit must also look after the body to which it is attached. The O.Z.E. society literally looks after the bodies of our people. In Eastern Europe it is working day and night to help our people there, on whom the economic depression has fallen particularly heavily, to keep body and soul together; while the O.R.T. society is trying to get rid of a severe social and economic handicap under which the Jews have laboured since the Middle Ages. Because we were then excluded from all directly productive occupations, we were forced into the purely commercial ones. The only way of really helping the Jew in Eastern countries is to give him access to new fields of activity, for which he is struggling all over the world. This is the grave problem which the O.R.T. society is successfully tackling.

It is to you English fellow-Jews that we now appeal to help us in this great enterprise which splendid men have set on foot. The last few years, nay, the last few days, have brought us a disappointment which must have touched you in particular nearly. Do not gird at fate, but rather look on these events as a reason for remaining true to the cause of the Jewish commonwealth. I am convinced that in doing that we shall also indirectly be promoting those general human ends which we must always recognize as the highest.

Remember that difficulties and obstacles are a valuable source of health and strength to any society. We should not have survived for thousands of years as a community if our bed had been of roses; of that I am quite sure.

But we have a still fairer consolation. Our friends are not exactly numerous, but among them are men of noble spirit and strong sense of justice, who have devoted their lives to uplifting human society and liberating the individual from degrading oppression.

We are happy and fortunate to have such men from the Gentile world among us to-night; their presence lends an added solemnity to this memorable evening. It gives me great pleasure to see before me Bernard Shaw and H. G. Wells, to whose view of life I am particularly attracted.

You, Mr. Shaw, have succeeded in winning the affection and joyous admiration of the world while pursuing a path that has led many others to a martyr's crown. You have not merely preached moral sermons to your fellows; you have actually mocked at things which many of them held sacred. You have done what only the born artist can do. From your magic box you have produced innumerable little figures which, while resembling human beings, are compact not of flesh and blood, but of brains, wit, and charm. And yet in a way they are more human than we are ourselves, and one almost forgets that they

are creations not of Nature, but of Bernard Shaw.
You make these charming little figures dance in
a miniature world in front of which the Graces
stand sentinel and permit no bitterness to enter.
He who has looked into this little world sees our
actual world in a new light; its puppets insinuate
themselves into real people, making them suddenly
look quite different. By thus holding the mirror
up to us all you have had a liberating effect on us
such as hardly any other of our contemporaries
has done and have relieved life of something of
its earth-bound heaviness. For this we are all
devoutly grateful to you, and also to fate, which
along with grievous plagues has also given us the
physician and liberator of our souls. I personally
am also grateful to you for the unforgettable
words which you have addressed to my mythical
namesake who makes life so difficult for me,
although he is really, for all his clumsy, formidable size, quite a harmless fellow.

To you all I say that the existence and destiny
of our people depend less on external factors than
on ourselves remaining faithful to the moral
traditions which have enabled us to survive for
thousands of years despite the heavy storms that
have broken over our heads. In the service of
life sacrifice becomes grace.

Working Palestine

Among Zionist organizations " Working Palestine " is the one whose work is of most direct
benefit to the most valuable class of people living
there—namely, those who are transforming deserts into flourishing settlements by the labour
of their hands. These workers are a selection,
made on a voluntary basis, from the whole

Jewish nation, an *élite* composed of strong, confident, and unselfish people. They are not ignorant labourers who sell the labour of their hands to the highest bidder, but educated, intellectually vigorous, free men, from whose peaceful struggle with a neglected soil the whole Jewish nation are the gainers, directly and indirectly. By lightening their heavy lot as far as we can we shall be saving the most valuable sort of human life; for the first settlers' struggle on ground not yet made habitable is a difficult and dangerous business involving a heavy personal sacrifice. How true this is, only they can judge who have seen it with their own eyes. Anyone who helps to improve the equipment of these men is helping on the good work at a crucial point.

It is, moreover, this working class alone that has it in its power to establish healthy relations with the Arabs, which is the most important political task of Zionism. Administrations come and go; but it is human relations that finally turn the scale in the lives of nations. Therefore to support " Working Palestine " is at the same time to promote a humane and worthy policy in Palestine, and to oppose an effective resistance to those undercurrents of narrow nationalism from which the whole political world, and in a less degree the small political world of Palestine affairs, is suffering.

Jewish Recovery

I gladly accede to your paper's request that I should address an appeal to the Jews of Hungary on behalf of Keren Hajessod.

The greatest enemies of the national consciousness and honour of the Jews are fatty degeneration—by which I mean the unconscionableness which comes from wealth and ease—and a kind of inner dependence on the surrounding Gentile world which comes from the loosening of the fabric of Jewish society. The best in man can flourish only when he loses himself in a community. Hence the moral danger of the Jew who has lost touch with his own people and is regarded as a foreigner by the people of his adoption. Only too often a contemptible and joyless egoism has resulted from such circumstances. The weight of outward oppression on the Jewish people is particularly heavy at the moment. But this very bitterness has done us good. A revival of Jewish national life, such as the last generation could never have dreamed of, has begun. Through the operation of a newly awakened sense of solidarity among the Jews, the scheme of colonizing Palestine launched by a handful of devoted and judicious leaders in the face of apparently insuperable difficulties, has already prospered so far that I feel no doubt about its permanent success. The value of this achievement for the Jews everywhere is very great. Palestine will be a centre of culture for all Jews, a refuge for the most grievously oppressed, a field of action for the best among us, a unifying ideal, and a means of attaining inward health for the Jews of the whole world.

Anti-Semitism and Academic Youth

So long as we lived in the ghetto our Jewish nationality involved for us material difficulties and sometimes physical danger, but no social or psychological problems. With emancipation the position changed, particularly for those Jews who turned to the intellectual professions. In school and at the university the young Jew is exposed to the influence of a society with a definite national tinge, which he respects and admires, from which he receives his mental sustenance, to which he feels himself to belong, while it, on the other hand, treats him, as one of an alien race, with a certain contempt and hostility. Driven by the suggestive influence of this psychological superiority rather than by utilitarian considerations, he turns his back on his people and his traditions, and considers himself as belonging entirely to the others while he tries in vain to conceal from himself and them the fact that the relation is not reciprocal. Hence that pathetic creature, the baptized Jewish *Geheimrat* of yesterday and to-day. In most cases it is not pushfulness and lack of character that have made him what he is, but, as I have said, the suggestive power of an environment superior in numbers and influence. He knows, of course, that many admirable sons of the Jewish people have made important contributions to the glory of European civilization; but have they not all, with a few exceptions, done much the same as he?

In this case, as in many mental disorders, the cure lies in a clear knowledge of one's condition and its causes. We must be conscious of our alien race and draw the logical conclusions from it. It is no use trying to convince the others of our spiritual and intellectual equality by arguments addressed to the reason, when their attitude does not originate in their intellects at all. Rather must we emancipate ourselves socially and supply our social needs, in the main, ourselves. We must have our own students' societies and adopt an attitude of courteous but consistent reserve to the Gentiles. And let us live after our own fashion there and not ape duelling and drinking customs which are foreign to our nature. It is possible to be a civilized European and a good citizen and at the same time a faithful Jew who loves his race and honours his fathers. If we remember this and act accordingly, the problem of anti-Semitism, in so far as it is of a social nature, is solved for us.

A Letter to Professor Dr. Hellpach, Minister of State

Dear Herr Hellpach,

I have read your article on Zionism and the Zurich Congress and feel, as a strong devotee of the Zionist idea, that I must answer you, even if it is only shortly.

The Jews are a community bound together by ties of blood and tradition, and not of religion only : the attitude of the rest of the world towards them is sufficient proof of this. When I came to Germany fifteen years ago I discovered for the first time that I was a Jew, and I owe this discovery more to Gentiles than Jews.

The tragedy of the Jews is that they are people of a definite historical type, who lack the support of a community to keep them together. The result is a want of solid foundations in the individual which amounts in its extremer forms to moral instability. I realized that the only possible salvation for the race was that every Jew in the world should become attached to a living society to which the individual rejoiced to belong and which enabled him to bear the hatred and the humiliations that he has to put up with from the rest of the world.

I saw worthy Jews basely caricatured, and the sight made my heart bleed. I saw how schools, comic papers, and innumerable other forces of the Gentile majority undermined the confidence even of the best of my fellow-Jews, and felt that this could not be allowed to continue.

Then I realized that only a common enterprise dear to the hearts of Jews all over the world could restore this people to health. It was a great achievement of Herzl's to have realized and proclaimed at the top of his voice that, the traditional attitude of the Jews being what it was, the establishment of a national home or, more accurately, a centre in Palestine, was a suitable object on which to concentrate our efforts.

All this you call nationalism, and there is something in the accusation. But a communal purpose, without which we can neither live nor die in this hostile world, can always be called by that ugly name. In any case it is a nationalism whose aim is not power but dignity and health. If we did not have to live among intolerant, narrow-minded, and violent people, I should be the first to throw over all nationalism in favour of universal humanity.

The objection that we Jews cannot be proper citizens of the German State, for example, if we want to be a " nation," is based on a misunderstanding of the nature of the State which springs from the intolerance of national majorities. Against that intolerance we shall never be safe, whether we call ourselves a " people " (or " nation ") or not.

I have put all this with brutal frankness for the

sake of brevity, but I know from your writings that you are a man who attends to the sense, not the form.

Letter to an Arab

March 15, 1930

Sir,

Your letter has given me great pleasure. It shows me that there is good will available on your side too for solving the present difficulties in a manner worthy of both our nations. I believe that these difficulties are more psychological than real, and that they can be got over if both sides bring honesty and good will to the task.

What makes the present position so bad is the fact that Jews and Arabs confront each other as opponents before the mandatory power. This state of affairs is unworthy of both nations and can only be altered by our finding a *via media* on which both sides agree.

I will now tell you how I think that the present difficulties might be remedied; at the same time I must add that this is only my personal opinion, which I have discussed with nobody. I am writing this letter in German because I am not capable of writing it in English myself and because I want myself to bear the entire responsibility for it. You will, I am sure, be able to get some Jewish friend of conciliation to translate it.

A Privy Council is to be formed to which the Jews and Arabs shall each send four representatives, who must be independent of all political parties.

Each group to be composed as follows :—

A doctor, elected by the Medical Association;

A lawyer, elected by the lawyers;
A working men's representative, elected by the
  trade unions;
An ecclesiastic, elected by the ecclesiastics.

These eight people are to meet once a week.
They undertake not to espouse the sectional
interests of their profession or nation but con-
scientiously and to the best of their power to aim
at the welfare of the whole population of the
country. Their deliberations shall be secret and
they are strictly forbidden to give any information
about them, even in private. When a decision
has been reached on any subject in which not
less than three members on each side concur, it
may be published, but only in the name of the
whole Council. If a member dissents he may
retire from the Council, but he is not thereby
released from the obligation to secrecy. If one
of the elective bodies above specified is dissatisfied
with a resolution of the Council, it may replace
its representative by another.

Even if this " Privy Council " has no definite
powers it may nevertheless bring about the
gradual composition of differences, and secure as
united representation of the common interests
of the country before the mandatory power, clear
of the dust of ephemeral politics.

Christianity and Judaism

If one purges the Judaism of the Prophets and
Christianity as Jesus Christ taught it of all subsequent additions, especially those of the priests,
one is left with a teaching which is capable of
curing all the social ills of humanity.

It is the duty of every man of good will to strive

steadfastly in his own little world to make this teaching of pure humanity a living force, so far as he can. If he makes an honest attempt in this direction without being crushed and trampled under foot by his contemporaries, he may consider himself and the community to which he belongs lucky.

OUT OF MY LATER YEARS

CONTENTS

CONTENTS

CONTENTS

Personalities

My People

1

PUBLISHER'S PREFACE

THIS SECOND VOLUME of collected essays by Albert Einstein covers a period of about fifteen years—1934 to 1950; the first anthology, published under the title *The World As I See It*, comprising material from 1922 to 1934.

Albert Einstein does not belong to that group of scholars who live in the "ivory tower" of their research work, oblivious to the world around them. On the contrary, he has always been an astute and critical observer of the trends and needs of his time. Indeed, frequently did he intervene by written as well as spoken appeal, and always, we should like to emphasize, for a humanitarian cause.

In this sense *Out of My Later Years* mirrors the philosophical, as well as political and social attitudes of its author. The chapters themselves represent addresses, articles, letters, appeals and miscellaneous papers hitherto unpublished.

We feel privileged to offer them to the public with hardly any editorial change—a moving document of the workings of a conscientious, profound and deeply humane mind.

Convictions and Beliefs

2

SELF-PORTRAIT

Of what is significant in one's own existence one is hardly aware, and it certainly should not bother the other fellow. What does a fish know about the water in which he swims all his life?

The bitter and the sweet come from the outside, the hard from within, from one's own efforts. For the most part I do the thing which my own nature drives me to do. It is embarrassing to earn so much respect and love for it. Arrows of hate have been shot at me too; but they never hit me, because somehow they belonged to another world, with which I have no connection whatsoever.

I live in that solitude which is painful in youth, but delicious in the years of maturity.

3

TEN FATEFUL YEARS

Reading once again the lines I wrote almost ten years ago,* I receive two strangely contrasting impressions. What I wrote then still seems essentially as true as ever; yet, it all seems curiously remote and strange. How can that be? Has the world changed so profoundly in ten years, or is it merely that I have grown ten years older, and my eyes see everything in a changed, dimmer light? What are ten years in the history of humanity? Must not all those forces that determine the life of man be regarded as constant compared with such a trifling interval? Is my critical reason so susceptible that the physiological change in my body during those ten years has been able to influence my concept of life so deeply? It seems clear to me that such considerations cannot throw light upon a change in the emotional approach to the general problems of life. Nor may the reasons for this curious change be sought in my own external circumstances; for I know that these have always played a subordinate part in my thoughts and emotions.

No, something quite different is involved. In these ten years confidence in the stability, yes, even the very basis for existence, of human society has largely vanished. One senses not only a threat to man's cultural heritage, but also that a lower value is placed upon all that one would like to see defended at all costs.

Conscious man, to be sure, has at all times been keenly

* To the volume *Living Philosophy*.

6

aware that life is an adventure, that life must, forever, be wrested from death. In part the dangers were external: one might fall downstairs and break one's neck, lose one's livelihood without fault, be condemned though innocent, or ruined by calumny. Life in human society meant dangers of all sorts; but these dangers were chaotic in nature, subject to chance. Human society, as a whole, seemed stable. Measured by the ideals of taste and morals it was decidedly imperfect. But, all in all, one felt at home with it and, apart from the many kinds of accidents, comparatively safe in it. One accepted its intrinsic qualities as a matter of course, as the air one breathed. Even standards of virtue, aspiration, and practical truth were taken for granted as an inviolable heritage, common to all civilized humanity.

To be sure, the first World War had already shaken this feeling of security. The sanctity of life vanished and the individual was no longer able to do as he pleased and to go where he liked. The lie was raised to the dignity of a political instrument. The war was, however, widely regarded as an external event, hardly or not at all as the result of man's conscious planful action. It was thought of as an interruption of man's normal life from the outside, universally considered unfortunate and evil. The feeling of security in regard to human aims and values remained, for the main part, unshaken.

The subsequent development is sharply marked by political events that are not as far-reaching as the less easily grasped socio-psychological background. First a brief, promising step forward characterized by the creation of the League of Nations through the grandiose initiative of Wilson, and the establishment of a system of collective security among the nations. Then the formation of Fascist states, attended by a series of broken pacts and undisguised acts of violence against humanity and against weaker nations. The system of collective security collapsed like a house of cards—a collapse the consequences of which cannot be measured even today. It was a manifestation of weakness of character and lack of responsibility on the part of the leaders in the affected countries, and of shortsighted selfishness in the democracies—those that still remain outwardly intact—which prevented any vigorous counterattack.

Things grew even worse than a pessimist of the deepest dye would have dared prophesy. In Europe to the east of the Rhine free exercise of the intellect exists no longer, the population is terrorized by gangsters who have seized power, and youth is poisoned by systematic lies. The pseudo-success of political adventurers has dazzled the rest of the world; it becomes apparent everywhere that this generation lacks the strength and force which enabled previous generations to win, in painful struggle and at great sacrifice, the political and individual freedom of man.

Awareness of this state of affairs overshadows every hour of my present existence, while ten years ago it did not yet occupy my thoughts. It is this that I feel so strongly in re-reading the words written in the past.

And yet I know that, all in all, man changes but little, even though prevailing notions make him appear in a very different light at different times, and even though current trends like the present bring him unimaginable sorrow. Nothing of all that will remain but a few pitiful pages in the history books, briefly picturing to the youth of future generations the follies of its ancestors.

4

MORAL DECAY

ALL RELIGIONS, arts and sciences are branches of the same tree. All these aspirations are directed toward ennobling man's life, lifting it from the sphere of mere physical existence and leading the individual toward freedom. It is no mere chance that our older universities have developed from clerical schools. Both churches and universities—insofar as they live up to their true function—serve the ennoblement of the individual. They seek to fulfill this great task by spreading moral and cultural understanding, renouncing the use of brute force.

The essential unity of ecclesiastical and secular cultural institutions was lost during the 19th century, to the point of senseless hostility. Yet there never was any doubt as to the striving for culture. No one doubted the sacredness of the goal. It was the approach that was disputed.

The political and economic conflicts and complexities of the last few decades have brought before our eyes dangers which even the darkest pessimists of the last century did not dream of. The injunctions of the Bible concerning human conduct were then accepted by believer and infidel alike as self-evident demands for individuals and society. No one would have been taken seriously who failed to acknowledge the quest for objective truth and knowledge as man's highest and eternal aim.

Yet today we must recognize with horror that these pillars of civilized human existence have lost their firmness. Nations that once ranked high bow down before tyrants who dare openly to assert: Right is that which serves us! The quest for truth for its own sake has no justification and is not to be tolerated. Arbitrary rule, oppression, persecution of individuals, faiths and communities are openly practiced in those countries and accepted as justifiable or inevitable.

And the rest of the world has slowly grown accustomed to these symptoms of moral decay. One misses the elementary reaction against injustice and for justice—that reaction which in the long run represents man's only protection against a relapse into barbarism. I am firmly convinced that the passionate will for justice and truth has done more to improve man's condition than calculating political shrewdness which in the long run only breeds general distrust. Who can doubt that Moses was a better leader of humanity than Machiavelli?

During the War someone tried to convince a great Dutch scientist that might went before right in the history of man. "I cannot disprove the accuracy of your assertion," he replied, "but I do know that I should not care to live in such a world!"

Let us think, feel and act like this man, refusing to accept fateful compromise. Let us not even shun the fight when it is unavoidable to preserve right and the dignity of man. If we do this we shall soon return to conditions that will allow us to rejoice in humanity.

5

MESSAGE FOR POSTERITY

OUR TIME IS RICH in inventive minds, the inventions of
which could facilitate our lives considerably. We are crossing
the seas by power and utilize power also in order to relieve
humanity from all tiring muscular work. We have learned to
fly and we are able to send messages and news without any
difficulty over the entire world through electric waves.

However, the production and distribution of commodities
is entirely unorganized so that everybody must live in fear
of being eliminated from the economic cycle, in this way suffering for the want of everything. Furthermore, people living
in different countries kill each other at irregular time intervals, so that also for this reason any one who thinks about the
future must live in fear and terror. This is due to the fact that
the intelligence and the character of the masses are incomparably lower than the intelligence and character of the few
who produce something valuable for the community.

I trust that posterity will read these statements with a feeling of proud and justified superiority.

6

ON FREEDOM

I KNOW THAT IT IS a hopeless undertaking to debate about fundamental value judgments. For instance if someone approves, as a goal, the extirpation of the human race from the earth, one cannot refute such a viewpoint on rational grounds. But if there is agreement on certain goals and values, one can argue rationally about the means by which these objectives may be attained. Let us, then, indicate two goals which may well be agreed upon by nearly all who read these lines.

1. Those instrumental goods which should serve to maintain the life and health of all human beings should be produced by the least possible labor of all.

2. The satisfaction of physical needs is indeed the indispensable precondition of a satisfactory existence, but in itself it is not enough. In order to be content men must also have the possibility of developing their intellectual and artistic powers to whatever extent accord with their personal characteristics and abilities.

The first of these two goals requires the promotion of all knowledge relating to the laws of nature and the laws of social processes, that is, the promotion of all scientific endeavor. For scientific endeavor is a natural whole the parts of which mutually support one another in a way which, to be sure, no one can anticipate. However, the progress of science presupposes the possibility of unrestricted communication of all results and judgments—freedom of expression and instruction in all realms of intellectual endeavor. By freedom I understand social conditions of such a kind that the expression of opinions and assertions about general and particular matters of knowledge will not involve dangers or serious disadvantages for him who expresses them. This freedom of communication is indispensable for the development and extension of scientific knowledge, a consideration of much practical import. In the first instance it must be guaranteed by law. But laws alone cannot secure freedom of expression; in order that every man may present his views without penalty there must be a spirit of tolerance in the entire population. Such an ideal of external liberty can never be fully attained but must be sought unremittingly if scientific thought, and philosophical and creative thinking in general, are to be advanced as far as possible.

If the second goal, that is, the possibility of the spiritual development of all individuals, is to be secured, a second kind of outward freedom is necessary. Man should not have to work for the achievement of the necessities of life to such an extent that he has neither time nor strength for personal activities. Without this second kind of outward liberty, freedom of expression is useless for him. Advances in technology would provide the possibility of this kind of freedom if the problem of a reasonable division of labor were solved.

The development of science and of the creative activities of the spirit in general requires still another kind of freedom, which may be characterized as inward freedom. It is this freedom of the spirit which consists in the independence of thought from the restrictions of authoritarian and social prejudices as well as from unphilosophical routinizing and habit in general. This inward freedom is an infrequent gift of nature and a worthy objective for the individual. Yet the community can do much to further this achievement, too, at least by not interfering with its development. Thus schools may interfere with the development of inward freedom through authoritarian influences and through imposing on young people excessive spiritual burdens; on the other hand schools may favor such freedom by encouraging independent thought. Only if outward and inner freedom are constantly and consciously pursued is there a possibility of spiritual development and perfection and thus of improving man's outward and inner life.

7

MORALS AND EMOTIONS

We ALL KNOW, from what we experience with and within ourselves, that our conscious acts spring from our desires and our fears. Intuition tells us that that is true also of our fellows and of the higher animals. We all try to escape pain and death, while we seek what is pleasant. We all are ruled in what we do by impulses; and these impulses are so organized that our actions in general serve for our self-preservation and that of the race. Hunger, love, pain, fear are some of those inner forces which rule the individual's instinct for self-preservation. At the same time, as social beings, we are moved in the relations with our fellow beings by such feelings as sympathy, pride, hate, need for power, pity, and so on. All these primary impulses, not easily described in words, are the springs of man's actions. All such action would cease if those powerful elemental forces were to cease stirring within us.

Though our conduct seems so very different from that of the higher animals, the primary instincts are much alike in them and in us. The most evident difference springs from the important part which is played in man by a relatively strong power of imagination and by the capacity to think, aided as it is by language and other symbolical devices. Thought is the organizing factor in man, intersected between the causal primary instincts and the resulting actions. In that way imagination and intelligence enter into our existence in the part of servants of the primary instincts. But their intervention makes our acts to serve ever less merely the immediate claims

15

of our instincts. Through them the primary instinct attaches itself to ends which become ever more distant. The instincts bring thought into action, and thought provokes intermediary actions inspired by emotions which are likewise related to the ultimate end. Through repeated performance, this process brings it about that ideas and beliefs acquire and retain a strong effective power even after the ends which gave them that power are long forgotten. In abnormal cases of such intensive borrowed emotions, which cling to objects emptied of their erstwhile effective meaning, we speak of fetishism.

Yet the process which I have indicated plays a very important part also in ordinary life. Indeed there is no doubt that to this process—which one may describe as a spiritualizing of the emotions and of thought—that to it man owes the most subtle and refined pleasures of which he is capable: the pleasure in the beauty of artistic creation and of logical trains of thought.

As far as I can see, there is one consideration which stands at the threshold of all moral teaching. If men as individuals surrender to the call of their elementary instincts, avoiding pain and seeking satisfaction only for their own selves, the result for them all taken together must be a state of insecurity, of fear, and of promiscuous misery. If, besides that, they use their intelligence from an individualist, i.e., a selfish standpoint, building up their life on the illusion of a happy unattached existence, things will be hardly better. In comparison with the other elementary instincts and impulses, the emotions of love, of pity and of friendship are too weak and too cramped to lead to a tolerable state of human society.

The solution of this problem, when freely considered, is simple enough, and it seems also to echo from the teachings of the wise men of the past always in the same strain: All men should let their conduct be guided by the same principles; and those principles should be such, that by following them there should accrue to all as great a measure as possible of security and satisfaction, and as small a measure as possible of suffering.

Of course, this general requirement is much too vague that we should be able to draw from it with confidence specific rules to guide the individuals in their actions. And indeed, these specific rules will have to change in keeping with changing circumstances. If this were the main difficulty that stands in the way of that keen conception, the millenary fate of man would have been incomparably happier than it actually was, or still is. Man would not have killed man, tortured each other, exploited each other by force and by guile.

The real difficulty, the difficulty which has baffled the sages of all times, is rather this: how can we make our teaching so potent in the emotional life of man, that its influence should withstand the pressure of the elemental psychic forces in the individual? We do not know, of course, if the sages of the past have really asked themselves this question, consciously and in this form; but we do know how they have tried to solve the problem.

Long before men were ripe, namely, to be faced with such a universal moral attitude, fear of the dangers of life had led them to attribute to various imaginary personal beings, not physically tangible, power to release those natural forces which men feared or perhaps welcomed. And they believed that those beings, which everywhere dominated their imagination, were psychically made in their own image, but were endowed with superhuman powers. These were the primitive precursors of the idea of God. Sprung in the first place from the fears which filled man's daily life, the belief in the existence of such beings, and in their extraordinary powers, has had so strong an influence on men and their conduct, that it is difficult for us to imagine. Hence it is not surprising that those who set out to establish the moral idea, as embracing all men equally, did so by linking it closely with religion. And the fact that those moral claims were the same for all men, may have had much to do with the development of mankind's religious culture from polytheism to monotheism.

The universal moral idea thus owed its original psychological potency to that link with religion. Yet in another sense that close association was fatal for the moral idea. Monotheistic religion acquired different forms with various peoples and groups. Although those differences were by no means fundamental, yet they soon were felt more strongly than the essentials that were common. And in that way religion often caused enmity and conflict, instead of binding mankind together with the universal moral idea.

Then came the growth of the natural sciences, with their great influence on thought and practical life, weakening still more in modern times the religious sentiment of the peoples. The causal and objective mode of thinking—though not necessarily in contradiction with the religious sphere—leaves in most people little room for a deepening religious sense. And because of the traditional close link between religion and morals, that has brought with it, in the last hundred years or so, a serious weakening of moral thought and sentiment. That, to my mind, is a main cause for the barbarization of political ways in our time. Taken together with the terrifying efficiency of the new technical means, the barbarization already forms a fearful threat for the civilized world.

Needless to say, one is glad that religion strives to work for the realization of the moral principle. Yet the moral imperative is not a matter for church and religion alone, but the most precious traditional possession of all mankind. Consider from this standpoint the position of the Press, or of the schools with their competitive method! Everything is dominated by the cult of efficiency and of success and not by the value of things and men in relation to the moral ends of human society. To that must be added the moral deterioration resulting from a ruthless economic struggle. The deliberate nurturing of the moral sense also outside the religious sphere, however, should help also in this, to lead men to look upon social problems as so many opportunities for joyous service towards a better life. For looked at from a simple human point of view, moral conduct does not mean merely a stern demand to renounce some of the desired joys of life, but rather a sociable interest in a happier lot for all men.

This conception implies one requirement above all—that every individual should have the opportunity to develop the gifts which may be latent in him. Alone in that way can the individual obtain the satisfaction to which he is justly entitled; and alone in that way can the community achieve its richest flowering. For everything that is really great and inspiring is created by the individual who can labour in freedom. Restriction is justified only in so far as it may be needed for the security of existence.

There is one other thing which follows from that conception—that we must not only tolerate differences between individuals and between groups, but we should indeed welcome them and look upon them as an enriching of our existence. That is the essence of all true tolerance; without tolerance in this widest sense there can be no question of true morality.

Morality in the sense here briefly indicated is not a fixed and stark system. It is rather a standpoint from which all questions which arise in life could and should be judged. It is a task never finished, something always present to guide our judgment and to inspire our conduct. Can you imagine that any man truly filled with this ideal could be content:—

Were he to receive from his fellow men a much greater return in goods and services than most other men ever receive?

Were his country, because it feels itself for the time being militarily secure, to stand aloof from the aspiration to create a supra-national system of security and justice?

Could he look on passively, or perhaps even with indifference, when elsewhere in the world innocent people are being brutally persecuted, deprived of their rights or even massacred?

To ask these questions is to answer them!

8

SCIENCE AND RELIGION

I

During the last century, and part of the one before, it was widely held that there was an unreconcilable conflict between knowledge and belief. The opinion prevailed among advanced minds that it was time that belief should be replaced increasingly by knowledge; belief that did not itself rest on knowledge was superstition, and as such had to be opposed. According to this conception, the sole function of education was to open the way to thinking and knowing, and the school, as the outstanding organ for the people's education, must serve that end exclusively.

One will probably find but rarely, if at all, the rationalistic standpoint expressed in such crass form; for any sensible man would see at once how one-sided is such a statement of the position. But it is just as well to state a thesis starkly and nakedly, if one wants to clear up one's mind as to its nature.

It is true that convictions can best be supported with experience and clear thinking. On this point one must agree unreservedly with the extreme rationalist. The weak point of his conception is, however, this, that those convictions which are necessary and determinant for our conduct and judgments, cannot be found solely along this solid scientific way.

For the scientific method can teach us nothing else beyond how facts are related to, and conditioned by, each other. The aspiration toward such objective knowledge belongs to the highest of which man is capable, and you will certainly not suspect me of wishing to belittle the achievements and the heroic efforts of man in this sphere. Yet it is equally clear that knowledge of what *is* does not open the door directly to what *should be.* One can have the clearest and most complete knowledge of what *is,* and yet not be able to deduct from that what should be the *goal* of our human aspirations. Objective knowledge provides us with powerful instruments for the achievements of certain ends, but the ultimate goal itself and the longing to reach it must come from another source. And it is hardly necessary to argue for the view that our existence and our activity acquire meaning only by the setting up of such a goal and of corresponding values. The knowledge of truth as such is wonderful, but it is so little capable of acting as a guide that it cannot prove even the justification and the value of the aspiration towards that very knowledge of truth. Here we face, therefore, the limits of the purely rational conception of our existence.

But it must not be assumed that intelligent thinking can play no part in the formation of the goal and of ethical judgments. When someone realizes that for the achievement of an end certain means would be useful, the means itself becomes thereby an end. Intelligence makes clear to us the interrelation of means and ends. But mere thinking cannot give us a sense of the ultimate and fundamental ends. To make clear these fundamental ends and valuations, and to set them fast in the emotional life of the individual, seems to me precisely the most important function which religion has to perform in the social life of man. And if one asks whence derives the authority of such fundamental ends, since they cannot be stated and justified merely by reason, one can only answer: they exist in a healthy society as powerful traditions, which act upon the conduct and aspirations and judgments of the individuals; they are there, that is, as something living, without its being necessary to find justification for their existence. They come into being not through demonstration but through revelation, through the medium of powerful personalities. One must not attempt to justify them, but rather to sense their nature simply and clearly.

The highest principles for our aspirations and judgments are given to us in the Jewish-Christian religious tradition. It is a very high goal which, with our weak powers, we can reach only very inadequately, but which gives a sure foundation to our aspirations and valuations. If one were to take that goal out of its religious form and look merely at its purely human side, one might state it perhaps thus: free and responsible development of the individual, so that he may place his powers freely and gladly in the service of all mankind.

There is no room in this for the divinization of a nation, of a class, let alone of an individual. Are we not all children of one father, as it is said in religious language? Indeed, even the divinization of humanity, as an abstract totality, would not be in the spirit of that ideal. It is only to the individual that a soul is given. And the high destiny of the individual is to serve rather than to rule, or to impose himself in any other way.

If one looks at the substance rather than at the form, then one can take these words as expressing also the fundamental democratic position. The true democrat can worship his nation as little as can the man who is religious, in our sense of the term.

What, then, in all this, is the function of education and of the school? They should help the young person to grow up in such a spirit that these fundamental principles should be to him as the air which he breathes. Teaching alone cannot do that.

If one holds these high principles clearly before one's eyes, and compares them with the life and spirit of our times, then it appears glaringly that civilized mankind finds itself at present in grave danger. In the totalitarian states it is the rulers themselves who strive actually to destroy that spirit of humanity. In less threatened parts it is nationalism and intolerance, as well as the oppression of the individuals by economic means, which threaten to choke these most precious traditions.

A realization of how great is the danger is spreading, however, among thinking people, and there is much search for means with which to meet the danger—means in the field of national and international politics, of legislation, of organization in general. Such efforts are, no doubt, greatly needed. Yet the ancients knew something which we seem to have forgotten. All means prove but a blunt instrument, if they have not behind them a living spirit. But if the longing for the achievement of the goal is powerfully alive within us, then shall we not lack the strength to find the means for reaching the goal and for translating it into deeds.

II

It would not be difficult to come to an agreement as to what we understand by science. Science is the century-old endeavor to bring together by means of systematic thought the perceptible phenomena of this world into as thoroughgoing an association as possible. To put it boldly, it is the attempt at the posterior reconstruction of existence by the process of conceptualization. But when asking myself what religion is I cannot think of the answer so easily. And even after finding an answer which may satisfy me at this particular moment I still remain convinced that I can never under any circumstances bring together, even to a slight extent, all those who have given this question serious consideration.

At first, then, instead of asking what religion is I should prefer to ask what characterizes the aspirations of a person who gives me the impression of being religious: A person who is religiously enlightened appears to me to be one who has, to the best of his ability, liberated himself from the fetters of his selfish desires and is preoccupied with thoughts, feelings, and aspirations to which he clings because of their super-personal value. It seems to me that what is important is the force of this super-personal content and the depth of the conviction concerning its overpowering meaningfulness, regardless of whether any attempt is made to unite this content with a divine Being, for otherwise it would not be possible to count Buddha and Spinoza as religious personalities. Accordingly, a religious person is devout in the sense that he has no doubt of the significance and loftiness of those super-personal objects and goals which neither require nor are capable of rational foundation. They exist with the same necessity and matter-of-factness as he himself. In this sense religion is the age-old endeavor of mankind to become clearly and completely conscious of these values and goals and constantly to strengthen and extend their effect. If one conceives of religion and science according to these definitions then a conflict between them appears impossible. For science can only ascertain what *is*, but not what *should be*, and outside of its domain value judgments of all kinds remain necessary. Religion, on the other hand, deals only with evaluations of human thought and action: it cannot justifiably speak of facts and relationships between facts. According to this interpretation the well-known conflicts between religion and science in the past must all be ascribed to a misapprehension of the situation which has been described.

For example, a conflict arises when a religious community insists on the absolute truthfulness of all statements recorded in the Bible. This means an intervention on the part of religion into the sphere of science; this is where the struggle of the Church against the doctrines of Galileo and Darwin belongs. On the other hand, representatives of science have often made an attempt to arrive at fundamental judgments with respect to values and ends on the basis of scientific method, and in this way have set themselves in opposition to religion. These conflicts have all sprung from fatal errors.

Now, even though the realms of religion and science in themselves are clearly marked off from each other, nevertheless there exist between the two strong reciprocal relationships and dependencies. Though religion may be that which determines the goal, it has, nevertheless, learned from science, in the broadest sense, what means will contribute to the attainment of the goals it has set up. But science can only be created by those who are thoroughly imbued with the aspiration towards truth and understanding. This source of feeling, however, springs from the sphere of religion. To this there also belongs the faith in the possibility that the regulations valid for the world of existence are rational, that is, comprehensible to reason. I cannot conceive of a genuine scientist without that profound faith. The situation may be expressed by an image: Science without religion is lame, religion without science is blind.

Though I have asserted above that in truth a legitimate conflict between religion and science cannot exist I must nevertheless qualify this assertion once again on an essential point, with reference to the actual content of historical religions. This qualification has to do with the concept of God. During the youthful period of mankind's spiritual evolution human fantasy created gods in man's own image, who, by the operations of their will were supposed to determine, or at any rate to influence the phenomenal world. Man sought to alter the disposition of these gods in his own favor by means of magic and prayer. The idea of God in the religions taught at present is a sublimation of that old conception of the gods. Its anthropomorphic character is shown, for instance, by the fact that men appeal to the Divine Being in prayers and plead for the fulfilment of their wishes.

Nobody, certainly, will deny that the idea of the existence of an omnipotent, just and omnibeneficent personal God is able to accord man solace, help, and guidance; also, by virtue of its simplicity it is accessible to the most undeveloped mind. But, on the other hand, there are decisive weaknesses attached to this idea in itself, which have been painfully felt since the beginning of history. That is, if this being is omnipotent then every occurrence, including every human action, every human thought, and every human feeling and aspiration is also His work; how is it possible to think of holding men responsible for their deeds and thoughts before such an almighty Being? In giving out punishment and rewards He would to a certain extent be passing judgment on Himself. How can this be combined with the goodness and righteousness ascribed to Him?

The main source of the present-day conflicts between the spheres of religion and of science lies in this concept of a personal God. It is the aim of science to establish general rules which determine the reciprocal connection of objects and events in time and space. For these rules, or laws of nature, absolutely general validity is required—not proven. It is mainly a program, and faith in the possibility of its accomplishment in principle is only founded on partial successes. But hardly anyone could be found who would deny these partial successes and ascribe them to human self-deception. The fact that on the basis of such laws we are able to predict the temporal behavior of phenomena in certain domains with great precision and certainty is deeply embedded in the consciousness of the modern man, even though he may have grasped very little of the contents of those laws. He need only consider that planetary courses within the solar system may be calculated in advance with great exactitude on the basis of a limited number of simple laws. In a similar way, though not with the same precision, it is possible to calculate in advance the mode of operation of an electric motor, a transmission system, or of a wireless apparatus, even when dealing with a novel development.

To be sure, when the number of factors coming into play in a phenomenological complex is too large scientific method in most cases fails us. One need only think of the weather, in which case prediction even for a few days ahead is impossible. Nevertheless no one doubts that we are confronted with a causal connection whose causal components are in the main known to us. Occurrences in this domain are beyond the reach of exact prediction because of the variety of factors in operation, not because of any lack of order in nature.

We have penetrated far less deeply into the regularities obtaining within the realm of living things, but deeply enough nevertheless to sense at least the rule of fixed necessity. One need only think of the systematic order in heredity, and in the effect of poisons, as for instance alcohol, on the behavior of organic beings. What is still lacking here is a grasp of connections of profound generality, but not a knowledge of order in itself.

The more a man is imbued with the ordered regularity of all events the firmer becomes his conviction that there is no room left by the side of this ordered regularity for causes of a different nature. For him neither the rule of human nor the rule of divine will exists as an independent cause of natural events. To be sure, the doctrine of a personal God interfering with natural events could never be *refuted*, in the real sense, by science, for this doctrine can always take refuge in those domains in which scientific knowledge has not yet been able to set foot.

But I am persuaded that such behavior on the part of the representatives of religion would not only be unworthy but also fatal. For a doctrine which is able to maintain itself not in clear light but only in the dark, will of necessity lose its effect on mankind, with incalculable harm to human progress. In their struggle for the ethical good, teachers of religion must have the stature to give up the doctrine of a personal God, that is, give up that source of fear and hope which in the past placed such vast power in the hands of priests. In their labors they will have to avail themselves of those forces which are capable of cultivating the Good, the True, and the Beautiful in humanity itself. This is, to be sure, a more difficult but an incomparably more worthy task.[1] After religious teachers accomplish the refining process indicated they will surely recognize with joy that true religion has been ennobled and made more profound by scientific knowledge.

If it is one of the goals of religion to liberate mankind as far as possible from the bondage of egocentric cravings, desires, and fears, scientific reasoning can aid religion in yet another sense. Although it is true that it is the goal of science to discover rules which permit the association and foretelling of facts, this is not its only aim. It also seeks to reduce the connections discovered to the smallest possible number of mutually independent conceptual elements. It is in this striving after the rational unification of the manifold that it encounters its greatest successes, even though it is precisely this attempt which causes it to run the greatest risk of falling a prey to illusions. But whoever has undergone the intense experience of successful advances made in this domain, is moved by profound reverence for the rationality made manifest in existence. By way of the understanding he achieves a far-reaching emancipation from the shackles of personal hopes and desires, and thereby attains that humble attitude of mind towards the grandeur of reason incarnate in existence, and which, in its profoundest depths, is inaccessible to man. This attitude, however, appears to me to be religious, in the highest sense of the word. And so it seems to me that science not only purifies the religious impulse of the dross of its anthropomorphism but also contributes to a religious spiritualization of our understanding of life.

The further the spiritual evolution of mankind advances,

[1] This thought is convincingly presented in Herbert Samuel's book, *Belief and Action*.

the more certain it seems to me that the path to genuine religiosity does not lie through the fear of life, and the fear of death, and blind faith, but through striving after rational knowledge. In this sense I believe that the priest must become a teacher if he wishes to do justice to his lofty educational mission.

9

ON EDUCATION

A DAY OF CELEBRATION generally is in the first place dedicated to retrospect, especially to the memory of personages who have gained special distinction for the development of the cultural life. This friendly service for our predecessors must indeed not be neglected, particularly as such a memory of the best of the past is proper to stimulate the well-disposed of today to a courageous effort. But this should be done by someone who, from his youth, has been connected with this State and is familiar with its past, not by one who like a gypsy has wandered about and gathered his experiences in all kinds of countries.

Thus, there is nothing else left for me but to speak about such questions as, independently of space and time, always have been and will be connected with educational matters. In this attempt I cannot lay any claim to being an authority, especially as intelligent and well-meaning men of all times have dealt with educational problems and have certainly repeatedly expressed their views clearly about these matters. From what source shall I, as a partial layman in the realm of pedagogy, derive courage to expound opinions with no foundations except personal experience and personal conviction? If it were really a scientific matter, one would probably be tempted to silence by such considerations.

However, with the affairs of active human beings it is different. Here knowledge of truth alone does not suffice; on the contrary this knowledge must continually be renewed by ceaseless effort, if it is not to be lost. It resembles a statue of marble which stands in the desert and is continuously threatened with burial by the shifting sand. The hands of service must ever be at work, in order that the marble continue lastingly to shine in the sun. To these serving hands mine also shall belong.

The school has always been the most important means of transferring the wealth of tradition from one generation to the next. This applies today in an even higher degree than in former times for, through modern development of the economic life, the family as bearer of tradition and education has been weakened. The continuance and health of human society is therefore in a still higher degree dependent on the school than formerly.

Sometimes one sees in the school simply the instrument for transferring a certain maximum quantity of knowledge to the growing generation. But that is not right. Knowledge is dead; the school, however, serves the living. It should develop in the young individuals those qualities and capabilities which are of value for the welfare of the commonwealth. But that does not mean that individuality should be destroyed and the individual become a mere tool of the community, like a bee or an ant. For a community of standardized individuals without personal originality and personal aims would be a poor community without possibilities for development. On the contrary, the aim must be the training of independently acting and thinking individuals, who, however, see in the service of the community their highest life problem. As far as I can judge, the English school system comes nearest to the realization of this ideal.

But how shall one try to attain this ideal? Should one perhaps try to realize this aim by moralizing? Not at all. Words are and remain an empty sound, and the road to perdition has ever been accompanied by lip service to an ideal. But personalities are not formed by what is heard and said, but by labor and activity.

The most important method of education accordingly always has consisted of that in which the pupil was urged to actual performance. This applies as well to the first attempts at writing of the primary boy as to the doctor's thesis on graduation from the university, or as to the mere memorizing of a poem, the writing of a composition, the interpretation and translation of a text, the solving of a mathematical problem or the practice of physical sport.

But behind every achievement exists the motivation which is at the foundation of it and which in turn is strengthened and nourished by the accomplishment of the undertaking. Here there are the greatest differences and they are of greatest importance to the educational value of the school. The same work may owe its origin to fear and compulsion, ambitious desire for authority and distinction, or loving interest in the object and a desire for truth and understanding, and thus to that divine curiosity which every healthy child possesses, but which so often early is weakened. The educational influence which is exercised upon the pupil by the accomplishment of one and the same work may be widely different, depending upon whether fear of hurt, egoistic passion or desire for pleasure and satisfaction are at the bottom of this work. And nobody will maintain that the administration of the school and the attitude of the teachers does not have an influence upon the molding of the psychological foundation for pupils.

To me the worst thing seems to be for a school principally to work with methods of fear, force and artificial authority. Such treatment destroys the sound sentiments, the sincerity and the self-confidence of the pupil. It produces the submissive subject. It is no wonder that such schools are the rule in Germany and Russia. I know that the schools in this country are free from this worst evil; this also is so in Switzerland and probably in all democratically governed countries. It is comparatively simple to keep the school free from this worst of all evils. Give into the power of the teacher the fewest possible coercive measures, so that the only source of the pupil's respect for the teacher is the human and intellectual qualities of the latter.

The second-named motive, ambition or, in milder terms, the aiming at recognition and consideration, lies firmly fixed in human nature. With absence of mental stimulus of this kind, human cooperation would be entirely impossible; the desire for the approval of one's fellowman certainly is one of the most important binding powers of society. In this complex of feelings, constructive and destructive forces lie closely together. Desire for approval and recognition is a healthy motive; but the desire to be acknowledged as better, stronger or more intelligent than a fellow being or fellow scholar easily leads to an excessively egoistic psychological adjustment, which may become injurious for the individual and for the community. Therefore the school and the teacher must guard against employing the easy method of creating individual ambition, in order to induce the pupils to diligent work.

Darwin's theory of the struggle for existence and the selectivity connected with it has by many people been cited as authorization of the encouragement of the spirit of competition. Some people also in such a way have tried to prove pseudo-scientifically the necessity of the destructive economic struggle of competition between individuals. But this is wrong, because man owes his strength in the struggle for existence to the fact that he is a socially living animal. As little as a battle between single ants of an ant hill is essential for survival, just so little is this the case with the individual members of a human community.

Therefore one should guard against preaching to the young man success in the customary sense as the aim of life. For a successful man is he who receives a great deal from his fellowmen, usually incomparably more than corresponds to his service to them. The value of a man, however, should be seen in what he gives and not in what he is able to receive.

The most important motive for work in the school and in life is the pleasure in work, pleasure in its result and the knowledge of the value of the result to the community. In the awakening and strengthening of these psychological forces in the young man, I see the most important task given by the school. Such a psychological foundation alone leads to a joyous desire for the highest possessions of men, knowledge and artistlike workmanship.

The awakening of these productive psychological powers is certainly less easy than the practice of force or the awakening of individual ambition but is the more valuable for it. The point is to develop the childlike inclination for play and the childlike desire for recognition and to guide the child over to important fields for society; it is that education which in the main is founded upon the desire for successful activity and acknowledgment. If the school succeeds in working successfully from such points of view, it will be highly honored by the rising generation and the tasks given by the school will be submitted to as a sort of gift. I have known children who preferred schooltime to vacation.

Such a school demands from the teacher that he be a kind of artist in his province. What can be done that this spirit be gained in the school? For this there is just as little a universal remedy as there is for an individual to remain well. But there are certain necessary conditions which can be met. First, teachers should grow up in such schools. Second, the teacher should be given extensive liberty in the selection of the material to be taught and the methods of teaching employed by him. For it is true also of him that pleasure in the shaping of his work is killed by force and exterior pressure.

If you have followed attentively my meditations up to this point, you will probably wonder about one thing. I have spoken fully about in what spirit, according to my opinion, youth should be instructed. But I have said nothing yet about the choice of subjects for instruction, nor about the method of teaching. Should language predominate or technical education in science?

To this I answer: In my opinion all this is of secondary importance. If a young man has trained his muscles and physical endurance by gymnastics and walking, he will later be fitted for every physical work. This is also analogous to the training of the mind and the exercising of the mental and manual skill. Thus the wit was not wrong who defined education in this way: "Education is that which remains, if one has forgotten everything he learned in school." For this reason I am not at all anxious to take sides in the struggle between the followers of the classical philologic-historical education and the education more devoted to natural science.

On the other hand, I want to oppose the idea that the school has to teach directly that special knowledge and those accomplishments which one has to use later directly in life. The demands of life are much too manifold to let such a specialized training in school appear possible. Apart from that, it seems to me, moreover, objectionable to treat the individual like a dead tool. The school should always have as its aim that the young man leave it as a harmonious personality, not as a specialist. This in my opinion is true in a certain sense even for technical schools, whose students will devote themselves to a quite definite profession. The development of general ability for independent thinking and judgment should always be placed foremost, not the acquisition of special knowledge. If a person masters the fundamentals of his subject and has learned to think and work independently, he will surely find his way and besides will better be able to adapt himself to progress and changes than the person whose training principally consists in the acquiring of detailed knowledge.

Finally, I wish to emphasize once more that what has been said here in a somewhat categorical form does not claim to mean more than the personal opinion of a man, which is founded upon *nothing but* his own personal experience, which he has gathered as a student and as a teacher.

Science

10

THE THEORY OF RELATIVITY

MATHEMATICS DEALS exclusively with the relations of concepts to each other without consideration of their relation to experience. Physics too deals with mathematical concepts; however, these concepts attain physical content only by the clear determination of their relation to the objects of experience. This in particular is the case for the concepts of motion, space, time.

The theory of relativity is that physical theory which is based on a consistent physical interpretation of these three concepts. The name "theory of relativity" is connected with the fact that motion from the point of view of possible experience always appears as the *relative* motion of one object with respect to another (e.g., of a car with respect to the ground, or the earth with respect to the sun and the fixed stars). Motion is never observable as "motion with respect to space" or, as it has been expressed, as "absolute motion." The "principle of relativity" in its widest sense is contained in the statement: The totality of physical phenomena is of such a character that it gives no basis for the introduction of the concept of "absolute motion"; or shorter but less precise: There is no absolute motion.

It might seem that our insight would gain little from such a negative statement. In reality, however, it is a strong restriction for the (conceivable) laws of nature. In this sense there exists an analogy between the theory of relativity and thermodynamics. The latter too is based on a negative statement: "There exists no perpetuum mobile."

41

The development of the theory of relativity proceeded in two steps, "special theory of relativity" and "general theory of relativity." The latter presumes the validity of the former as a limiting case and is its consistent continuation.

A. *Special theory of relativity.*

Physical interpretation of space and time in classical mechanics.

Geometry, from a physical standpoint, is the totality of laws according to which rigid bodies mutually at rest can be placed with respect to each other (e.g., a triangle consists of three rods whose ends touch permanently). It is assumed that with such an interpretation the Euclidean laws are valid. "Space" in this interpretation is in principle an infinite rigid body (or skeleton) to which the position of all other bodies is related (body of reference). Analytic geometry (Descartes) uses as the body of reference, which represents space, three mutually perpendicular rigid rods on which the "coordinates" (x, y, z) of space points are measured in the known manner as perpendicular projections (with the aid of a rigid unit-measure).

Physics deals with "events" in space and time. To each event belongs, besides its place coordinates x, y, z, a time value t. The latter was considered measurable by a clock (ideal periodic process) of negligible spatial extent. This clock C is to be considered at rest at one point of the coordinate system, e.g., at the coordinate origin (x = y = z = O). The time of an event taking place at a point P(x, y, z) is then defined as the time shown on the clock C simultaneously with the event. Here the concept "simultaneous" was assumed as physically meaningful without special definition. This is a lack of exactness which seems harmless only since with the help of light (whose velocity is practically infinite from the point of view of daily experience) the simultaneity of spatially distant events can apparently be decided immediately.

The special theory of relativity removes this lack of precision by defining simultaneity physically with the use of light signals. The time t of the event in P is the reading of the clock C at the time of arrival of a light signal emitted from the event, corrected with respect to the time needed for the light signal to travel the distance. This correction presumes (postulates) that the velocity of light is constant.

This definition reduces the concept of simultaneity of spatially distant events to that of the simultaneity of events happening at the same place (coincidence), namely the arrival of the light signal at C and the reading of C.

Classical mechanics is based on Galileo's principle: A body is in rectilinear and uniform motion as long as other bodies do not act on it. This statement cannot be valid for arbitrary moving systems of coordinates. It can claim validity only for so-called "inertial systems". Inertial systems are in rectilinear and uniform motion with respect to each other. In classical physics laws claim validity only with respect to all inertial systems (special principle of relativity).

It is now easy to understand the dilemma which has led to the special theory of relativity. Experience and theory have gradually led to the conviction that light in empty space always travels with the same velocity c independent of its color and the state of motion of the source of light (principle of the constancy of the velocity of light—in the following referred to as "L-principle"). Now elementary intuitive considerations seem to show that the same light ray *cannot* move with respect to all inertial systems with the same velocity c. The L-principle seems to contradict the special principle of relativity.

It turns out, however, that this contradiction is only an apparent one which is based essentially on the prejudice about the absolute character of time or rather of the simultaneity of distant events. We just saw that x, y, z and t of an event can, for the moment, be defined only with respect to a certain chosen system of coordinates (inertial system). The transformation of the x, y, z, t of events which has to be carried out with the passage from one inertial system to another (coordinate transformation), is a problem which cannot be solved without special physical assumptions. However, the following postulate is exactly sufficient for a solution: *The L-principle holds for all inertial systems* (application of the special principle of relativity to the L-principle). The transformations thus defined, which are linear in x, y, z, t, are called Lorentz transformations. Lorentz transformations are formally characterized by the demand that the expression

$$dx^2 + dy^2 + dz^2 - c^2dt^2,$$

which is formed from the coordinate differences dx, dy, dz, dt of two infinitely close events, be invariant (i.e., that through the transformation it goes over into the *same* expression formed from the coordinate differences in the new system).

With the help of the Lorentz transformations the special principle of relativity can be expressed thus: The laws of nature are invariant with respect to Lorentz-transformations (i.e., a law of nature does not change its form if one introduces into it a new inertial system with the help of a Lorentz-transformation on x, y, z, t).

The special theory of relativity has led to a clear understanding of the physical concepts of space and time and in connection with this to a recognition of the behavior of moving measuring rods and clocks. It has in principle removed the concept of absolute simultaneity and thereby also that of instantaneous action at a distance in the sense of Newton. It has shown how the law of motion must be modified in dealing with motions that are not negligibly small as compared with the velocity of light. It has led to a formal clarification of Maxwell's equations of the electromagnetic field; in particular it has led to an understanding of the essential oneness of the electric and the magnetic field. It has unified the laws of conservation of momentum and of energy into one single law and has demonstrated the equivalence of mass and energy. From a formal point of view one may characterize the achievement of the special theory of relativity thus: it has shown generally the role which the universal constant c (velocity of light) plays in the laws of nature and has demonstrated that there exists a close connection between the form in which time on the one hand and the spatial coordinates on the other hand enter into the laws of nature.

B. *General theory of relativity.*

The special theory of relativity retained the basis of classical mechanics in one fundamental point, namely the statement: The laws of nature are valid only with respect to inertial systems. The "permissible" transformations for the coordinates (i.e., those which leave the form of the laws unchanged) are *exclusively* the (linear) Lorentz-transformations. Is this restriction really founded in physical facts? The following argument convincingly denies it.

Principle of equivalence. A body has an inertial mass (resistance to acceleration) and a heavy mass (which determines the weight of the body in a given gravitational field, e.g., that at the surface of the earth). These two quantities, so different according to their definition, are according to experience measured by one and the same number. There must be a deeper reason for this. The fact can also be described thus: In a gravitational field different masses receive the same acceleration. Finally, it can also be expressed thus: Bodies in a gravitational field behave as in the absence of a gravitational field if, in the latter case, the system of reference used is a uniformly accelerated coordinate system (instead of an inertial system).

There seems, therefore, to be no reason to ban the following interpretation of the latter case. One considers the system as being "at rest" and considers the "apparent" gravitational field which exists with respect to it as a "real" one. This gravitational field "generated" by the acceleration of the coordinate system would of course be of unlimited extent in such a way that it could not be caused by gravitational masses in a finite region; however, if we are looking for a field-like theory, this fact need not deter us. With this interpretation the inertial system loses its meaning and one has an "explanation" for the equality of heavy and inertial mass (the same property of matter appears as weight or as inertia depending on the mode of description).

Considered formally, the admission of a coordinate system which is accelerated with respect to the original "inertial" coordinates means the admission of non-linear coordinate transformations, hence a mighty enlargement of the idea of invariance, i.e., the principle of relativity.

First, a penetrating discussion, using the results of the special theory of relativity, shows that with such a generalization the coordinates can no longer be interpreted directly as the results of measurements. Only the coordinate difference together with the field quantities which describe the gravitational field determine measurable distances between events. After one has found oneself forced to admit non-linear coordinate transformations as transformations between equivalent coordinate systems, the simplest demand appears to admit all continuous coordinate transformations (which form a group), i.e., to admit arbitrary curvilinear coordinate systems in which the fields are described by regular functions (general principle of relativity).

Now it is not difficult to understand why the general principle of relativity (*on the basis of the equivalence principle*) has led to a theory of gravitation. There is a special kind of space whose physical structure (field) we can presume as precisely known on the basis of the special theory of relativity. This is empty space without electromagnetic field and without matter. It is completely determined by its "metric" property: Let dx_0, dy_0, dz_0, dt_0 be the coordinate differences of two infinitesimally near points (events); then

$$(1) \qquad ds^2 = dx_0{}^2 + dy_0{}^2 + dz_0{}^2 - c^2 dt_0{}^2$$

is a measurable quantity which is independent of the special choice of the inertial system. If one introduces in this space the new coordinates x_1, x_2, x_3, x_4 through a general transformation of coordinates, then the quantity ds^2 for the same pair of points has an expression of the form

$$(2) \quad ds^2 = \Sigma g_{ik} dx^i dx^k \text{ (summed for i and k from 1 to 4)}$$

where $g_{ik} = g_{ki}$. The g_{ik} which form a "symmetric tensor" and are continuous functions of x_1, . . . x_4 then describe according to the "principle of equivalence" a gravitational field of a special kind (namely one which can be retransformed to the form (1)). From Riemann's investigations on metric spaces the mathematical properties of this g_{ik} field can be given exactly ("Riemann-condition"). However, what we are looking for are the equations satisfied by "general" gravitational fields. It is natural to assume that they too can be described as tensor-fields of the type g_{ik}, which in general do *not* admit a transformation to the form (1), i.e., which do not satisfy the "Riemann condition," but weaker conditions, which, just as the Riemann condition, are independent of the choice of coordinates (i.e., are generally invariant). A simple formal consideration leads to weaker conditions which are closely connected with the Riemann condition. These conditions are the very equations of the pure gravitational field (on the outside of matter and at the absence of an electromagnetic field).

These equations yield Newton's equations of gravitational mechanics as an approximate law and in addition certain small effects which have been confirmed by observation (deflection of light by the gravitational field of a star, influence of the gravitational potential on the frequency of emitted light, slow rotation of the elliptic circuits of planets—perihelion motion of the planet Mercury). They further yield an explanation for the expanding motion of galactic systems, which is manifested by the red-shift of the light omitted from these systems.

The general theory of relativity is as yet incomplete insofar as it has been able to apply the general principle of relativity satisfactorily only to gravitational fields, but not to the total field. We do not yet know with certainty, by what mathematical mechanism the total field in space is to be described and what the general invariant laws are to which this total field is subject. One thing, however, seems certain: namely, that the general principle of relativity will prove a necessary and effective tool for the solution of the problem of the total field.

11

E = M C²

IN ORDER TO UNDERSTAND the law of the equivalence of mass and energy, we must go back to two conservation or "balance" principles which, independent of each other, held a high place in pre-relativity physics. These were the principle of the conservation of energy and the principle of the conservation of mass. The first of these, advanced by Leibnitz as long ago as the seventeenth century, was developed in the nineteenth century essentially as a corollary of a principle of mechanics.

Drawing from Dr. Einstein's manuscript.

Consider, for example, a pendulum whose mass swings back and forth between the points A and B. At these points the mass m is higher by the amount h than it is at C, the lowest point of the path (see drawing). At C, on the other hand, the lifting height has disappeared and instead of it the mass has a velocity v. It is as though the lifting height could be converted entirely into velocity, and vice versa. The exact relation would be expressed as mgh $= \frac{m}{2}$ v², with g representing the acceleration of gravity. What is interesting here is that this relation is independent of both the length of the

49

pendulum and the form of the path through which the mass moves.

The significance is that something remains constant throughout the process, and that something is energy. At A and at B it is an energy of position, or "potential" energy; at C it is an energy of motion, or "kinetic" energy. If this concept is correct, then the sum $mgh + m\frac{v^2}{2}$ must have the same value for any position of the pendulum, if h is understood to represent the height above C, and v the velocity at that point in the pendulum's path. And such is found to be actually the case. The generalization of this principle gives us the law of the conservation of mechanical energy. But what happens when friction stops the pendulum?

The answer to that was found in the study of heat phenomena. This study, based on the assumption that heat is an indestructible substance which flows from a warmer to a colder object, seemed to give us a principle of the "conservation of heat." On the other hand, from time immemorial it has been known that heat could be produced by friction, as in the fire-making drills of the Indians. The physicists were for long unable to account for this kind of heat "production." Their difficulties were overcome only when it was successfully established that, for any given amount of heat produced by friction, an exactly proportional amount of energy had to be expended. Thus did we arrive at a principle of the "equivalence of work and heat." With our pendulum, for example, mechanical energy is gradually converted by friction into heat.

In such fashion the principles of the conservation of mechanical and thermal energies were merged into one. The physicists were thereupon persuaded that the conservation principle could be further extended to take in chemical and electromagnetic processes—in short, could be applied to all fields. It appeared that in our physical system there was a sum total of energies that remained constant through all changes that might occur.

Now for the principle of the conservation of mass. Mass is defined by the resistance that a body opposes to its acceleration (inert mass). It is also measured by the weight of the body (heavy mass). That these two radically different definitions lead to the same value for the mass of a body is, in itself, an astonishing fact. According to the principle—namely, that masses remain unchanged under any physical or chemical changes—the mass appeared to be the essential (because unvarying) quality of matter. Heating, melting, vaporization, or combining into chemical compounds would not change the total mass.

Physicists accepted this principle up to a few decades ago. But it proved inadequate in the face of the special theory of relativity. It was therefore merged with the energy principle —just as, about 60 years before, the principle of the conservation of mechanical energy had been combined with the principle of the conservation of heat. We might say that the principle of the conservation of energy, having previously swallowed up that of the conservation of heat, now proceeded to swallow that of the conservation of mass—and holds the field alone.

It is customary to express the equivalence of mass and energy (though somewhat inexactly) by the formula $E = mc^2$, in which c represents the velocity of light, about 186,000 miles per second. E is the energy that is contained in a stationary body; m is its mass. The energy that belongs to the mass m is equal to this mass, multiplied by the square of the enormous speed of light—which is to say, a vast amount of energy for every unit of mass.

But if every gram of material contains this tremendous energy, why did it go so long unnoticed? The answer is simple enough: so long as none of the energy is given off externally, it cannot be observed. It is as though a man who is fabulously rich should never spend or give away a cent; no one could tell how rich he was.

Now we can reverse the relation and say that an increase of E in the amount of energy must be accompanied by an increase of $\frac{E}{c^2}$ in the mass. I can easily supply energy to the mass—for instance, if I heat it by 10 degrees. So why not measure the mass increase, or weight increase, connected with this change? The trouble here is that in the mass increase the enormous factor c^2 occurs in the denominator of the fraction. In such a case the increase is too small to be measured directly; even with the most sensitive balance.

For a mass increase to be measurable, the change of energy per mass unit must be enormously large. We know of only one sphere in which such amounts of energy per mass unit are released: namely, radioactive disintegration. Schematically, the process goes like this: An atom of the mass M splits into two atoms of the mass M′ and M″, which separate with tremendous kinetic energy. If we imagine these two masses as brought to rest—that is, if we take this energy of motion from them—then, considered together, they are essentially poorer in energy than was the original atom. According to the equivalence principle, the mass sum M′ + M″ of the disintegration products must also be somewhat smaller than the original mass M of the disintegrating atom—in contradiction to the old principle of the conservation of mass. The relative difference of the two is on the order of $\frac{1}{10}$ of one percent.

Now, we cannot actually weigh the atoms individually. However, there are indirect methods for measuring their weights exactly. We can likewise determine the kinetic energies that are transferred to the disintegration products M′ and M″. Thus it has become possible to test and confirm the equivalence formula. Also, the law permits us to calculate in advance, from precisely determined atom weights, just how much energy will be released with any atom disintegration we have in mind. The law says nothing, of course, as to whether—or how—the disintegration reaction can be brought about.

What takes place can be illustrated with the help of our rich man. The atom M is a rich miser who, during his life, gives away no money (*energy*). But in his will he bequeaths his fortune to his sons M' and M'', on condition that they give to the community a small amount, less than one thousandth of the whole estate (*energy or mass*). The sons together have somewhat less than the father had (*the mass sum M' + M'' is somewhat smaller than the mass M of the radioactive atom*). But the part given to the community, though relatively small, is still so enormously large (*considered as kinetic energy*) that it brings with it a great threat of evil. Averting that threat has become the most urgent problem of our time.

12

WHAT IS THE THEORY OF RELATIVITY?

I GLADLY accede to the request of your colleague to write something for *The Times* on relativity. After the lamentable breakdown of the old active intercourse between men of learning, I welcome this opportunity of expressing my feelings of joy and gratitude towards the astronomers and physicists of England. It is thoroughly in keeping with the great and proud traditions of scientific work in your country that eminent scientists should have spent much time and trouble, and your scientific institutions have spared no expense, to test the implications of a theory which was perfected and published during the War in the land of your enemies. Even though the investigation of the influence of the gravitational field of the sun on light rays is a purely objective matter, I cannot forbear to express my personal thanks to my English colleagues for their work; for without it I could hardly have lived to see the most important implication of my theory tested.

We can distinguish various kinds of theories in physics. Most of them are constructive. They attempt to build up a picture of the more complex phenomena out of the materials of a relatively simple formal scheme from which they start out. Thus the kinetic theory of gases seeks to reduce mechanical, thermal and diffusional processes to movements of molecules—i.e., to build them up out of the hypothesis of molecular motion. When we say that we have succeeded in understanding a group of natural processes, we invariably mean that a constructive theory has been found which covers the processes in question.

Along with this most important class of theories there exists a second, which I will call "principle-theories." These employ the analytic, not the synthetic, method. The elements which form their basis and starting-point are not hypothetically constructed but empirically discovered ones, general characteristics of natural processes, principles that give rise to mathematically formulated criteria which the separate processes or the theoretical representations of them have to satisfy. Thus the science of thermodynamics seeks by analytical means to deduce necessary connections, which separate events have to satisfy, from the universally experienced fact that perpetual motion is impossible.

The advantages of the constructive theory are completeness, adaptability and clearness, those of the principle theory are logical perfection and security of the foundations.

The theory of relativity belongs to the latter class. In order to grasp its nature, one needs first of all to become acquainted with the principles on which it is based. Before I go into these, however, I must observe that the theory of relativity resembles a building consisting of two separate stories, the special theory and the general theory. The special theory, on which the general theory rests, applies to all physical phenomena with the exception of gravitation; the general theory provides the law of gravitation and its relations to the other forces of nature.

It has, of course, been known since the days of the ancient Greeks that in order to describe the movement of a body, a second body is needed to which the movement of the first is referred. The movement of a vehicle is considered in reference to the earth's surface, that of a planet to the totality of the visible fixed stars. In physics the body to which events are spatially referred is called the co-ordinate system.

The laws of the mechanics of Galileo and Newton, for instance, can only be formulated with the aid of a co-ordinate system.

The state of motion of the co-ordinate system may not, however, be arbitrarily chosen, if the laws of mechanics are to be valid (it must be free from rotation and acceleration). A co-ordinate system which is admitted in mechanics is called an "inertial system." The state of motion of an inertial system is according to mechanics not one that is determined uniquely by nature. On the contrary, the following definition holds good:—a co-ordinate system that is moved uniformly and in a straight line relatively to an inertial system is likewise an inertial system. By the "special principle of relativity" is meant the generalization of this definition to include any natural event whatever: thus, every universal law of nature which is valid in relation to a co-ordinate system C, must also be valid, as it stands, in relation to a co-ordinate system C', which is in uniform translatory motion relatively to C.

The second principle, on which the special theory of relativity rests, is the "principle of the constant velocity of light in vacuo." This principle asserts that light in vacuo always has a definite velocity of propagation (independent of the state of motion of the observer or of the source of the light). The confidence which physicists place in this principle springs from the successes achieved by the electro-dynamics of Clerk Maxwell and Lorentz.

Both the above-mentioned principles are powerfully supported by experience, but appear not to be logically reconcilable. The special theory of relativity finally succeeded in reconciling them logically by a modification of kinematics— i.e., of the doctrine of the laws relating to space and time (from the point of view of physics). It became clear that to speak of the simultaneity of two events had no meaning except in relation to a given co-ordinate system, and that the shape of measuring devices and the speed at which clocks move depend on their state of motion with respect to the co-ordinate system.

But the old physics, including the laws of motion of Galileo and Newton, did not fit in with the suggested relativist kinematics. From the latter, general mathematical conditions issued, to which natural laws had to conform, if the above-mentioned two principles were really to apply. To these, physics had to be adapted. In particular, scientists arrived at a new law of motion for (rapidly moving) mass points, which was admirably confirmed in the case of electrically charged particles. The most important upshot of the special theory of relativity concerned the inert mass of corporeal systems. It turned out that the inertia of a system necessarily depends on its energy-content, and this led straight to the notion that inert mass is simply latent energy. The principle of the conservation of mass lost its independence and became fused with that of the conservation of energy.

The special theory of relativity, which was simply a systematic development of the electro-dynamics of Clerk Maxwell and Lorentz, pointed beyond itself, however. Should the independence of physical laws of the state of motion of the co-ordinate system be restricted to the uniform translatory motion of co-ordinate systems in respect to each other? What has nature to do with our co-ordinate systems and their state of motion? If it is necessary for the purpose of describing nature, to make use of a co-ordinate system arbitrarily introduced by us, then the choice of its state of motion ought to be subject to no restriction; the laws ought to be entirely independent of this choice (general principle of relativity).

The establishment of this general principle of relativity is made easier by a fact of experience that has long been known, namely that the weight and the inertia of a body are controlled by the same constant. (Equality of inertial and gravitational mass.) Imagine a co-ordinate system which is rotating uniformly with respect to an inertial system in the Newtonian manner. The centrifugal forces which manifest themselves in relation to this system must, according to Newton's teaching, be regarded as effects of inertia. But these centrifugal forces are, exactly like the forces of gravity, proportional to the masses of the bodies. Ought it not to be possible in this case to regard the co-ordinate system as stationary and the centrifugal forces as gravitational forces? This seems the obvious view, but classical mechanics forbid it.

This hasty consideration suggests that a general theory of relativity must supply the laws of gravitation, and the consistent following up of the idea has justified our hopes.

But the path was thornier than one might suppose, because it demanded the abandonment of Euclidean geometry. This is to say, the laws according to which fixed bodies may be arranged in space, do not completely accord with the spatial laws attributed to bodies by Euclidean geometry. This is what we mean when we talk of the "curvature of space." The fundamental concepts of the "straight line," the "plane," etc., thereby lose their precise significance in physics.

In the general theory of relativity the doctrine of space and time, or kinematics, no longer figures as a fundamental independent of the rest of physics. The geometrical behavior of bodies and the motion of clocks rather depend on gravitational fields, which in their turn are produced by matter.

The new theory of gravitation diverges considerably, as regards principles, from Newton's theory. But its practical results agree so nearly with those of Newton's theory that it is difficult to find criteria for distinguishing them which are accessible to experience. Such have been discovered so far:—

(1) In the revolution of the ellipses of the planetary orbits round the sun (confirmed in the case of Mercury).

(2) In the curving of light rays by the action of gravitational fields (confirmed by the English photographs of eclipses).

(3) In a displacement of the spectral lines towards the red end of the spectrum in the case of light transmitted to us from stars of considerable magnitude (unconfirmed so far).[1]

The chief attraction of the theory lies in its logical completeness. If a single one of the conclusions drawn from it proves wrong, it must be given up; to modify it without destroying the whole structure seems to be impossible.

Let no one suppose, however, that the mighty work of Newton can really be superseded by this or any other theory. His great and lucid ideas will retain their unique significance for all time as the foundation of our whole modern conceptual structure in the sphere of natural philosophy.

NOTE: Some of the statements in your paper concerning my life and person owe their origin to the lively imagination of the writer. Here is yet another application of the principle of relativity for the delectation of the reader:—Today I am described in Germany as a "German savant," and in England as a "Swiss Jew." Should it ever be my fate to be represented as a *bête noire*, I should, on the contrary, become a "Swiss Jew" for the Germans and a "German savant" for the English.

---

[1] Editor's Note: This criterion has also been confirmed in the meantime.

13

PHYSICS AND REALITY

IT HAS OFTEN BEEN SAID, and certainly not without justification, that the man of science is a poor philosopher. Why then should it not be the right thing for the physicist to let the philosopher do the philosophizing? Such might indeed be the right thing at a time when the physicist believes he has at his disposal a rigid system of fundamental concepts and fundamental laws which are so well established that waves of doubt can not reach them; but, it can not be right at a time when the very foundations of physics itself have become problematic as they are now. At a time like the present, when experience forces us to seek a newer and more solid foundation, the physicist cannot simply surrender to the philosopher the critical contemplation of the theoretical foundations; for, he himself knows best, and feels more surely where the shoe pinches. In looking for a new foundation, he must try to make clear in his own mind just how far the concepts which he uses are justified, and are necessities.

The whole of science is nothing more than a refinement of every day thinking. It is for this reason that the critical thinking of the physicist cannot possibly be restricted to the examination of the concepts of his own specific field. He cannot proceed without considering critically a much more difficult problem, the problem of analyzing the nature of everyday thinking.

On the stage of our subconscious mind appear in colorful succession sense experiences, memory pictures of them, representations and feelings. In contrast to psychology, physics treats directly only of sense experiences and of the "understanding" of their connection. But even the concept of the "real external world" of everyday thinking rests exclusively on sense impressions.

Now we must first remark that the differentiation between sense impressions and representations is not possible; or, at least it is not possible with absolute certainty. With the discussion of this problem, which affects also the notion of reality, we will not concern ourselves but we shall take the existence of sense experiences as given, that is to say as psychic experiences of special kind.

I believe that the first step in the setting of a "real external world" is the formation of the concept of bodily objects and of bodily objects of various kinds. Out of the multitude of our sense experiences we take, mentally and arbitrarily, certain repeatedly occurring complexes of sense impression (partly in conjunction with sense impressions which are interpreted as signs for sense experiences of others), and we attribute to them a meaning—the meaning of the bodily object. Considered logically this concept is not identical with the totality of sense impressions referred to; but it is an arbitrary creation of the human (or animal) mind. On the other hand, the concept owes its meaning and its justification exclusively to the totality of the sense impressions which we associate with it.

The second step is to be found in the fact that, in our thinking (which determines our expectation), we attribute to this concept of the bodily object a significance, which is to a high degree independent of the sense impression which originally gives rise to it. This is what we mean when we attribute to the bodily object "a real existence." The justification of such a setting rests exclusively on the fact that, by means of such concepts and mental relations between them, we are able to orient ourselves in the labyrinth of sense impressions. These notions and relations, although free statements of our thoughts, appear to us as stronger and more unalterable than the individual sense experience itself, the character of which as anything other than the result of an illusion or hallucination is never completely guaranteed. On the other hand, these concepts and relations, and indeed the setting of real objects and, generally speaking, the existence of "the real world," have justification only in so far as they are connected with sense impressions between which they form a mental connection.

The very fact that the totality of our sense experiences is such that by means of thinking (operations with concepts, and the creation and use of definite functional relations between them, and the coordination of sense experiences to these concepts) it can be put in order, this fact is one which leaves us in awe, but which we shall never understand. One may say "the eternal mystery of the world is its comprehensibility." It is one of the great realizations of Immanuel Kant that the setting up of a real external world would be senseless without this comprehensibility.

In speaking here concerning "comprehensibility," the expression is used in its most modest sense. It implies: the production of some sort of order among sense impressions, this order being produced by the creation of general concepts, relations between these concepts, and by relations between the concepts and sense experience, these relations being determined in any possible manner. It is in this sense that the world of our sense experiences is comprehensible. The fact that it is comprehensible is a miracle.

In my opinion, nothing can be said concerning the manner in which the concepts are to be made and connected, and how we are to coordinate them to the experiences. In guiding us in the creation of such an order of sense experiences, success in the result is alone the determining factor. All that is necessary is *the statement* of a set of rules, since without such rules the acquisition of knowledge in the desired sense would be impossible. One may compare these rules with the rules of a game in which, while the rules themselves are arbitrary, it is their rigidity alone which makes the game possible. However, the fixation will never be final. It will have validity only for a special field of application (i.e. there are no final categories in the sense of Kant).

The connection of the elementary concepts of every day thinking with complexes of sense experiences can only be comprehended intuitively and it is unadaptable to scientifically logical fixation. The totality of these connections—none of which is expressible in notional terms—is the only thing which differentiates the great building which is science from a logical but empty scheme of concepts. By means of these connections, the purely notional theorems of science become statements about complexes of sense experiences.

We shall call "primary concepts" such concepts as are directly and intuitively connected with typical complexes of sense experiences. All other notions are—from the physical point of view—possessed of meaning, only in so far as thev are connected, by theorems, with the primary notions. These theorems are partially definitions of the concepts (and of the statements derived logically from them) and partially theorems not derivable from the definitions, which express at least indirect relations between the "primary concepts," and in this way between sense experiences. Theorems of the latter kind are "statements about reality" or laws of nature, i.e. theorems which have to show their usefulness when applied to sense experiences comprehended by primary concepts. The question as to which of the theorems shall be considered as definitions and which as natural laws will depend largely upon the chosen representation. It really becomes absolutely necessary to make this differentiation only when one examines the degree to which the whole system of concepts considered is not empty from the physical point of view.

STRATIFICATION OF THE SCIENTIFIC SYSTEM

The aim of science is, on the one hand, a comprehension, as *complete* as possible, of the connection between the sense experiences in their totality, and, on the other hand, the accomplishment of this aim *by the use of a minimum of primary concepts and relations.* (Seeking, as far as possible, logical unity in the world picture, i.e. paucity in logical elements.)

Science concerns the totality of the primary concepts, i.e. concepts directly connected with sense experiences, and theorems connecting them. In its first stage of development, science does not contain anything else. Our everyday thinking is satisfied on the whole with this level. Such a state of affairs cannot, however, satisfy a spirit which is really scientifically minded; because, the totality of concepts and relations obtained in this manner is utterly lacking in logical unity. In order to supplement this deficiency, one invents a system poorer in concepts and relations, a system retaining the primary concepts and relations of the "first layer" as logically derived concepts and relations. This new "secondary system" pays for its higher logical unity by having, as its own elementary concepts (concepts of the second layer), only those which are no longer directly connected with complexes of sense experiences. Further striving for logical unity brings us to a tertiary system, still poorer in concepts and relations, for the deduction of the concepts and relations of the secondary (and so indirectly of the primary) layer. Thus the story goes on until we have arrived at a system of the greatest conceivable unity, and of the greatest poverty of concepts of the logical foundations, which are still compatible with the observation made by our senses. We do not know whether or not this ambition will ever result in a definite system. If one is asked for his opinion, he is inclined to answer no. While wrestling with the problems, however, one will never give up the hope that this greatest of all aims can really be attained to a very high degree.

An adherent to the theory of abstraction or induction might call our layers "degrees of abstraction"; but, I do not consider it justifiable to veil the logical independence of the concept from the sense experiences. The relation is not analogous to that of soup to beef but rather of wardrobe number to over-coat.

The layers are furthermore not clearly separated. It is not even absolutely clear which concepts belong to the primary layer. As a matter of fact, we are dealing with freely formed concepts, which, with a certainty sufficient for practical use, are intuitively connected with complexes of sense experiences in such a manner that, in any given case of experience, there is no uncertainty as to the applicability or non-applicability of the statement, The essential thing is the aim to represent the multitude of concepts and theorems, close to experience, as theorems, logically deduced and belonging to a basis, as narrow as possible, of fundamental concepts and fundamental relations which themselves can be chosen freely (axioms). The liberty of choice, however, is of a special kind; it is not in any way similar to the liberty of a writer of fiction. Rather, it is similar to that of a man engaged in solving a well de-signed word puzzle. He may, it is true, propose any word as the solution; but, there is only *one* word which really solves the puzzle in all its forms. It is an outcome of faith that nature —as she is perceptible to our five senses—takes the character of such a well formulated puzzle. The successes reaped up to now by science do, it is true, give a certain encouragement for this faith.

The multitude of layers discussed above corresponds to the several stages of progress which have resulted from the struggle for unity in the course of development. As regards the final aim, intermediary layers are only of temporary nature. They must eventually disappear as irrelevant. We have to deal, however, with the science of today, in which these strata represent problematic partial successes which support one another but which also threaten one another, because today's systems of concepts contain deep seated incongruities which we shall meet later on.

It will be the aim of the following lines to demonstrate what paths the constructive human mind has entered, in order to arrive at a basis of physics which is logically as uniform as possible.

§ 2. Mechanics and the Attempts to Base All Physics upon It

An important property of our sense experiences, and, more generally, of all of our experience, is its time-like order. This kind of order leads to the mental conception of a subjective time, an ordinating scheme for our experience. The subjective time leads then through the concept of the bodily object and of space, to the concept of objective time, as we shall see later on.

Ahead of the notion of objective time there is, however, the concept of space; and, ahead of the latter we find the concept of the bodily object. The latter is directly connected with complexes of sense experiences. It has been pointed out that one property which is characteristic of the notion "bodily object" is the property which provides that we coordinate to it an existence, independent of (subjective) time, and independent of the fact that it is perceived by our senses. We do this in spite of the fact that we perceive temporal alterations in it. Poincaré has justly emphasized the fact that we distinguish two kinds of alterations of the bodily object, "changes of state" and "changes of position." The latter, he remarked, are alterations which we can reverse by arbitrary motions of our bodies.

That there are bodily objects to which we have to ascribe,

within a certain sphere of perception, no alteration of state, but only alterations of position, is a fact of fundamental importance for the formation of the concept of space (in a certain degree even for the justification of the notion of the bodily object itself). Let us call such an object "practically rigid."

If, as the object of our perception, we consider simultaneously (i.e. as a single unit) two practically rigid bodies, then there exist for this ensemble such alterations as can *not* possibly be considered as changes of position of the whole, notwithstanding the fact that this is the case for each one of the two constituents. This leads to the notion of "change of relative position" of the two objects; and, in this way, also to the notion of "relative position" of the two objects. It is found moreover that among the relative positions, there is one of a specific kind which we designate as "Contact." [1] Permanent contact of two bodies in three or more "points" means that they are united as a quasi rigid compound body. It is permissible to say that the second body forms then a (quasi rigid) continuation on the first body and may, in its turn, be continued quasi rigidly. The possibility of the quasi rigid continuation of a body is unlimited. The real essence of the conceivable quasi rigid continuation of a body B_0 is the infinite "space" determined by it.

In my opinion, the fact that every bodily object situated in any arbitrary manner can be put into contact with the quasi rigid continuation of a predetermined and chosen body B_0 (body of relation), this fact is the empirical basis of our conception of space. In pre-scientific thinking, the solid earth's crust plays the role of B_0 and its continuation. The very name geometry indicates that the concept of space is

---

[1] It is in the nature of things that we are able to talk about these objects only by means of concepts of our own creation, concepts which themselves are not subject to definition. It is essential, however, that we make use only of such concepts concerning whose coordination to our experience we feel no doubt.

psychologically connected with the earth as an assigned body.

The bold notion of "space" which preceded all scientific geometry transformed our mental concept of the relations of positions of bodily objects into the notion of the position of these bodily objects in "space." This, of itself, represents a great formal simplification. Through this concept of space one reaches, moreover, an attitude in which any description of position is admittedly a description of contact; the statement that a point of a bodily object is located at a point P of space means that the object touches the point P of the standard body of reference B_0 (supposed appropriately continued) at the point considered.

In the geometry of the Greeks, space plays only a qualitative role, since the position of bodies in relation to space is considered as given, it is true, but is not described by means of numbers. Descartes was the first to introduce this method. In his language, the whole content of Euclidian geometry can axiomatically be founded upon the following statements: (1) Two specified points of a rigid body determine a distance. (2) We may coordinate triplets of numbers X_1, X_2, X_3, to points of space in such a manner that for every distance $P' - P''$ under consideration, the coordinates of whose end points are X_1', X_2', X_3'; X_1'', X_2'', X_3'', the expression

$$S^2 = (X_1'' - X_1')^2 + (X_2'' - X_2')^2 + (X_3'' - X_3')^2$$

is independent of the position of the body, and of the positions of any and all other bodies.

The (positive) number S means the length of the stretch, or the distance between the two points P' and P'' of space (which are coincident with the points P' and P'' of the stretch).

The formulation is chosen, intentionally, in such a way that it expresses clearly, not only the logical and axiomatic, but also the empirical content of Euclidian geometry. The purely logical (axiomatic) representation of Euclidian geometry has, it is true, the advantage of greater simplicity and clarity. It pays for this, however, by renouncing representation of the connection between the notional construction and the sense experience upon which connection, alone, the significance of geometry for physics rests. The fatal error that the necessity of thinking, preceding all experience, was at the basis of Euclidian geometry and the concept of space belonging to it, this fatal error arose from the fact that the empirical basis, on which the axiomatic construction of Euclidian geometry rests, had fallen into oblivion.

In so far as one can speak of the existence of rigid bodies in nature, Euclidian geometry is a physical science, the usefulness of which must be shown by application to sense experiences. It relates to the totality of laws which must hold for the relative positions of rigid bodies independently of time. As one may see, the physical notion of space also, as originally used in physics, is tied to the existence of rigid bodies.

From the physicist's point of view, the central importance of Euclidian geometry rests in the fact that its laws are independent of the specific nature of the bodies whose relative positions it discusses. Its formal simplicity is characterized by the properties of homogeneity and isotropy (and the existence of similar entities).

The concept of space is, it is true, useful, but not indispensable for geometry proper, i.e. for the formulation of rules about the relative positions of rigid bodies. In opposition to this, the concept of objective time, without which the formulation of the fundamentals of classical mechanics is impossible, is linked with the concept of the spacial continuum.

The introduction of objective time involves two statements which are independent of each other.

(1) The introduction of the objective local time by connecting the temporal sequence of experiences with the indications of a "clock," i.e. of a closed system with periodical occurrence.

(2) The introduction of the notion of objective time for the happenings in the whole space, by which notion alone the idea of local time is enlarged to the idea of time in physics.

Note concerning (1). As I see it, it does not mean a "petitio principii" if one puts the concept of periodical occurrence ahead of the concept of time, while one is concerned with the clarification of the origin and of the empirical content of the concept of time. Such a conception corresponds exactly to the precedence of the concept of the rigid (or quasi rigid) body in the interpretation of the concept of space.

Further discussion of (2). The illusion which prevailed prior to the enunciation of the theory of relativity—that, from the point of view of experience the meaning of simultaneity in relation to happenings distant in space and consequently that the meaning of time in physics is a priori clear—this illusion had its origin in the fact that in our everyday experience, we can neglect the time of propagation of light. We are accustomed on this account to fail to differentiate between "simultaneously seen" and "simultaneously happening"; and, as a result the difference between time and local time fades away.

The lack of definiteness which, from the point of view of empirical importance, adheres to the notion of time in classical mechanics was veiled by the axiomatic representation of space and time as things given independently of our senses. Such a use of notions—independent of the empirical basis, to which they owe their existence—does not necessarily damage science. One may however easily be led into the error of believing that these notions, whose origin is forgotten, are necessary and unalterable accompaniments to our thinking, and this error may constitute a serious danger to the progress of science.

It was fortunate for the development of mechanics and hence also for the development of physics in general, that the lack of definiteness in the concept of objective time remained obscured from the earlier philosophers as regards its empirical interpretation. Full of confidence in the real meaning of the space-time construction they developed the foundations of mechanics which we shall characterize, schematically, as follows:

(a) Concept of a material point: a bodily object which—as regards its position and motion—can be described with sufficient exactness as a point with coordinates X_1, X_2, X_3. Description of its motion (in relation to the "space" B_0) by giving X_1, X_2, X_3, as functions of the time.

(b) Law of inertia: the disappearance of the components of acceleration for the material point which is sufficiently far away from all other points.

(c) Law of motion (for the material point): Force = mass × acceleration.

(d) Laws of force (actions and reactions between material points).

In this (b) is nothing more than an important special case of (c). A real theory exists only when the laws of force are given. The forces must in the first place only obey the law of equality of action and reaction in order that a system of points —permanently connected to each other—may behave like *one* material point.

These fundamental laws, together with Newton's law for gravitational force, form the basis of the mechanics of celestial bodies. In this mechanics of Newton, and in contrast to the above conceptions of space derived from rigid bodies, the space B_0 enters in a form which contains a new idea; it is not for every B_0 that validity is required (for a given law of force) by (b) and (c), but only for a B_0 in the appropriate condition of motion (inertial system). On account of this fact, the coordinate space acquired an independent physical property which is not contained in the purely geometrical notion of space, a circumstance which gave Newton considerable food for thought (pail-experiment).[2]

Classical mechanics is only a general scheme; it becomes a theory only by explicit indication of the force laws (*d*) as was done so very successfully by Newton for celestial mechanics. From the point of view of the aim of the greatest logical simplicity of the foundations, this theoretical method is deficient in so far as the laws of force cannot be obtained by logical and formal considerations, so that their choice is *a priori* to a large extent arbitrary. Also Newton's gravitation law of force is distinguished from other conceivable laws of force exclusively by its *success*.

In spite of the fact that, today, we know positively that classical mechanics fails as a foundation dominating all physics, it still occupies the center of all of our thinking in physics. The reason for this lies in the fact that, regardless of important progress reached since the time of Newton, we have not yet arrived at a new foundation of physics concerning which we may be certain that the whole complexity of investigated phenomena, and of partial theoretical systems of a successful kind, could be deduced logically from it. In the following lines I shall try to describe briefly how the matter stands.

First we try to get clearly in our minds how far the system of classical mechanics has shown itself adequate to serve as a basis for the whole of physics. Since we are dealing here only with the foundations of physics and with its development, we need not concern ourselves with the purely *formal* progresses of mechanics (equation of Lagrange, canonical

---

[2] This defect of the theory could only be eliminated by such a formulation of mechanics as would command validity for all B_0. This is one of the steps which lead to the general theory of relativity. A second defect, also eliminated only by the introduction of the general theory of relativity, lies in the fact that there is no reason given by mechanics itself for the equality of the gravitational and inertial mass of the material point.

equations, etc.). *One* remark, however, appears indispensable. The notion "material point" is fundamental for mechanics. If now we seek the mechanics of a bodily object which itself can *not* be treated as a material point—and strictly speaking every object "perceptible to our senses" is of this category—then the question arises: How shall we imagine the object to be built up out of material points, and what forces must we assume as acting between them? The formulation of this question is indispensable, if mechanics is to pretend to describe the object *completely*.

It is natural to the tendency of mechanics to assume these material points, and the laws of forces acting between them, as invariable, since time alterations would lie outside of the scope of mechanical explanation. From this we can see that classical mechanics must lead us to an atomistic construction of matter. We now realize, with special clarity, how much in error are those theorists who believe that theory comes inductively from experience. Even the great Newton could not free himself from this error ("Hypotheses non fingo").*

In order to save itself from becoming hopelessly lost in this line of thought (atomistic), science proceeded first in the following manner. The mechanics of a system is determined if its potential energy is given as a function of its configuration. Now, if the acting forces are of such a kind as to guarantee maintenance of certain qualities of order of the system's configuration, then the configuration may be described with sufficient accuracy by a relatively small number of configuration variables q_r; the potential energy is considered only insofar as it is dependent upon *these* variables (for instance, description of the configuration of a practically rigid body by six variables).

A second method of application of mechanics, which avoids the consideration of a subdivision of matter down to "real" material points, is the mechanics of so-called continuous

* "I make no hypotheses."

media. This mechanics is characterized by the fiction that the density of matter and speed of matter is dependent in a continuous manner upon coordinates and time, and that the part of the interactions not explicitly given can be considered as surface forces (pressure forces) which again are continuous functions of location. Herein we find the hydrodynamic theory, and the theory of elasticity of solid bodies. These theories avoid the explicit introduction of material points by fictions which, in the light of the foundation of classical mechanics, can only have an approximate significance.

In addition to their great *practical* significance, these categories of science have—by enlargement of the mathematical world of ideas—created those formal auxiliary instruments (partial differential equations) which have been necessary for the subsequent attempts at formulating the total scheme of physics in a manner which is new as compared with that of Newton.

These two modes of application of mechanics belong to the so-called "phenomenological" physics. It is characteristic of this kind of physics that it makes as much use as possible of concepts which are close to experience but which, for this reason, have to give up, to a large degree, unity in the foundations. Heat, electricity and light are described by special variables of state and constants of matter other than the mechanical state; and to determine all of these variables in their relative dependence was a rather empirical task. Many contemporaries of Maxwell saw in such a manner of presentation the ultimate aim of physics, which they thought could be obtained purely inductively from experience on account of the relative closeness of the concepts used to the experience. From the point of view of theories of knowledge St. Mill and E. Mach took their stand approximately on this ground.

According to my belief, the greatest achievement of Newton's mechanics lies in the fact that its consistent application has led beyond this phenomenological representation, particularly in the field of heat phenomena. This occurred in the kinetic theory of gases and, in a general way, in statistical mechanics. The former connected the equation of state of the ideal gases, viscosity, diffusion and heat conductivity of gases and radiometric phenomena of gases, and gave the logical connection of phenomena which, from the point of view of direct experience, had nothing whatever to do with one another. The latter gave a mechanical interpretation of the thermodynamic ideas and laws as well as the discovery of the limit of applicability of the notions and laws to the classical theory of heat. This kinetic theory which surpassed, by far, the phenomenological physics as regards the logical unity of its foundations, produced moreover definite values for the true magnitudes of atoms and molecules which resulted from several independent methods and were thus placed beyond the realm of reasonable doubt. These decisive progresses were paid for by the coordination of atomistic entities to the material points, the constructively speculative character of which entities being obvious. Nobody could hope ever to "perceive directly" an atom. Laws concerning variables connected more directly with experimental facts (for example: temperature, pressure, speed) were deduced from the fundamental ideas by means of complicated calculations. In this manner physics (at least part of it), originally more phenomenologically constructed, was reduced, by being founded upon Newton's mechanics for atoms and molecules, to a basis further removed from direct experiment, but more uniform in character.

§ 3. THE FIELD CONCEPT

In explaining optical and electrical phenomena Newton's mechanics has been far less successful than it had been in the fields cited above. It is true that Newton tried to reduce light to the motion of material points in his corpuscular theory of light. Later on, however, as the phenomena of polarization, diffraction and interference of light forced upon his theory more and more unnatural modifications, Huyghens' undulatory theory of light, prevailed. Probably this theory owes its origin essentially to the phenomena of crystallographic optics and to the theory of sound, which was then already elaborated to a certain degree. It must be admitted that Huyghens' theory also was based in the first instance upon classical mechanics; but, the all-penetrating ether had to be assumed as the carrier of the waves and the structure of the ether, formed from material points, could not be explained by any known phenomenon. One could never get a clear picture of the interior forces governing the ether, nor of the forces acting between the ether and the "ponderable" matter. The foundations of this theory remained, therefore, eternally in the dark. The true basis was a partial differential equation, the reduction of which to mechanical elements remained always problematic.

For the theoretical conception of electric and magnetic phenomena one introduced, again, masses of a special kind, and between these masses one assumed the existence of forces acting at a distance, similar to Newton's gravitational forces. This special kind of matter, however, appeared to be lacking in the fundamental property of inertia; and, the forces acting between these masses and the ponderable matter remained obscure. To these difficulties there had to be added the polar character of these kinds of matter which did not fit into the scheme of classical mechanics. The basis of the theory became still more unsatisfactory when electrodynamic phenomena became known, notwithstanding the fact that these phenomena brought the physicist to the explanation of magnetic phenomena through electrodynamic phenomena and, in this way, made the assumption of magnetic masses superfluous. This progress had, indeed, to be paid for by increasing the complexity of the forces of interaction which had to be assumed as existing between electrical masses in motion.

The escape from this unsatisfactory situation by the electric field theory of Faraday and Maxwell represents probably the most profound transformation which has been experienced by the foundations of physics since Newton's time. Again, it has been a step in the direction of constructive speculation which has increased the distance between the foundation of the theory and what can be experienced by means of our five senses. The existence of the field manifests itself, indeed, only when electrically charged bodies are introduced into it. The differential equations of Maxwell connect the spacial and temporal differential coefficients of the electric and magnetic fields. The electric masses are nothing more than places of non-disappearing divergency of the electric field. Light waves appear as undulatory electromagnetic field processes in space.

To be sure, Maxwell still tried to interpret his field theory mechanically by means of mechanical ether models. But these attempts receded gradually to the background following the representation—purged of any unnecessary additions —by Heinrich Hertz, so that, in this theory the field finally took the fundamental position which had been occupied in Newton's mechanics by the material points. At first, however, this applies only for electromagnetic fields in empty space.

In its initial stage the theory was yet quite unsatisfactory for the interior of matter, because there, two electric vectors had to be introduced, which were connected by relations dependent on the nature of the medium, these relations being inaccessible to any theoretical analysis. An analogous situation arose in connection with the magnetic field, as well as in the relation between electric current density and the field.

Here H. A. Lorentz found an escape which showed, at the same time, the way to an electrodynamic theory of bodies in motion, a theory which was more or less free of arbitrary assumption. His theory was built on the following fundamental hypothesis:

Everywhere (including the interior of ponderable bodies)

the seat of the field is the empty space. The participation of matter in electromagnetic phenomena has its origin only in the fact that the elementary particles of matter carry unalterable electric charges, and, on this account are subject on the one hand to the actions of ponderomotive forces and on the other hand possess the property of generating a field. The elementary particles obey Newton's law of motion for the material point.

This is the basis on which H. A. Lorentz obtained his synthesis of Newton's mechanics and Maxwell's field theory. The weakness of this theory lies in the fact that it tried to determine the phenomena by a combination of partial differential equations (Maxwell's field equations for empty space) and total differential equations (equations of motion of points), which procedure was obviously unnatural. The unsatisfactory part of the theory showed up externally by the necessity of assuming finite dimensions for the particles in order to prevent the electromagnetic field existing at their surfaces from becoming infinitely great. The theory failed moreover to give any explanation concerning the tremendous forces which hold the electric charges on the individual particles. H. A. Lorentz accepted these weaknesses of his theory, which were well known to him, in order to explain the phenomena correctly at least as regards their general lines.

Furthermore, there was one consideration which reached beyond the frame of Lorentz's theory. In the environment of an electrically charged body there is a magnetic field which furnishes an (apparent) contribution to its inertia. Should it not be possible to explain the *total* inertia of the particles electromagnetically? It is clear that this problem could be worked out satisfactorily only if the particles could be interpreted as regular solutions of the electromagnetic partial differential equations. The Maxwell equations in their original form do not, however, allow such a description of particles, because their corresponding solutions contain a singularity.

Theoretical physicists have tried for a long time, therefore, to reach the goal by a modification of Maxwell's equations. These attempts have, however, not been crowned with success. Thus it happened that the goal of erecting a pure electromagnetic field theory of matter remained unattained for the time being, although in principle no objection could be raised against the possibility of reaching such a goal. The thing which deterred one in any further attempt in this direction was the lack of any systematic method leading to the solution. What appears certain to me, however, is that, in the foundations of any consistent field theory, there shall not be, in addition to the concept of field, any concept concerning particles. The whole theory must be based solely on partia differential equations and their singularity-free solutions.

§ 4. The Theory of Relativity

There is no inductive method which could lead to the fundamental concepts of physics. Failure to understand this fact constituted the basic philosophical error of so many investigators of the nineteenth century. It was probably the reason why the molecular theory, and Maxwell's theory were able to establish themselves only at a relatively late date. Logical thinking is necessarily deductive; it is based upon hypothetical concepts and axioms. How can we hope to choose the latter in such a manner as to justify us in expecting success as a consequence?

The most satisfactory situation is evidently to be found in cases where the new fundamental hypotheses are suggested by the world of experience itself. The hypothesis of the non-existence of perpetual motion as a basis for thermodynamics affords such an example of a fundamental hypothesis suggested by experience; the same thing holds for the principle of inertia of Galileo. In the same category, moreover, we find the fundamental hypotheses of the theory of relativity, which theory has led to an unexpected expansion and broadening of the field theory, and to the superseding of the foundations of classical mechanics.

The successes of the Maxwell-Lorentz theory have given great confidence in the validity of the electromagnetic equations for empty space and hence, in particular, to the statement that light travels "in space" with a certain constant speed c. Is this law of the invariability of light velocity in relation to any desired inertial system valid? If it were not, then one specific inertial system or more accurately, one specific state of motion (of a body of reference), would be distinguished from all others. In opposition to this idea, however, stand all the mechanical and electromagnetic-optical facts of our experience.

For these reasons it was necessary to raise to the degree of a principle, the validity of the law of constancy of light velocity for all inertial systems. From this, it follows that the spacial coordinates X_1, X_2, X_3, and the time X_4, must be transformed according to the "Lorentz-transformation" which is characterized by invariance of the expression

$$ds^2 = dx_1{}^2 + dx_2{}^2 + dx_3{}^2 - dx_4{}^2$$

(if the unit of time is chosen in such a manner that the speed of light $c = 1$).

By this procedure time lost its absolute character, and was included with the "spacial" coordinates as of algebraically (nearly) similar character. The absolute character of time and particularly of simultaneity were destroyed, and the four dimensional description became introduced as the only adequate one.

In order to account, also, for the equivalence of all inertial systems with regard to all the phenomena of nature, it is necessary to postulate invariance of all systems of physical equations which express general laws, with regard to the Lorentzian transformation. The elaboration of this requirement forms the content of the special theory of relativity.

This theory is compatible with the equations of Maxwell; but, it is incompatible with the basis of classical mechanics. It is true that the equations of motion of the material point can be modified (and with them the expressions for momentum and kinetic energy of the material point) in such a manner as to satisfy the theory; but, the concept of the force of interaction, and with it the concept of potential energy of a system, lose their basis, because these concepts rest upon the idea of absolute instantaneousness. The field, as determined by differential equations, takes the place of the force.

Since the foregoing theory allows interaction only by fields, it requires a field theory of gravitation. Indeed, it is not difficult to formulate such a theory in which, as in Newton's theory, the gravitational fields can be reduced to a scalar which is the solution of a partial differential equation. However, the experimental facts expressed in Newton's theory of gravitation lead in another direction, that of the general theory of relativity.

Classical mechanics contains one point which is unsatisfactory in that, in the fundamentals, the same mass constant is met twice over in two different rôles, namely as "inertial mass" in the law of motion, and as "gravitational mass" in the law of gravitation. As a result of this, the acceleration of a body in a pure gravitational field is independent of its material; or, in a coordinate system of *uniform acceleration* (accelerated in relation to an "inertial system") the motions take place as they would in a homogeneous gravitational field (in relation to a "motionless" system of coordinates). If one assumes that the equivalence of these two cases is complete, then one attains an adaptation of our theoretical thinking to the fact that the gravitational and inertial masses are identical.

From this it follows that there is no longer any reason for favoring, as a fundamental principle, the "inertial systems"; and, we must admit as equivalent in their own right, also *non-linear* transformations of the coordinates (x_1, x_2, x_3, x_4). If we make such a transformation of a system of coordinates of the special theory of relativity, then the metric

$$ds^2 = dx_1{}^2 + dx_2{}^2 + dx_3{}^2 - dx_4{}^2$$

goes over to a general (Riemannian) metric of Bane

$$ds^2 = g_{\mu\nu}\, dx_\mu\, dx_\nu \quad \text{(Summed over } \mu \text{ and } \nu)$$

where the $g_{\mu\nu}$, symmetrical in μ and ν, are certain functions of $x_1 \cdots x_4$ which describe both the metric property, and the gravitational field in relation to the new system of coordinates.

The foregoing improvement in the interpretation of the mechanical basis must, however, be paid for in that—as becomes evident on closer scrutiny—the new coordinates could no longer be interpreted, as results of measurements by rigid bodies and clocks, as they could in the original system (an inertial system with vanishing gravitational field).

The passage to the general theory of relativity is realized by the assumption that such a representation of the field properties of space already mentioned, by functions $g_{\mu\nu}$ (that is to say by a Riemann metric), is also justified in the *general* case in which there is no system of coordinates in relation to which the metric takes the simple quasi-Euclidian form of the special theory of relativity.

Now the coordinates, by themselves, no longer express metric relations, but only the "neighborliness" of the things described, whose coordinates differ but little from one another. All transformations of the coordinates have to be admitted so long as these transformations are free from singularities. Only such equations as are covariant in relation to arbitrary transformations in this sense have meaning as expressions of general laws of nature (postulate of general covariancy).

The first aim of the general theory of relativity was a preliminary statement which, by giving up the requirement of constituting a closed thing in itself, could be connected in as simple a manner as possible with the "facts directly observed." Newton's gravitational theory gave an example, by restricting itself to the pure mechanics of gravitation. This preliminary statement may be characterized as follows:

(1) The concept of the material point and of its mass is retained. A law of motion is given for it, this law of motion being the translation of the law of inertia into the language of the general theory of relativity. This law is a system of total differential equations, the system characteristic of the geodetic line.

(2) In place of Newton's law of interaction by gravitation, we shall find the system of the simplest generally covariant differential equations which can be set up for the $g_{\mu\nu}$-tensor. It is formed by equating to zero the once contracted Riemannian curvature tensor, ($R_{\mu\nu} = 0$).

This formulation permits the treatment of the problem of the planets. More accurately speaking, it allows the treatment of the problem of motion of material points of practically negligible mass in the gravitational field produced by a material point which itself is supposed to have no motion (central symmetry). It does not take into account the reaction of the "moved" material points on the gravitational field, nor does it consider how the central mass produces this gravitational field.

Analogy with classical mechanics shows that the following is a way to complete the theory. One sets up as field equation

$$R_{ik} - \tfrac{1}{2}g_{ik}R = -T_{ik}$$

where R represents the scalar of Riemannian curvature, T_{ik} the energy tensor of the matter in a phenomenological representation. The left side of the equation is chosen in such a manner that its divergence disappears identically. The resulting disappearance of the divergence of the right side produces the "equations of motion" of matter, in the form of partial differential equations for the case where T_{ik} introduces, for the description of the matter, only *four* further functions independent of each other (for instance, density, pressure, and velocity components, where there is between the latter an identity, and between pressure and density an equation of condition).

By this formulation one reduces the whole mechanics of gravitation to the solution of a single system of covariant partial differential equations. The theory avoids all internal discrepancies which we have charged against the basis of classical mechanics. It is sufficient—as far as we know—for the representation of the observed facts of celestial mechanics. But, it is similar to a building, one wing of which is made of fine marble (left part of the equation), but the other wing of which is built of low grade wood (right side of equation). The phenomenological representation of matter is, in fact, only a crude substitute for a representation which would correspond to all known properties of matter.

There is no difficulty in connecting Maxwell's theory of the electromagnetic field with the theory of the gravitational field so long as one restricts himself to space, free of ponderable matter and free of electric density. All that is necessary is to put on the right hand side of the above equation for T_{ik}, the energy tensor of the electromagnetic field in empty space and to associate with the so modified system of equations the Maxwell field equation for empty space, written in general covariant form. Under these conditions there will exist, between all these equations, a sufficient number of the differential identities to guarantee their consistency. We may add that this necessary formal property of the total system of equations leaves arbitrary the choice of the sign of the member T_{ik}, a fact which was later shown to be important.

The desire to have, for the foundations of the theory, the greatest possible unity has resulted in several attempts to include the gravitational field and the electromagnetic field in one formal but homogeneous picture. Here we must mention particularly the five-dimensional theory of Kaluza and Klein. Having considered this possibility very carefully I feel that it is more desirable to accept the lack of internal uniformity of the original theory, because I do not consider that the totality of the hypothetical basis of the five-dimensional theory contains less of an arbitrary nature than does the original theory. The same statement may be made for the projective variety of the theory, which has been elaborated with great care, in particular, by v. Dantzig and by Pauli.

The foregoing considerations concern, exclusively, the theory of the field, free of matter. How are we to proceed from this point in order to obtain a complete theory of atomically constructed matter? In such a theory, singularities must certainly be excluded, since without such exclusion the differential equations do not completely determine the total field. Here, in the field theory of general relativity, we meet the same problem of a theoretical field-representation of matter as was met originally in connection with the pure Maxwell theory.

Here again the attempt to construct particles out of the field theory, leads apparently to singularities. Here also the endeavor has been made to overcome this defect by the introduction of new field variables and by elaborating and extending the system of field equations. Recently, however, I discovered, in collaboration with Dr. Rosen, that the above mentioned simplest combination of the field equations of gravitation and electricity produces centrally symmetrical solutions which can be represented as free of singularity (the well known centrally symmetrical solutions of Schwarzschild for the pure gravitational field, and those of Reissner for the electric field with consideration of its gravitational action). We shall refer to this shortly in the paragraph next but one. In this way it seems possible to get for matter and its interactions a pure field theory free of additional hypotheses, one moreover whose test by submission to facts of experience does not result in difficulties other than purely mathematical ones, which difficulties, however, are very serious.

§ 5. QUANTUM THEORY AND THE FUNDAMENTALS OF PHYSICS

The theoretical physicists of our generation are expecting the erection of a new theoretical basis for physics which would make use of fundamental concepts greatly different from those of the field theory considered up to now. The reason is that it has been found necessary to use—for the mathematical representation of the so-called quantum phenomena—new sorts of methods of consideration.

While the failure of classical mechanics, as revealed by the theory of relativity, is connected with the finite speed of light (its avoidance of being ∞), it was discovered at the beginning of our century that there were other kinds of inconsistencies between deductions from mechanics and experimental facts, which inconsistencies are connected with the finite magnitude (the avoidance of being zero) of Planck's constant h. In particular, while molecular mechanics requires that both, heat content and (monochromatic) radiation density, of solid bodies should decrease *in proportion* to the decreasing absolute temperature, experience has shown that they decrease much more rapidly than the absolute temperature. For a theoretical explanation of this behavior it was necessary to assume that the energy of a mechanical system cannot assume any sort of value, but only certain discrete values whose mathematical expressions were always dependent upon Planck's constant h. Moreover, this conception was essential for the theory of the atom (Bohr's theory). For the transitions of these states into one another—with or without emission or absorption of radiation—no causal laws could be given, but only statistical ones; and, a similar conclusion holds for the radioactive decomposition of atoms, which decomposition was carefully investigated about the same time. For more than two decades physicists tried vainly to find a uniform interpretation of this "quantum character" of systems and phenomena. Such an attempt was successful about ten years ago, through the agency of two entirely different theoretical methods of attack. We owe one of these to Heisenberg and Dirac, and the other to de Broglie and Schrödinger. The mathematical equivalence of the two methods was soon recognized by Schrödinger. I shall try here to sketch the line of thought of de Broglie and Schrödinger, which lies closer to the physicist's method of thinking, and shall accompany the description with certain general considerations.

The question is first: How can one assign a discrete succession of energy value H_σ to a system specified in the sense of classical mechanics (the energy function is a given function of the coordinates q_r and the corresponding momenta p_r)? Planck's constant h relates the frequency H_σ/h to the energy values H_σ. It is therefore sufficient to give to the system a succession of discrete *frequency* values. This reminds us of the fact that in acoustics, a series of discrete frequency values is coordinated to a linear partial differential equation (if boundary values are given) namely the sinusoidal periodic solutions. In corresponding manner, Schrödinger set himself the task of coordinating a partial differential equation for a scalar function ψ to the given energy function $\mathcal{E}(q_r, p_r)$, where the q_r and the time t are independent variables. In this he succeeded (for a complex function ψ) in such a manner that the theoretical values of the energy H_σ, as required by the statistical theory, actually resulted in a satisfactory manner from the periodic solution of the equation.

To be sure, it did not happen to be possible to associate a definite movement, in the sense of mechanics of material points, with a definite solution $\psi(q_r, t)$ of the Schrödinger equation. This means that the ψ function does not determine, at any rate *exactly*, the story of the q_r as functions of the time t. According to Born, however, an interpretation of the physical meaning of the ψ functions was shown to be possible in the following manner: $\psi\psi$ (the square of the absolute value of the complex function ψ) is the probability density at the point under consideration in the configuration-space of the q_r, at the time t. It is therefore possible to characterize the content of the Schrödinger equation in a manner, easy to be understood, but not quite accurate, as follows: it determines how the probability density of a statistical ensemble of systems varies in the configuration-space with the time. Briefly: the Schrödinger equation determines the alteration of the function ψ of the q_r with the time.

It must be mentioned that the result of this theory contains —as limiting values—the result of the particle mechanics if the wave-length encountered during the solution of the Schrödinger problem is everywhere so small that the potential energy varies by a practically infinitely small amount for a change of one wave-length in the configuration-space. Under these conditions the following can in fact be shown: We choose a region G_0 in the configuration-space which, although large (in every dimension) in relation to the wave length, is small in relation to the practical dimensions of the configuration-space. Under these conditions it is possible to choose a function of ψ for an initial time t_0 in such a manner that it vanishes outside of the region G_0, and behaves, according to the Schrödinger equation, in such a manner that it retains this property—approximately at least—also for a later time, but with the region G_0 having passed at that time t into another region G. In this manner one can, with a certain degree of approximation, speak of the motion of the region G as a whole, and one can approximate this motion by the motion of a point in the configuration-space. This motion then coincides with the motion which is required by the equations of classical mechanics.

Experiments on interference made with particle rays have given a brilliant proof that the wave character of phenomena of motion as assumed by the theory does, really, correspond to the facts. In addition to this, the theory succeeded, easily, in demonstrating the statistical laws of the transition of a system from one quantum condition to another under the action of external forces, which, from the standpoint of classical mechanics, appears as a miracle. The external forces were here represented by small additions of the potential energy as functions of the time. Now, while in classical mechanics, such additions can produce only correspondingly small alterations of the system, in the quantum mechanics they produce alterations of any magnitude however large, but with correspondingly small probability, a consequence in perfect harmony with experience. Even an understanding of the laws of radioactive decomposition, at least in their broad lines, was provided by the theory.

Probably never before has a theory been evolved which has given a key to the interpretation and calculation of such a heterogeneous group of phenomena of experience as has the quantum theory. In spite of this, however, I believe that the theory is apt to beguile us into error in our search for a uniform basis for physics, because, in my belief, it is an *incomplete* representation of real things, although it is the only one which can be built out of the fundamental concepts of force and material points (quantum corrections to classical mechanics). The incompleteness of the representation is the outcome of the statistical nature (incompleteness) of the laws. I will now justify this opinion.

I ask first: How far does the ψ function describe a real condition of a mechanical system? Let us assume the ψ_r to be the periodic solutions (put in the order of increasing energy values) of the Schrödinger equation. I shall leave open, for the time being, the question as to how far the individual ψ_r are *complete* descriptions of physical conditions. A system is first in the condition ψ_1 of lowest energy $\mathcal{E}_1$. Then during a finite time a small disturbing force acts upon the system. At a later instant one obtains then from the Schrödinger equation a ψ function of the form

$$\psi = \Sigma \, c_r \psi_r$$

where the c_r are (complex) constants. If the ψ_r are "normalized," then $|c_1|$ is nearly equal to 1, $|c_2|$ etc. is small compared with 1. One may now ask: Does ψ describe a real condition of the system? If the answer is yes, then we can hardly do otherwise than ascribe [8] to this condition a definite energy $\mathcal{E}$, and, in particular, such an energy as exceeds $\mathcal{E}_1$ by a small amount (in any case $\mathcal{E}_1 < \mathcal{E} < \mathcal{E}_2$). Such an assumption is, however, at variance with the experiments on electron impact such as have been made by J. Franck and G. Hertz, if, in addition to this, one accepts Millikan's demonstration of the discrete nature of electricity. As a matter of fact, these experiments lead to the conclusion that energy values of a state lying between the quantum values do not exist. From this it follows that our function ψ does not in any way describe a homogeneous condition of the body, but represents rather a statistical description in which the c_r represent probabilities of the individual energy values. It seems to be clear, therefore, that the Born statistical interpretation of the quantum theory is the only possible one. The ψ function does not in any way describe a condition which could be that of a single system; it relates rather to many systems, to "an ensemble of systems" in the sense of statistical mechanics. If, except for certain special cases, the ψ function furnishes only *statistical* data concerning measurable magnitudes, the reason lies not only in the fact that the *operation of measuring* introduces unknown elements, which can be grasped only statistically, but because of the very fact that the ψ function

[8] Because, according to a well established consequence of the relativity theory, the energy of a complete system (at rest) is equal to its inertia (as a whole). This, however, must have a well defined value.

does not, in any sense, describe the condition of *one* single system. The Schrödinger equation determines the time variations which are experienced by the ensemble of systems which may exist with or without external action on the single system.

Such an interpretation eliminates also the paradox recently demonstrated by myself and two collaborators, and which relates to the following problem.

Consider a mechanical system constituted of two partial systems A and B which have interaction with each other only during limited time. Let the ψ function before their interaction be given. Then the Schrödinger equation will furnish the ψ function after the interaction has taken place. Let us now determine the physical condition of the partial system A as completely as possible by measurements. Then the quantum mechanics allows us to determine the ψ function of the partial system B from the measurements made, and from the ψ function of the total system. This determination, however, gives a result which depends upon *which* of the determining magnitudes specifying the condition of A has been measured (for instance coordinates *or* momenta). Since there can be only *one* physical condition of B after the interaction and which can reasonably not be considered as dependent on the particular measurement we perform on the system A separated from B it may be concluded that the ψ function is *not* unambiguously coordinated with the physical condition. This coordination of several ψ functions with the same physical condition of system B shows again that the ψ function cannot be interpreted as a (complete) description of a physical condition of a unit system. Here also the coordination of the ψ function to an ensemble of systems eliminates every difficulty.[4]

[4] The operation of measuring A, for example, thus involves a transition to a narrower ensemble of systems. The latter (hence also its ψ function) depends upon the point of view according to which this narrowing of the ensemble of systems is made.

The fact that quantum mechanics affords, in such a simple manner, statements concerning (apparently) discontinuous transitions from one total condition to another without actually giving a representation of the specific process, this fact is connected with another, namely the fact that the theory, in reality, does not operate with the single system, but with a totality of systems. The coefficients c_r of our first example are really altered very little under the action of the external force. With this interpretation of quantum mechanics one can understand why this theory can easily account for the fact that weak disturbing forces are able to produce alterations of any magnitude in the physical condition of a system. Such disturbing forces produce, indeed, only correspondingly small alterations of the *statistical density* in the ensemble of systems, and hence only infinitely weak alterations of the ψ functions, the mathematical description of which offers far less difficulty than would be involved in the mathematical representation of finite alterations experienced by part of the single systems. What happens to the single system remains, it is true, entirely unclarified by this mode of consideration; this enigmatic happening is entirely eliminated from the representation by the statistical manner of consideration.

But now I ask: Is there really any physicist who believes that we shall never get any inside view of these important alterations in the single systems, in their structure and their causal connections, and this regardless of the fact that these single happenings have been brought so close to us, thanks to the marvelous inventions of the Wilson chamber and the Geiger counter? To believe this is logically possible without contradiction; but, it is so very contrary to my scientific instinct that I cannot forego the search for a more complete conception.

To these considerations we should add those of another kind which also voice their plea against the idea that the methods introduced by quantum mechanics are likely to give a useful basis for the whole of physics. In the Schrödinger equation, absolute time, and also the potential energy, play a decisive role, while these two concepts have been recognized by the theory of relativity as inadmissible in principle. If one wishes to escape from this difficulty he must found the theory upon field and field laws instead of upon forces of interaction. This leads us to transpose the statistical methods of quantum mechanics to fields, that is to systems of infinitely many degrees of freedom. Although the attempts so far made are restricted to linear equations, which, as we know from the results of the general theory of relativity, are insufficient, the complications met up to now by the very ingenious attempts are already terrifying. They certainly will rise sky high if one wishes to obey the requirements of the general theory of relativity, the justification of which in principle nobody doubts.

To be sure, it has been pointed out that the introduction of a space-time continuum may be considered as contrary to nature in view of the molecular structure of everything which happens on a small scale. It is maintained that perhaps the success of the Heisenberg method points to a purely algebraical method of description of nature, that is to the elimination of continuous functions from physics. Then, however, we must also give up, by principle, the space-time continuum. It is not unimaginable that human ingenuity will some day find methods which will make it possible to proceed along such a path. At the present time, however, such a program looks like an attempt to breathe in empty space.

There is no doubt that quantum mechanics has seized hold of a beautiful element of truth, and that it will be a test stone for any future theoretical basis, in that it must be deducible as a limiting case from that basis, just as electrostatics is deducible from the Maxwell equations of the electromagnetic field or as thermodynamics is deducible from classical mechanics. However, I do not believe that quantum mechanics will be the *starting point* in the search for this basis, just as, vice versa, one could not go from thermodynamics (resp. statistical mechanics) to the foundations of mechanics.

In view of this situation, it seems to be entirely justifiable seriously to consider the question as to whether the basis of field physics cannot by *any* means be put into harmony with the facts of the quantum theory. Is this not the only basis which, consistently with today's possibility of mathematical expression, can be adapted to the requirements of the general theory of relativity? The belief, prevailing among the physicists of today, that such an attempt would be hopeless, may have its root in the unjustifiable idea that such a theory should lead, as a first approximation, to the equations of classical mechanics for the motion of corpuscles, or at least to total differential equations. As a matter of fact up to now we have never succeeded in representing corpuscles theoretically by fields free of singularities, and we can, a priori, say nothing about the behavior of such entities. *One thing*, however, is certain: if a field theory results in a representation of corpuscles free of singularities, then the behavior of these corpuscles with time is determined solely by the differential equations of the field.

§ 6. Relativity Theory and Corpuscles

I shall now show that, according to the general theory of relativity, there exist singularity-free solutions of field equations which can be interpreted as representing corpuscles. I restrict myself here to neutral particles because, in another recent publication in collaboration with Dr. Rosen, I have treated this question in a detailed manner, and because the essentials of the problem can be completely shown by this case.

The gravitational field is entirely described by the tensor $g_{\mu\nu}$. In the three-index symbols $\Gamma_{\mu\nu}{}^{\sigma}$, there appear also the contravariants $g^{\mu\nu}$ which are defined as the minors of the $g_{\mu\nu}$ divided by the determinant $g(=|g_{\alpha\beta}|)$. In order that the R_{ik} shall be defined and finite, it is not sufficient that there shall be, for the environment of every part of the continuum, a system of coordinates in which the $g_{\mu\nu}$ and their first differential quotients are continuous and differentiable, but it is also necessary that the determinant g shall nowhere vanish. This last restriction is, however, eliminated if one replaces the differential equations $R_{ik} = 0$ by $g^2 R_{ik} = 0$, the left hand sides of which are *whole* rational functions of the g_{ik} and of their derivatives.

These equations have the centrally symmetrical solutions indicated by Schwarzschild

$$ds^2 = -\frac{1}{1-2m/r}dr^2 - r^2(d\theta^2 + \sin^2\theta d\varphi^2) + \left(1 - \frac{2m}{r}\right)dt^2$$

This solution has a singularity at $r = 2m$, since the coefficient of dr^2 (i.e. g_{11}), becomes infinite on this hypersurface. If, however, we replace the variable r by ρ defined by the equation

$$\rho^2 = r - 2m$$

we obtain

$$ds^2 = -4(2m + \rho^2)d\rho^2 - (2m + \rho^2)^2(d\theta^2 + \sin^2\theta d\varphi^2)$$
$$+ \frac{\rho^2}{2m + \rho^2}dt^2$$

This solution behaves regularly for all values of ρ. The vanishing of the coefficient of dt^2 i.e. (g_{44}) for $\rho = 0$ results, it is true, in the consequence that the determinant g vanishes for this value; but, with the methods of writing the field equations actually adopted, this does not constitute a singularity.

If ρ extends from $-\infty$ to $+\infty$, then r runs from $+\infty$ to $r = 2m$ and then back to $+\infty$, while for such values of r as correspond to $r < 2m$ there are no corresponding real values of ρ. Hence the Schwarzschild solution becomes a regular solution by representation of the physical space as consisting of two identical "shells" neighboring upon the hypersurface $\rho = 0$, that is $r = 2m$, while for this hypersurface the determinant g vanishes. Let us call such a connection between the two (identical) shells a "bridge." Hence the existence of such a bridge between the two shells in the finite realm corresponds to the existence of a material neutral particle which is described in a manner free from singularities.

The solution of the problem of the motion of neutral particles evidently amounts to the discovery of such solutions of the gravitational equations (written free of denominators), as contain several bridges.

The conception sketched above corresponds, a priori, to the atomistic structure of matter insofar as the "bridge" is by its nature a discrete element. Moreover, we see that the mass constant m of the neutral particles must necessarily be positive, since no solution free of singularities can correspond to the Schwarzschild solution for a negative value of m. Only the examination of the several-bridge-problem, can show whether or not this theoretical method furnishes an explanation of the empirically demonstrated equality of the masses of the particles found in nature, and whether it takes into account the facts which the quantum mechanics has so wonderfully comprehended.

In an analogous manner, it is possible to demonstrate that the combined equations of gravitation and electricity (with appropriate choice of the sign of the electrical member in the gravitational equations) produce a singularity-free bridge-representation of the electric corpuscle. The simplest solution of this kind is that for an electrical particle without gravitational mass.

So long as the important mathematical difficulties concerned with the solution of the several-bridge-problem, are not overcome, nothing can be said concerning the usefulness of the theory from the physicist's point of view. However, it constitutes, as a matter of fact, the first attempt towards the consistent elaboration of a field theory which presents a possibility of explaining the properties of matter. In favor of this attempt one should also add that it is based on the simplest possible relativistic field equations known today.

Summary

Physics constitutes a logical system of thought which is in a state of evolution, and whose basis cannot be obtained through distillation by any inductive method from the experiences lived through, but which can only be attained by free invention. The justification (truth content) of the system rests in the proof of usefulness of the resulting theorems on the basis of sense experiences, where the relations of the latter to the former can only be comprehended intuitively. Evolution is going on in the direction of increasing simplicity of the logical basis. In order further to approach this goal, we must make up our mind to accept the fact that the logical basis departs more and more from the facts of experience, and that the path of our thought from the fundamental basis to these resulting theorems, which correlate with sense experiences, becomes continually harder and longer.

Our aim has been to sketch, as briefly as possible, the development of the fundamental concepts in their dependence upon the facts of experience and upon the strife towards the goal of internal perfection of the system. Today's state of affairs had to be illuminated by these considerations, as they appear to me. (It is unavoidable that historic schematic representation is of a personal color.)

I try to demonstrate how the concepts of bodily objects, space, subjective and objective time, are connected with one another and with the nature of the experience. In classical mechanics the concepts of space and time become independent. The concept of the bodily object is replaced in the foundations by the concept of the material point, by which means mechanics becomes fundamentally atomistic. Light and electricity produce insurmountable difficulties when one attempts to make mechanics the basis of all physics. We are thus led to the field theory of electricity, and, later on to the attempt to base physics entirely upon the concept of the field (after an attempted compromise with classical mechanics). This attempt leads to the theory of relativity (evolution of the notion of space and time into that of the continuum with metric structure).

I try to demonstrate, furthermore, why in my opinion the quantum theory does not seem likely to be able to produce a usable foundation for physics: one becomes involved in contradictions if one tries to consider the theoretical quantum description as a *complete* description of the individual physical system or happening.

On the other hand, up to the present time, the field theory is unable to give an explanation of the molecular structure of matter and of quantum phenomena. It is shown, however, that the conviction to the effect that the field theory is unable to give, by its methods, a solution of these problems rests upon prejudice.

14

THE FUNDAMENTS OF
THEORETICAL PHYSICS

SCIENCE IS THE ATTEMPT to make the chaotic diversity of our sense-experience correspond to a logically uniform system of thought. In this system single experiences must be correlated with the theoretic structure in such a way that the resulting coordination is unique and convincing.

The sense-experiences are the given subject-matter. But the theory that shall interpret them is man-made. It is the result of an extremely laborious process of adaptation: hypothetical, never completely final, always subject to question and doubt.

The scientific way of forming concepts differs from that which we use in our daily life, not basically, but merely in the more precise definition of concepts and conclusions; more painstaking and systematic choice of experimental material; and greater logical economy. By this last we mean the effort to reduce all concepts and correlations to as few as possible logically independent basic concepts and axioms.

What we call physics comprises that group of natural sciences which base their concepts on measurements; and whose concepts and propositions lend themselves to mathematical formulation. Its realm is accordingly defined as that part of the sum total of our knowledge which is capable of being expressed in mathematical terms. With the progress of science, the realm of physics has so expanded that it seems to be limited only by the limitations of the method itself.

The larger part of physical research is devoted to the development of the various branches of physics, in each of which the object is the theoretical understanding of more or less restricted fields of experience, and in each of which the laws and concepts remain as closely as possible related to experience. It is this department of science, with its ever-growing specialization, which has revolutionized practical life in the last centuries, and given birth to the possibility that man may at last be freed from the burden of physical toil.

On the other hand, from the very beginning there has always been present the attempt to find a unifying theoretical basis for all these single sciences, consisting of a minimum of concepts and fundamental relationships, from which all the concepts and relationships of the single disciplines might be derived by logical process. This is what we mean by the search for a foundation of the whole of physics. The confident belief that this ultimate goal may be reached is the chief source of the passionate devotion which has always animated the researcher. It is in this sense that the following observations are devoted to the foundations of physics.

From what has been said it is clear that the word foundations in this connection does not mean something analogous in all respects to the foundations of a building. Logically considered, of course, the various single laws of physics rest upon this foundation. But whereas a building may be seriously damaged by a heavy storm or spring flood, yet its foundations remain intact, in science the logical foundation is always in greater peril from new experiences or new knowledge than are the branch disciplines with their closer experimental contacts. In the connection of the foundation with all the single parts lies its great significance, but likewise its greatest danger in face of any new factor. When we realize this, we are led to wonder why the so-called revolutionary epochs of the science of physics have not more often and more completely changed its foundation than has actually been the case.

The first attempt to lay a uniform theoretical foundation was the work of Newton. In his system everything is reduced to the following concepts: (1) Mass points with invariable mass; (2) action at a distance between any pair of mass points; (3) law of motion for the mass point. There was not, strictly speaking, any all-embracing foundation, because an explicit law was formulated only for the actions-at-a-distance of gravitation; while for other actions-at-a-distance nothing was established *a priori* except the law of equality of *actio* and *reactio*. Moreover, Newton himself fully realized that time and space were essential elements, as physically effective factors, of his system, if only by implication.

This Newtonian basis proved eminently fruitful and was regarded as final up to the end of the nineteenth century. It not only gave results for the movements of the heavenly bodies, down to the most minute details, but also furnished a theory of the mechanics of discrete and continuous masses, a simple explanation of the principle of the conservation of energy and a complete and brilliant theory of heat. The explanation of the facts of electrodynamics within the Newtonian system was more forced; least convincing of all, from the very beginning, was the theory of light.

It is not surprising that Newton would not listen to a wave theory of light; for such a theory was most unsuited to his theoretical foundation. The assumption that space was filled with a medium consisting of material points that propagated light waves without exhibiting any other mechanical properties must have seemed to him quite artificial. The strongest empirical arguments for the wave nature of light, fixed speeds of propagation, interference, diffraction, polarization, were either unknown or else not known in any well-ordered synthesis. He was justified in sticking to his corpuscular theory of light.

During the nineteenth century the dispute was settled in favor of the wave theory. Yet no serious doubt of the mechanical foundation of physics arose, in the first place because nobody knew where to find a foundation of another sort. Only slowly, under the irresistible pressure of facts, there developed a new foundation of physics, field-physics.

From Newton's time on, the theory of action-at-a-distance was constantly found artificial. Efforts were not lacking to explain gravitation by a kinetic theory, that is, on the basis of collision forces of hypothetical mass particles. But the attempts were superficial and bore no fruit. The strange part played by space (or the inertial system) within the mechanical foundation was also clearly recognized, and criticized with especial clarity by Ernst Mach.

The great change was brought about by Faraday, Maxwell and Hertz—as a matter of fact half-unconsciously and against their will. All three of them, throughout their lives, considered themselves adherents of the mechanical theory. Hertz had found the simplest form of the equations of the electromagnetic field, and declared that any theory leading to these equations was Maxwellian theory. Yet toward the end of his short life he wrote a paper in which he presented as the foundation of physics a mechanical theory freed from the force-concept.

For us, who took in Faraday's ideas so to speak with our mother's milk, it is hard to appreciate their greatness and audacity. Faraday must have grasped with unerring instinct the artificial nature of all attempts to refer electromagnetic phenomena to actions-at-a-distance between electric particles reacting on each other. How was each single iron filing among a lot scattered on a piece of paper to know of the single electric particles running round in a nearby conductor? All these electric particles together seemed to create in the surrounding space a condition which in turn produced a certain order in the filings. These spatial states, to-day called fields, if their geometrical structure and interdependent action were once rightly grasped, would, he was convinced, furnish the clue to the mysterious electromagnetic inter-actions. He conceived these fields as states of mechanical stress in a space-filling medium, similar to the states of stress in an elastically distended body. For at that time this was the only way one could conceive of states that were appar-ently continuously distributed in space. The peculiar type of mechanical interpretation of these fields remained in the background—a sort of placation of the scientific conscience in view of the mechanical tradition of Faraday's time. With the help of these new field concepts Faraday succeeded in form-ing a qualitative concept of the whole complex of electro-magnetic effects discovered by him and his predecessors. The precise formulation of the time-space laws of those fields was the work of Maxwell. Imagine his feelings when the differ-ential equations he had formulated proved to him that elec-tromagnetic fields spread in the form of polarized waves and with the speed of light! To few men in the world has such an experience been vouchsafed. At that thrilling moment he surely never guessed that the riddling nature of light, appar-ently so completely solved, would continue to baffle succeed-ing generations. Meantime, it took physicists some decades to grasp the full significance of Maxwell's discovery, so bold was the leap that his genius forced upon the conceptions of his fellow-workers. Only after Hertz had demonstrated ex-perimentally the existence of Maxwell's electromagnetic waves, did resistance to the new theory break down.

But if the electromagnetic field could exist as a wave inde-pendent of the material source, then the electrostatic inter-action could no longer be explained as action-at-a-distance. And what was true for electrical action could not be denied for gravitation. Everywhere Newton's actions-at-a-distance gave way to fields spreading with finite velocity.

Of Newton's foundation there now remained only the ma-terial mass points subject to the law of motion. But J. J. Thom-son pointed out that an electrically charged body in motion must, according to Maxwell's theory, possess a magnetic field whose energy acted precisely as does an increase of kinetic energy to the body. If, then, a part of kinetic energy consists of field energy, might that not then be true of the whole of the kinetic energy? Perhaps the basic property of matter, its inertia, could be explained within the field theory? The question led to the problem of an interpretation of matter in terms of field theory, the solution of which would furnish an explanation of the atomic structure of matter. It was soon realized that Maxwell's theory could not accomplish such a program. Since then many scientists have zealously sought to complete the field theory by some generalization that should comprise a theory of matter; but so far such efforts have not been crowned with success. In order to construct a theory, it is not enough to have a clear conception of the goal. One must also have a formal point of view which will sufficiently restrict the unlimited variety of possibilities. So far this has not been found; accordingly the field theory has not succeeded in furnishing a foundation for the whole of physics.

For several decades most physicists clung to the conviction that a mechanical substructure would be found for Maxwell's theory. But the unsatisfactory results of their efforts led to gradual acceptance of the new field concepts as irreducible fundamentals—in other words, physicists resigned themselves to giving up the idea of a mechanical foundation.

Thus physicists held to a field-theory program. But it could not be called a foundation, since nobody could tell whether a consistent field theory could ever explain on the one hand gravitation, on the other hand the elementary components of matter. In this state of affairs it was necessary to think of material particles as mass points subject to Newton's laws of motion. This was the procedure of Lorentz in creating his electron theory and the theory of the electromagnetic phenomena of moving bodies.

Such was the point at which fundamental conceptions had

arrived at the turn of the century. Immense progress was made in the theoretical penetration and understanding of whole groups of new phenomena; but the establishment of a unified foundation for physics seemed remote indeed. And this state of things has even been aggravated by subsequent developments. The development during the present century is characterized by two theoretical systems essentially independent of each other: the theory of relativity and the quantum theory. The two systems do not directly contradict each other; but they seem little adapted to fusion into one unified theory. We must briefly discuss the basic idea of these two systems.

The theory of relativity arose out of efforts to improve, with reference to logical economy, the foundation of physics as it existed at the turn of the century. The so-called special or restricted relativity theory is based on the fact that Maxwell's equations (and thus the law of propagation of light in empty space) are converted into equations of the same form, when they undergo Lorentz transformation. This formal property of the Maxwell equations is supplemented by our fairly secure empirical knowledge that the laws of physics are the same with respect to all inertial systems. This leads to the result that the Lorentz transformation—applied to space and time coordinates—must govern the transition from one inertial system to any other. The content of the restricted relativity theory can accordingly be summarized in one sentence: all natural laws must be so conditioned that they are covariant with respect to Lorentz transformations. From this it follows that the simultaneity of two distant events is not an invariant concept and that the dimensions of rigid bodies and the speed of clocks depend upon their state of motion. A further consequence was a modification of Newton's law of motion in cases where the speed of a given body was not small compared with the speed of light. There followed also the principle of the equivalence of mass and energy, with the laws of conservation of mass and energy becoming one and the same. Once it was shown that simultaneity was relative and depended on the frame of reference, every possibility of retaining actions-at-a-distance within the foundation of physics disappeared, since that concept presupposed the absolute character of simultaneity (it must be possible to state the location of the two interacting mass points "at the same time").

The general theory of relativity owes its origin to the attempt to explain a fact known since Galileo's and Newton's time but hitherto eluding all theoretical interpretation: the inertia and the weight of a body, in themselves two entirely distinct things, are measured by one and the same constant, the mass. From this correspondence follows that it is impossible to discover by experiment whether a given system of coordinates is accelerated, or whether its motion is straight and uniform and the observed effects are due to a gravitational field (this is the equivalence principle of the general relativity theory). It shatters the concepts of the inertial system, as soon as gravitation enters in. It may be remarked here that the inertial system is a weak point of the Galilean-Newtonian mechanics. For there is presupposed a mysterious property of physical space, conditioning the kind of coordination-systems for which the law of inertia and the Newtonian law of motion hold good.

These difficulties can be avoided by the following postulate: natural laws are to be formulated in such a way that their form is identical for coordinate systems of any kind of states of motion. To accomplish this is the task of the general theory of relativity. On the other hand, we deduce from the restricted theory the existence of a Riemannian metric within the time-space continuum, which, according to the equivalence principle, describes both the gravitational field and the metric properties of space. Assuming that the field equations of gravitation are of the second differential order, the field law is clearly determined.

Aside from this result, the theory frees field physics from the disability it suffered from, in common with the Newtonian mechanics, of ascribing to space those independent physical properties which heretofore had been concealed by the use of an inertial system. But it can not be claimed that those parts of the general relativity theory which can to-day be regarded as final have furnished physics with a complete and satisfactory foundation. In the first place, the total field appears in it to be composed of two logically unconnected parts, the gravitational and the electromagnetic. And in the second place, this theory, like the earlier field theories, has not up till now supplied an explanation of the atomistic structure of matter. This failure has probably some connection with the fact that so far it has contributed nothing to the understanding of quantum phenomena. To take in these phenomena, physicists have been driven to the adoption of entirely new methods, the basic characteristics of which we shall now discuss.

In the year nineteen hundred, in the course of a purely theoretic investigation, Max Planck made a very remarkable discovery: the law of radiation of bodies as a function of temperature could not be derived solely from the laws of Maxwellian electrodynamics. To arrive at results consistent with the relevant experiments, radiation of a given frequency had to be treated as though it consisted of energy atoms of the individual energy h.v., where h is Planck's universal constant. During the years following it was shown that light was everywhere produced and absorbed in such energy quanta. In particular Niels Bohr was able largely to understand the structure of the atom, on the assumption that atoms can have only discrete energy values, and that the discontinuous transitions between them are connected with the emission or absorption of such an energy quantum. This threw some light on the fact that in their gaseous state elements and their compounds radiate and absorb only light of certain sharply defined frequencies. All this was quite inexplicable within the frame of the hitherto existing theories. It was clear that at least in the field of atomistic phenomena the character of everything that happens is determined by discrete states and by apparently discontinuous transitions between them, Planck's constant h playing a decisive role.

The next step was taken by De Broglie. He asked himself how the discrete states could be understood by the aid of the current concepts, and hit on a parallel with stationary waves, as for instance in the case of the proper frequencies of organ pipes and strings in acoustics. True, wave actions of the kind here required were unknown; but they could be constructed, and their mathematical laws formulated, employing Planck's constant h. De Broglie conceived an electron revolving about the atomic nucleus as being connected with such a hypothetical wave train, and made intelligible to some extent the discrete character of Bohr's "permitted" paths by the stationary character of the corresponding waves.

Now in mechanics the motion of material points is determined by the forces or fields of force acting upon them. Hence it was to be expected that those fields of force would also influence De Broglie's wave fields in an analogous way. Erwin Schrödinger showed how this influence was to be taken into account, re-interpreting by an ingenious method certain formulations of classical mechanics. He even succeeded in expanding the wave mechanical theory to a point where without the introduction of any additional hypotheses, it became applicable to any mechanical system consisting of an arbitrary number of mass points, that is to say possessing an arbitrary number of degrees of freedom. This was possible because a mechanical system consisting of n mass points is mathematically equivalent to a considerable degree, to one single mass point moving in a space of 3 n dimensions.

On the basis of this theory there was obtained a surprisingly good representation of an immense variety of facts which otherwise appeared entirely incomprehensible. But on one point, curiously enough, there was failure: it proved impossible to associate with these Schrödinger waves definite motions of the mass points—and that, after all, had been the original purpose of the whole construction.

The difficulty appeared insurmountable, until it was overcome by Born in a way as simple as it was unexpected. The De Broglie-Schrödinger wave fields were not to be interpreted as a mathematical description of how an event actually takes place in time and space, though, of course, they have reference to such an event. Rather they are a mathematical description of what we can actually know about the system. They serve only to make statistical statements and predictions of the results of all measurements which we can carry out upon the system.

Let me illustrate these general features of quantum mechanics by means of a simple example: we shall consider a mass point kept inside a restricted region G by forces of finite strength. If the kinetic energy of the mass point is below a certain limit, then the mass point, according to classical mechanics, can never leave the region G. But according to quantum mechanics, the mass point, after a period not immediately predictable, is able to leave the region G, in an unpredictable direction, and escape into surrounding space. This case, according to Gamow, is a simplified model of radioactive disintegration.

The quantum theoretical treatment of this case is as follows: at the time t_0 we have a Schrödinger wave system entirely inside G. But from the time t_0 onwards, the waves leave the interior of G in all directions, in such a way that the amplitude of the outgoing wave is small compared to the initial amplitude of the wave system inside G. The further these outside waves spread, the more the amplitude of the waves inside G diminishes, and correspondingly the intensity of the later waves issuing from G. Only after infinite time has passed is the wave supply inside G exhausted, while the outside wave has spread over an ever-increasing space.

But what has this wave process to do with the first object of our interest, the particle originally enclosed in G? To answer this question, we must imagine some arrangement which will permit us to carry out measurements on the particle. For instance, let us imagine somewhere in the surrounding space a screen so made that the particle sticks to it on coming into contact with it. Then from the intensity of the waves hitting the screen at some point, we draw conclusions as to the probability of the particle hitting the screen there at that time. As soon as the particle has hit any particular point of the screen, the whole wave field loses all its physical meaning; its only purpose was to make probability predictions as to the place and time of the particle hitting the screen (or, for instance, its momentum at the time when it hits the screen).

All other cases are analogous. The aim of the theory is to determine the probability of the results of measurement upon a system at a given time. On the other hand, it makes no attempt to give a mathematical representation of what is actually present or goes on in space and time. On this point the quantum theory of to-day differs fundamentally from all previous theories of physics, mechanistic as well as field theories. Instead of a model description of actual space-time events, it gives the probability distributions for possible measurements as functions of time.

It must be admitted that the new theoretical conception owes its origin not to any flight of fancy but to the compelling force of the facts of experience. All attempts to represent the particle and wave features displayed in the' phenomena of light and matter, by direct course to a space-time model, have so far ended in failure. And Heisenberg has convincingly shown, from an empirical point of view, any decision as to a rigorously deterministic structure of nature is definitely ruled out, because of the atomistic structure of our experimental apparatus. Thus it is probably out of the question that any future knowledge can compel physics again to relinquish our present statistical theoretical foundation in favor of a deterministic one which would deal directly with physical reality. Logically the problem seems to offer two possibilities, between which we are in principle given a choice. In the end the choice will be made according to which kind of description yields the formulation of the simplest foundation, logically speaking. At the present, we are quite without any deterministic theory directly describing the events themselves and in consonance with the facts.

For the time being, we have to admit that we do not possess any general theoretical basis for physics, which can be regarded as its logical foundation. The field theory, so far, has failed in the molecular sphere. It is agreed on all hands that the only principle which could serve as the basis of quantum theory would be one that constituted a translation of the field theory into the scheme of quantum statistics. Whether this will actually come about in a satisfactory manner, nobody can venture to say.

Some physicists, among them myself, can not believe that we must abandon, actually and forever, the idea of direct representation of physical reality in space and time; or that we must accept the view that events in nature are analogous to a game of chance. It is open to every man to choose the direction of his striving; and also every man may draw comfort from Lessing's fine saying, that the search for truth is more precious than its possession.

15

THE COMMON LANGUAGE OF SCIENCE

THE FIRST STEP towards language was to link acoustically or otherwise commutable signs to sense-impressions. Most likely all sociable animals have arrived at this primitive kind of communication—at least to a certain degree. A higher development is reached when further signs are introduced and understood which establish relations between those other signs designating sense-impression. At this stage it is already possible to report somewhat complex series of impressions; we can say that language has come to existence. If language is to lead at all to understanding, there must be rules concerning the relations between the signs on the one hand and on the other hand there must be a stable correspondence between signs and impressions. In their childhood individuals connected by the same language grasp these rules and relations mainly by intuition. When man becomes conscious of the rules concerning the relations between signs the so-called grammar of language is established.

In an early stage the words may correspond directly to impressions. At a later stage this direct connection is lost insofar as some words convey relations to perceptions only if used in connection with other words (for instance such words as: "is," "or," "thing"). Then word-groups rather than single words refer to perceptions. When language becomes thus partially independent from the background of impressions a greater inner coherence is gained.

Only at this further development where frequent use is

made of so-called abstract concepts, language becomes an instrument of reasoning in the true sense of the word. But it is also this development which turns language into a dangerous source of error and deception. Everything depends on the degree to which words and word-combinations correspond to the world of impression.

What is it that brings about such an intimate connection between language and thinking? Is there no thinking without the use of language, namely in concepts and concept-combinations for which words need not necessarily come to mind? Has not everyone of us struggled for words although the connection between "things" was already clear?

We might be inclined to attribute to the act of thinking complete independence from language if the individual formed or were able to form his concepts without the verbal guidance of his environment. Yet most likely the mental shape of an individual, growing up under such conditions, would be very poor. Thus we may conclude that the mental development of the individual and his way of forming concepts depend to a high degree upon language. This makes us realize to what extent the same language means the same mentality. In this sense thinking and language are linked together.

What distinguishes the language of science from language as we ordinarily understand the word? How is it that scientific language is international? What science strives for is an utmost acuteness and clarity of concepts as regards their mutual relation and their correspondence to sensory data. As an illustration let us take the language of Euclidian geometry and Algebra. They manipulate with a small number of independently introduced concepts, respectively symbols, such as the integral number, the straight line, the point, as well as with signs which designate the fundamental operations, that is the connections between those fundamental concepts. This is the basis for the construction, respectively definition of all other statements and concepts. The connection between concepts and statements on the one hand and the sensory data on the other hand is established through acts of counting and measuring whose performance is sufficiently well determined.

The super-national character of scientific concepts and scientific language is due to the fact that they have been set up by the best brains of all countries and all times. In solitude and yet in cooperative effort as regards the final effect they created the spiritual tools for the technical revolutions which have transformed the life of mankind in the last centuries. Their system of concepts have served as a guide in the bewildering chaos of perceptions so that we learned to grasp general truths from particular observations.

What hopes and fears does the scientific method imply for mankind? I do not think that this is the right way to put the question. Whatever this tool in the hand of man will produce depends entirely on the nature of the goals alive in this mankind. Once these goals exist, the scientific method furnishes means to realize them. Yet it cannot furnish the very goals. The scientific method itself would not have led anywhere, it would not even have been born without a passionate striving for clear understanding.

Perfections of means and confusion of goals seem—in my opinion—to characterize our age. If we desire sincerely and passionately the safety, the welfare and the free development of the talents of all men, we shall not be in want of the means to approach such a state. Even if only a small part of mankind strives for such goals, their superiority will prove itself in the long run.

16

THE LAWS OF SCIENCE AND THE LAWS OF ETHICS

Science searches for relations which are thought to exist independently of the searching individual. This includes the case where man himself is the subject. Or the subject of scientific statements may be concepts created by ourselves, as in mathematics. Such concepts are not necessarily supposed to correspond to any objects in the outside world. However, all scientific statements and laws have one characteristic in common: they are "true or false" (adequate or inadequate). Roughly speaking, our reaction to them is "yes" or "no."

The scientific way of thinking has a further characteristic. The concepts which it uses to build up its coherent systems are not expressing emotions. For the scientist, there is only "being," but no wishing, no valuing, no good, no evil; no goal. As long as we remain within the realm of science proper, we can never meet with a sentence of the type: "Thou shalt not lie." There is something like a Puritan's restraint in the scientist who seeks truth: he keeps away from everything voluntaristic or emotional. Incidentally, this trait is the result of a slow development, peculiar to modern Western thought.

From this it might seem as if logical thinking were irrelevant for ethics. Scientific statements of facts and relations, indeed, cannot produce ethical directives. However, ethical directives can be made rational and coherent by logical thinking and empirical knowledge. If we can agree on some fundamental ethical propositions, then other ethical propositions can be derived from them, provided that the original premises are stated with sufficient precision. Such ethical premises play a similar role in ethics, to that played by axioms in mathematics.

This is why we do not feel at all that it is meaningless to ask such questions as: "Why should we not lie?" We feel that such questions are meaningful because in all discussions of this kind some ethical premises are tacitly taken for granted. We then feel satisfied when we succeed in tracing back the ethical directive in question to these basic premises. In the case of lying this might perhaps be done in some way such as this: Lying destroys confidence in the statements of other people. Without such confidence, social cooperation is made impossible or at least difficult. Such cooperation, however, is essential to make human life possible and tolerable. This means that the rule "Thou shalt not lie" has been traced back to the demands: "Human life shall be preserved" and "Pain and sorrow shall be lessened as much as possible."

But what is the origin of such ethical axioms? Are they arbitrary? Are they based on mere authority? Do they stem from experiences of men and are they conditioned indirectly by such experiences?

For pure logic all axioms are arbitrary, including the axioms of ethics. But they are by no means arbitrary from a psychological and genetic point of view. They are derived from our inborn tendencies to avoid pain and annihilation, and from the accumulated emotional reaction of individuals to the behavior of their neighbors.

It is the privilege of man's moral genius, impersonated by inspired individuals, to advance ethical axioms which are so comprehensive and so well founded that men will accept them as grounded in the vast mass of their individual emotional experiences. Ethical axioms are found and tested not very differently from the axioms of science. Truth is what stands the test of experience.

17

AN ELEMENTARY DERIVATION OF THE EQUIVALENCE OF MASS AND ENERGY

THE FOLLOWING DERIVATION of the law of equivalence, which has not been published before, has two advantages. Although it makes use of the principle of special relativity, it does not presume the formal machinery of the theory but uses only three previously known laws:

(1) The law of the conservation of momentum.
(2) The expression for the pressure of radiation; that is, the momentum of a complex of radiation moving in a fixed direction.
(3) The well known expression for the aberration of light (influence of the motion of the earth on the apparent location of the fixed stars—Bradley).

We now consider the following system. Let the body B rest

116

freely in space with respect to the system K_0. Two complexes of radiation S, S' each of energy $\frac{E}{2}$ move in the positive and negative x_0 direction respectively and are eventually absorbed by B. With this absorption the energy of B increases by E. The body B stays at rest with respect to K_0 by reasons of symmetry.

Now we consider this same process with respect to the system K, which moves with respect to K_0 with the constant velocity v in the negative Z_0 direction. With respect to K the description of the process is as follows:

The body B moves in the positive Z direction with velocity v. The two complexes of radiation now have directions with respect to K which make an angle α with the x axis. The law of aberration states that in the first approximation $\alpha = \frac{c}{v}$, where c is the velocity of light. From the consideration with respect to K_0 we know that the velocity v of B remains unchanged by the absorption of S and S'.

Now we apply the law of conservation of momentum with respect to the z direction to our system in the coordinate-frame K.

I. *Before the absorption* let M be the mass of B; Mv is then the expression of the momentum of B (according to classical mechanics). Each of the complexes has the energy $\frac{E}{2}$ and hence, by a well known conclusion of Maxwell's theory, it has the momentum $\frac{E}{2c}$. Rigorously speaking this is the momentum of S with respect to K_0. However, when v is small with respect to c, the momentum with respect to K is the same except for a quantity of second order of magnitude ($\frac{v^2}{c^2}$ compared to 1). The z-component of this momentum is $\frac{E}{2c}$ sin α or with sufficient accuracy (except for quantities of higher order of magnitude) $\frac{E}{2c}$ α or $\frac{E}{2} \cdot \frac{v}{c^2}$. S and S′ together therefore have a momentum $E\frac{v}{c^2}$ in the z direction. The total momentum of the system before absorption is therefore

$$Mv + \frac{E}{c^2} \cdot v$$

II. *After the absorption* let M′ be the mass of B. We anticipate here the possibility that the mass increased with the absorption of the energy E (this is necessary so that the final result of our consideration be consistent). The momentum of the system after absorption is then

$$M'v$$

We now assume the law of the conservation of momentum and apply it with respect to the z direction. This gives the equation

$$Mv + \frac{E}{c^2} v = M'v$$

or

$$M' - M = \frac{E}{c^2}$$

This equation expresses the law of the equivalence of energy and mass. The energy increase E is connected with the mass increase $\frac{E}{c^2}$. Since energy according to the usual definition leaves an additive constant free, we may so choose the latter that

$$E = Mc^2$$

Public Affairs

18

WHY SOCIALISM?

Is it advisable for one who is not an expert on economic and social issues to express views on the subject of socialism? I believe for a number of reasons that it is.

Let us first consider the question from the point of view of scientific knowledge. It might appear that there are no essential methodological differences between astronomy and economics: scientists in both fields attempt to discover laws of general acceptability for a circumscribed group of phenomena in order to make the interconnection of these phenomena as clearly understandable as possible. But in reality such methodological differences do exist. The discovery of general laws in the field of economics is made difficult by the circumstance that observed economic phenomena are often affected by many factors which are very hard to evaluate separately. In addition, the experience which has accumulated since the beginning of the so-called civilized period of human history has—as is well known—been largely influenced and limited by causes which are by no means exclusively economic in nature. For example, most of the major states of history owed their existence to conquest. The conquering peoples established themselves, legally and economically, as the privileged class of the conquered country. They seized for themselves a monopoly of the land ownership and appointed a priesthood from among their own ranks. The priests, in control of education, made the class division of society into a permanent institution and created a system of values by which the people were thenceforth, to a large extent unconsciously, guided in their social behavior.

But historic tradition is, so to speak, of yesterday; nowhere have we really overcome what Thorstein Veblen called "the predatory phase" of human development. The observable economic facts belong to that phase and even such laws as we can derive from them are not applicable to other phases. Since the real purpose of socialism is precisely to overcome and advance beyond the predatory phase of human development, economic science in its present state can throw little light on the socialist society of the future.

Second, socialism is directed towards a social-ethical end. Science, however, cannot create ends and, even less, instill them in human beings; science, at most, can supply the means by which to attain certain ends. But the ends themselves are conceived by personalities with lofty ethical ideals and—if these ends are not stillborn, but vital and vigorous—are adopted and carried forward by those many human beings who, half unconsciously, determine the slow evolution of society.

For these reasons, we should be on our guard not to over-estimate science and scientific methods when it is a question of human problems; and we should not assume that experts are the only ones who have a right to express themselves on questions affecting the organization of society.

Innumerable voices have been asserting for some time now that human society is passing through a crisis, that its stability has been gravely shattered. It is characteristic of such a situation that individuals feel indifferent or even hostile toward the group, small or large, to which they belong. In order to illustrate my meaning, let me record here a personal experience. I recently discussed with an intelligent and well-disposed man the threat of another war, which in my opinion would seriously endanger the existence of mankind, and I remarked that only a supra-national organization would offer protection from that danger. Thereupon my visitor, very calmly and coolly, said to me: "Why are you so deeply opposed to the disappearance of the human race?"

I am sure that as little as a century ago no one would have so lightly made a statement of this kind. It is the statement of a man who has striven in vain to attain an equilibrium within himself and has more or less lost hope of succeeding. It is the expression of a painful solitude and isolation from which so many people are suffering in these days. What is the cause? Is there a way out?

It is easy to raise such questions, but difficult to answer them with any degree of assurance. I must try, however, as best I can, although I am very conscious of the fact that our feelings and strivings are often contradictory and obscure and that they cannot be expressed in easy and simple formulas.

Man is, at one and the same time, a solitary being and a social being. As a solitary being, he attempts to protect his own existence and that of those who are closest to him, to satisfy his personal desires, and to develop his innate abilities. As a social being, he seeks to gain the recognition and affection of his fellow human beings, to share in their pleasures, to comfort them in their sorrows, and to improve their conditions of life. Only the existence of these varied, frequently conflicting, strivings accounts for the special character of a man, and their specific combination determines the extent to which an individual can achieve an inner equilibrium and can contribute to the well-being of society. It is quite possible that the relative strength of these two drives is, in the main, fixed by inheritance. But the personality that finally emerges is largely formed by the environment in which a man happens to find himself during his development, by the structure of the society in which he grows up, by the tradition of that society, and by its appraisal of particular types of behavior. The abstract concept "society" means to the individual human being the sum total of his direct and indirect relations to his contemporaries and to all the people of earlier generations. The individual is able to think, feel, strive, and work by himself; but he depends so much upon society—in his physical, intellectual, and emotional existence—that it is impossible to think of him, or to understand him, outside the framework of society. It is "society" which provides man with food, clothing, a home, the tools of work, language, the forms of thought, and most of the content of thought; his life is made possible through the labor and the accomplishments of the many millions past and present who are all hidden behind the small word "society."

It is evident, therefore, that the dependence of the individual upon society is a fact of nature which cannot be abolished—just as in the case of ants and bees. However, while the whole life process of ants and bees is fixed down to the smallest detail by rigid, hereditary instincts, the social pattern and interrelationships of human beings are very variable and susceptible to change. Memory, the capacity to make new combinations, the gift of oral communication have made possible developments among human beings which are not dictated by biological necessities. Such developments manifest themselves in traditions, institutions, and organizations; in literature; in scientific and engineering accomplishments; in works of art. This explains how it happens that, in a certain sense, man can influence his life through his own conduct, and that in this process conscious thinking and wanting can play a part.

Man acquires at birth, through heredity, a biological constitution which we must consider fixed and unalterable, including the natural urges which are characteristic of the human species. In addition, during his lifetime, he acquires a cultural constitution which he adopts from society through communication and through many other types of influences. It is this cultural constitution which, with the passage of time, is subject to change and which determines to a very large extent the relationship between the individual and society. Modern anthropology has taught us, through comparative investigation of so-called primitive cultures, that the social behavior of human beings may differ greatly, depending upon prevailing cultural patterns and the types of organization which predominate in society. It is on this that those who are striving to improve the lot of man may ground their hopes: human beings are *not* condemned, because of their biological constitution, to annihilate each other or to be at the mercy of a cruel, self-inflicted fate.

If we ask ourselves how the structure of society and the cultural attitude of man should be changed in order to make human life as satisfying as possible, we should constantly be conscious of the fact that there are certain conditions which we are unable to modify. As mentioned before, the biological nature of man is, for all practical purposes, not subject to change. Furthermore, technological and demographic developments of the last few centuries have created conditions which are here to stay. In relatively densely settled populations with the goods which are indispensable to their continued existence, an extreme division of labor and a highly-centralized productive apparatus are absolutely necessary. The time—which, looking back, seems so idyllic—is gone forever when individuals or relatively small groups could be completely self-sufficient. It is only a slight exaggeration to say that mankind constitutes even now a planetary community of production and consumption.

I have now reached the point where I may indicate briefly what to me constitutes the essence of the crisis of our time. It concerns the relationship of the individual to society. The individual has become more conscious than ever of his dependence upon society. But he does not experience this dependence as a positive asset, as an organic tie, as a protective force, but rather as a threat to his natural rights, or even to his economic existence. Moreover, his position in society is such that the egotistical drives of his make-up are constantly being accentuated, while his social drives, which are by nature weaker, progressively deteriorate. All human beings, whatever their position in society, are suffering from this process of deterioration. Unknowingly prisoners of their own egotism, they feel insecure, lonely, and deprived of the naive, simple, and unsophisticated enjoyment of life. Man can find meaning in life, short and perilous as it is, only through devoting himself to society.

The economic anarchy of capitalist society as it exists today is, in my opinion, the real source of the evil. We see before us a huge community of producers the members of which are unceasingly striving to deprive each other of the fruits of their collective labor—not by force, but on the whole in faithful compliance with legally established rules. In this respect, it is important to realize that the means of production—that is to say, the entire productive capacity that is needed for producing consumer goods as well as additional capital goods —may legally be, and for the most part are, the private property of individuals.

For the sake of simplicity, in the discussion that follows I shall call "workers" all those who do not share in the ownership of the means of production—although this does not quite correspond to the customary use of the term. The owner of the means of production is in a position to purchase the labor power of the worker. By using the means of production, the worker produces new goods which become the property of the capitalist. The essential point about this process is the relation between what the worker produces and what he is paid, both measured in terms of real value. Insofar as the labor contract is "free," what the worker receives is determined not by the real value of the goods he produces, but by his minimum needs and by the capitalists' requirements for labor power in relation to the number of workers competing for jobs. It is important to understand that even in theory the payment of the worker is not determined by the value of his product.

Private capital tends to become concentrated in few hands, partly because of competition among the capitalists, and partly because technological development and the increasing division of labor encourage the formation of larger units of production at the expense of the smaller ones. The result of these developments is an oligarchy of private capital the enormous power of which cannot be effectively checked even by a democratically organized political society. This is true since the members of legislative bodies are selected by political parties, largely financed or otherwise influenced by private capitalists who, for all practical purposes, separate the electorate from the legislature. The consequence is that the representatives of the people do not in fact sufficiently protect the interests of the underprivileged sections of the population. Moreover, under existing conditions, private capitalists inevitably control, directly or indirectly, the main sources of information (press, radio, education). It is thus extremely difficult, and indeed in most cases quite impossible, for the individual citizen to come to objective conclusions and to make intelligent use of his political rights.

The situation prevailing in an economy based on the private ownership of capital is thus characterized by two main principles: first, means of production (capital) are privately owned and the owners dispose of them as they see fit; second, the labor contract is free. Of course, there is no such thing as a *pure* capitalist society in this sense. In particular, it should be noted that the workers, through long and bitter political struggles, have succeeded in securing a somewhat improved form of the "free labor contract" for certain categories of workers. But taken as a whole, the present day economy does not differ much from "pure" capitalism.

Production is carried on for profit, not for use. There is no provision that all those able and willing to work will always be in a position to find employment; an "army of unemployed" almost always exists. The worker is constantly in fear of losing his job. Since unemployed and poorly paid workers do not provide a profitable market, the production of consumers' goods is restricted, and great hardship is the consequence. Technological progress frequently results in more unemployment rather than in an easing of the burden of work for all. The profit motive, in conjunction with competition among capitalists, is responsible for an instability in the accumulation and utilization of capital which leads to increasingly severe depressions. Unlimited competition leads to a huge waste of labor, and to that crippling of the social consciousness of individuals which I mentioned before.

This crippling of individuals I consider the worst evil of capitalism. Our whole educational system suffers from this evil. An exaggerated competitive attitude is inculcated into the student, who is trained to worship acquisitive success as a preparation for his future career.

I am convinced there is only *one* way to eliminate these grave evils, namely through the establishment of a socialist economy, accompanied by an educational system which would be oriented toward social goals. In such an economy, the means of production are owned by society itself and are utilized in a planned fashion. A planned economy, which adjusts production to the needs of the community, would distribute the work to be done among all those able to work and would guarantee a livelihood to every man, woman, and child. The education of the individual, in addition to promoting his own innate abilities, would attempt to develop in him a sense of responsibility for his fellow men in place of the glorification of power and success in our present society.

Nevertheless, it is necessary to remember that a planned economy is not yet socialism. A planned economy as such may be accompanied by the complete enslavement of the individual. The achievement of socialism requires the solution of some extremely difficult socio-political problems: how is it possible, in view of the far-reaching centralization of political and economic power, to prevent bureaucracy from becoming all-powerful and overweening? How can the rights of the individual be protected and therewith a democratic counterweight to the power of bureaucracy be assured?

19
THE NEGRO QUESTION

I AM WRITING AS ONE who has lived among you in America only a little more than ten years. And I am writing seriously and warningly. Many readers may ask: "What right has he to speak out about things which concern us alone, and which no newcomer should touch?"

I do not think such a standpoint is justified. One who has grown up in an environment takes much for granted. On the other hand, one who has come to this country as a mature person may have a keen eye for everything peculiar and characteristic. I believe he should speak out freely on what he sees and feels, for by so doing he may perhaps prove himself useful.

What soon makes the new arrival devoted to this country is the democratic trait among the people. I am not thinking here so much of the democratic political constitution of this country, however highly it must be praised. I am thinking of the relationship between individual people and of the attitude they maintain toward one another.

In the United States everyone feels assured of his worth as an individual. No one humbles himself before another person or class. Even the great difference in wealth, the superior power of a few, cannot undermine this healthy self-confidence and natural respect for the dignity of one's fellow-man.

There is, however, a somber point in the social outlook of Americans. Their sense of equality and human dignity is mainly limited to men of white skins. Even among these there are prejudices of which I as a Jew am clearly conscious; but they are unimportant in comparison with the attitude of the "Whites" toward their fellow-citizens of darker complexion, particularly toward Negroes. The more I feel an American, the more this situation pains me. I can escape the feeling of complicity in it only by speaking out.

Many a sincere person will answer me: "Our attitude towards Negroes is the result of unfavorable experiences which we have had by living side by side with Negroes in this country. They are not our equals in intelligence, sense of responsibility, reliability."

I am firmly convinced that whoever believes this suffers from a fatal misconception. Your ancestors dragged these black people from their homes by force; and in the white man's quest for wealth and an easy life they have been ruthlessly suppressed and exploited, degraded into slavery. The modern prejudice against Negroes is the result of the desire to maintain this unworthy condition.

The ancient Greeks also had slaves. They were not Negroes but white men who had been taken captive in war. There could be no talk of racial differences. And yet Aristotle, one of the great Greek philosophers, declared slaves inferior beings who were justly subdued and deprived of their liberty. It is clear that he was enmeshed in a traditional prejudice from which, despite his extraordinary intellect, he could not free himself.

A large part of our attitude toward things is conditioned by opinions and emotions which we unconsciously absorb as children from our environment. In other words, it is tradition —besides inherited aptitudes and qualities—which makes us what we are. We but rarely reflect how relatively small as compared with the powerful influence of tradition is the influence of our conscious thought upon our conduct and convictions.

It would be foolish to despise tradition. But with our growing self-consciousness and increasing intelligence we must begin to control tradition and assume a critical attitude toward it, if human relations are ever to change for the better. We must try to recognize what in our accepted tradition is damaging to our fate and dignity—and shape our lives accordingly.

I believe that whoever tries to think things through honestly will soon recognize how unworthy and even fatal is the traditional bias against Negroes.

What, however, can the man of good will do to combat this deeply rooted prejudice? He must have the courage to set an example by word and deed, and must watch lest his children become influenced by this racial bias.

I do not believe there is a way in which this deeply entrenched evil can be quickly healed. But until this goal is reached there is no greater satisfaction for a just and well-meaning person than the knowledge that he has devoted his best energies to the service of the good cause.

20

SCIENCE AND SOCIETY

THERE ARE TWO WAYS in which science affects human affairs. The first is familiar to everyone: Directly, and to an even greater extent indirectly, science produces aids that have completely transformed human existence. The second way is educational in character—it works on the mind. Although it may appear less obvious to cursory examination, it is no less incisive than the first.

The most conspicuous practical effect of science is that it makes possible the contriving of things that enrich life, though they complicate it at the same time—inventions such as the steam engine, the railway, electric power and light, the telegraph, radio, automobile, airplane, dynamite, etc. To these must be added the life-preserving achievements of biology and medicine, especially the production of pain relievers and preservative methods of storing food. The greatest practical benefit which all these inventions confer on man I see in the fact that they liberate him from the excessive muscular drudgery that was once indispensable for the preservation of bare existence. Insofar as we may at all claim that slavery has been abolished today, we owe its abolition to the practical consequences of science.

On the other hand, technology—or applied science—has confronted mankind with problems of profound gravity. The very survival of mankind depends on a satisfactory solution of these problems. It is a matter of creating the kind of social institutions and traditions without which the new tools must inevitably bring disaster of the worst kind.

135

Mechanical means of production in an unorganized economy have had the result that a substantial proportion of mankind is no longer needed for the production of goods and is thus excluded from the process of economic circulation. The immediate consequences are the weakening of purchasing power and the devaluation of labor because of excessive competition, and these give rise, at ever shortening intervals, to a grave paralysis in the production of goods. Ownership of the means of production, on the other hand, carries a power to which the traditional safeguards of our political institutions are unequal. Mankind is caught up in a struggle for adaptation to these new conditions—a struggle that may bring true liberation, if our generation shows itself equal to the task.

Technology has also shortened distances and created new and extraordinarily effective means of destruction which, in the hands of nations claiming unrestricted freedom of action, become threats to the security and very survival of mankind. This situation requires a single judicial and executive power for the entire planet, and the creation of such a central authority is desperately opposed by national traditions. Here too we are in the midst of a struggle whose issue will decide the fate of all of us.

Means of communication, finally—reproduction processes for the printed word, and the radio—when combined with modern weapons, have made it possible to place body and soul under bondage to a central authority—and here is a third source of danger to mankind. Modern tyrannies and their destructive effects show plainly how far we are from exploiting these achievements organizationally for the benefit of mankind. Here too circumstances require an international solution, with the psychological foundation for such a solution not yet laid.

Let us now turn to the intellectual effects that proceed from science. In prescientific times it was not possible by means of thought alone to attain results that all mankind could have accepted as certain and necessary. Still less was there a conviction that all that happens in nature is subject to inexorable laws. The fragmentary character of natural law, as seen by the primitive observer, was such as to foster a belief in ghosts and spirits. Hence even today primitive man lives in constant fear that supernatural and arbitrary forces will intervene in his destiny.

It stands to the everlasting credit of science that by acting on the human mind it has overcome man's insecurity before himself and before nature. In creating elementary mathematics the Greeks for the first time wrought a system of thought whose conclusions no one could escape. The scientists of the Renaissance then devised the combination of systematic experiment with mathematical method. This union made possible such precision in the formulation of natural laws and such certainty in checking them by experience that as a result there was no longer room for basic differences of opinion in natural science. Since that time each generation has built up the heritage of knowledge and understanding, without the slightest danger of a crisis that might jeopardize the whole structure.

The general public may be able to follow the details of scientific research to only a modest degree; but it can register at least one great and important gain: confidence that human thought is dependable and natural law universal.

21
TOWARDS A WORLD GOVERNMENT

A CONVERSATION I HAD with three students of the University of Chicago has made a strong impression on me. It showed me that a sense of responsibility and initiative is at work in the young generation of this country. These students are aware of the fact that the destiny of the new generation will be decided in these few years. They are determined to influence the pace of events within the framework of their possibilities.

What is the situation? The development of technology and of the implements of war has brought about something akin to a shrinking of our planet. Economic interlinking has made the destinies of nations interdependent to a degree far greater than in previous years. The available weapons of destruction are of a kind such that no place on earth is safeguarded against sudden total destruction. The only hope for protection lies in the securing of peace in a supranational way. A world government must be created which is able to solve conflicts between nations by judicial decision. This government must be based on a clearcut constitution which is approved by the governments and the nations and which gives it the sole disposition of offensive weapons. A person or a nation can be considered peace loving only if it is ready to cede its military force to the international authorities and to renounce every attempt or even the means, of achieving its interests abroad by the use of force.

It is apparent that the development of political relations in the year which has elapsed since the conclusion of the second world war, has brought us in no way nearer to the achievement of this goal. The U. N. as it stands today has neither the military force nor the legal basis to bring about a state of international security. Nor does it take account of the actual distribution of power. Real power is at present in the hands of few. It is no exaggeration to say that the solution of the real problem is linked solely to an agreement on a grand scale between this country and Russia. For, if such an agreement would be achieved then these two powers alone would be able to cause the other nations to give up their sovereignty to the degree necessary for the establishment of military security for all.

Now many will say that fundamental agreement with Russia is impossible under the present circumstances. Such a statement would be justified if the United States had made a serious attempt in this direction during the past year. I find, however, that the opposite has happened. There was no need to accept fascist Argentina into the U. N. against Russia's opposition. There was no need to manufacture new atomic bombs without letup and to appropriate twelve billion dollars for defense in a year in which no military threat was to be expected for the nearest future. Nor was it necessary to delay the proposed measures against Franco-Spain. It is senseless to recount here the details which all show that nothing has been done in order to alleviate Russia's distrust, a distrust which can very well be understood in the light of the events of the last decades and to whose origin we have contributed no little.

A permanent peace cannot be prepared by threats but only by the honest attempt to create mutual trust. One should think that the wish to create a decent form of life on this planet and to avert the danger of unspeakable destruction would tame the passions of responsible men. You cannot rely on that, my young friends. May you succeed in activating the young generation in this sense, so that it will strive for a policy of peace on a grand scale. Thus you can not only defend yourself successfully but you can serve your country and your descendants in a degree as was not given to any previous generation.

22

THE WAY OUT

THE CONSTRUCTION of the atom bomb has brought about
the effect that all the people living in cities are threatened,
everywhere and constantly, with sudden destruction. There
is no doubt that this condition has to be abolished if man is
to prove himself worthy, at least to some extent, of the self-
chosen name of *homo sapiens*. However, there still exist
widely divergent opinions concerning the degree to which
traditional social and political forms, historically developed,
will have to be sacrificed in order to achieve the desired
security.

After the First World War, we were confronted with a
paradoxical situation regarding the solution of international
conflicts. An international court of justice had been established for a peaceful solution of these conflicts on the basis
of international law. Furthermore, a political instrument for
securing peace by means of international negotiation in a
sort of world parliament had been created in the form of the
League of Nations. The nations united in the League had
further outlawed as criminal the method of solving conflicts
by means of war.

Thus the nations were imbued with an illusion of security
that led inevitably to bitter disappointment. For the best
court of justice is meaningless unless it is backed by the authority and power to execute its decisions, and exactly the
same thing is true of a world parliament. An individual state
with sufficient military and economic power can easily resort
to violence and voluntarily destroy the entire structure of

supranational security built on nothing but words and documents. Moral authority alone is an inadequate means of securing the peace.

The United Nations Organization is now in the process of being tested. It may eventually emerge as the agency of "security without illusion" that we so badly need. But it has not as yet gone beyond the area of moral authority as, in my opinion, it must.

Our situation is rendered more acute by other circumstances, only two of which will be presented here. So long as the individual state, despite its official condemnation of war, has to consider the possibility of engaging in war, it must influence and educate its citizens—and its youth in particular—in such a way that they can easily be converted into efficient soldiers in the event of war. Therefore it is compelled not only to cultivate a technical-military training and type of thinking but also to implant a spirit of national vanity in its people in order to secure their inner readiness for the outbreak of war. Of course, this kind of education counteracts all endeavors to establish moral authority for any supranational security organization.

The danger of war in our time is further heightened by another technical factor. Modern weapons, in particular the atom bomb, have led to a considerable advantage in the means of offense or attack over those of defense. And this could well bring about the result that even responsible statesmen might find themselves compelled to wage a preventive war.

In view of these evident facts there is, in my opinion, only *one* way out.

It is necessary that conditions be established that guarantee the individual state the right to solve its conflicts with other states on a legal basis and under international jurisdiction.

It is necessary that the individual state be prevented from

making war by a supranational organization supported by a military power that is exclusively under its control.

Only when these two conditions have been fully met can we have some assurance that we shall not vanish into the atmosphere, dissolved into atoms, one of these days.

From the viewpoint of the political mentality prevailing at present, it may seem illusory, even fantastic, to hope for the realization of such conditions within a period of a few years. Yet their realization cannot wait for a gradual historical development to take its course. For, so long as we do not achieve supranational military security, the above-mentioned factors can always and forcibly lead us into war. Even more than the will for power, the fear of sudden attack will prove to be disastrous for us if we do not openly and decisively meet the problem of depriving national spheres of power of their military strength, turning such power over to a supranational authority.

With due consideration for the difficulties involved in this task, I have no doubt about *one* point. *We shall be able to solve the problem when it will be clearly evident to all that there is no other, no cheaper way out of the present situation.*

Now I feel it my obligation to say something about the individual steps which might lead to a solution of the security problem.

1. Mutual inspection by the leading military powers of methods and installations used for the production of offensive weapons, combined with an interchange of pertinent technical and scientific discoveries, would diminish fear and distrust, at least for the time being. In the breathing spell thus provided we would have to prepare more thorough measures. For this preliminary step should be taken with conscious awareness that the ultimate goal is the denationalization of military power altogether.

This first step is necessary to make any successive moves possible. However, we should be wary of believing that its execution would immediately result in security. There still would remain the possibility of an armament race with regard to a possible future war, and there always exists the temptation to resort once more, by "underground" methods, to the military secret, that is, keeping secret the knowledge about methods and means of and actual preparations for warfare. Real security is tied to the denationalization of military power.

2. This denationalization can be prepared through a steadily increasing interchange of military and scientific-technical personnel among the armies of the different nations. The interchange should follow a carefully elaborated plan, aimed at converting the national armies systematically into a supranational military force. A national army, one might say, is the last place where national feeling may be expected to weaken. Even so, the nationalism can be progressively immunized at a rate proportionate at least to the building of the supranational army; and the whole process can be facilitated by integrating it with the recruiting and training of the latter. The process of interchanging personnel would further lessen the danger of surprise attacks and in itself would lay the psychological foundation for internationalization of military resources.

Simultaneously the strongest military powers could draft the working papers for a supranational security organization and for an arbitration committee, as well as the legal basis for, and the precise stipulation of, obligations, competencies, and restrictions of the latter with respect to the individual nations. They could further decide upon the terms of election for establishing and maintaining these bodies.

When an agreement on these points shall have been reached, a guarantee against wars of world-wide dimensions can be assured.

3. The above-named bodies can now begin to function. The vestiges of national armies can then be either disbanded

or placed under the high command of the supranational authority.

4. After the cooperation of the nations of highest military importance has been secured, the attempt should be made to incorporate, if possible, all nations into the supranational organization, provided that it is their voluntary decision to join.

This outline may perhaps create the impression that the presently prevailing military powers are to be assigned too dominant a role. I have tried, however, to present the problem with a view to a sufficiently swift realization that will allow us to avoid difficulties greater than those already inherent in the nature of such a task. It may be simpler, of course, to reach preliminary agreement among the strongest military powers than among *all* nations, big and small, for a body of representatives of all nations is a hopelessly clumsy instrument for the speedy achievement of even preliminary results. Even so, the task confronting us requires of all concerned the utmost sagacity and tolerance, which can be achieved only through awareness of the harsh necessity we have to face.

23

ON RECEIVING THE ONE
WORLD AWARD

I AM GREATLY TOUCHED by the signal honor which you have wished to confer upon me. In the course of my long life I have received from my fellow-men far more recognition than I deserve, and I confess that my sense of shame has always outweighed my pleasure therein. But never, on any previous occasion, has the pain so far outweighed the pleasure as now. For all of us who are concerned for peace and the triumph of reason and justice must today be keenly aware how small an influence reason and honest good will exert upon events in the political field. But however that may be, and whatever fate may have in store for us, yet we may rest assured that without the tireless efforts of those who are concerned with the welfare of humanity as a whole, the lot of mankind would be still worse than in fact it even now is.

In this time of decisions so heavy with fate what we must say to our fellow-citizens seems above all to be this: where belief in the omnipotence of physical force gets the upper hand in political life this force takes on a life of its own, and proves stronger than the men who think to use force as a tool. The proposed militarization of the nation not only immediately threatens us with war; it will also slowly but surely destroy the democratic spirit and the dignity of the individual in our land. The assertion that events abroad force us to arm is wrong, we must combat it with all our strength. Actually, our own rearmament, through the reaction of other nations to it, will bring about that very situation on which its advocates seek to base their proposals.

There is only *one* path to peace and security: the path of supra-national organization. One-sided armament on a national basis only heightens the general uncertainty and confusion without being an effective protection.

24

SCIENCE AND CIVILIZATION

I<small>T IS IN TIMES</small> of economic distress such as we experience
everywhere today, one sees very clearly the strength of the
moral forces that live in a people. Let us hope that a historian
delivering judgment in some future period when Europe is
politically and economically united, will be able to say that
in our days the liberty and honour of this Continent was
saved by its Western nations, which stood fast in hard times
against the temptations of hatred and oppression; and that
Western Europe defended successfully the liberty of the individual which has brought us every advance of knowledge
and invention—liberty without which life to a self-respecting
man is not worth living.

It cannot be my task today to act as judge of the conduct
of a nation which for many years has considered me as her
own; perhaps it is an idle task to judge in times when action
counts.

Today, the questions which concern us are: how can we
save mankind and its spiritual acquisitions of which we are
the heirs? How can one save Europe from a new disaster?

It cannot be doubted that the world crisis and the suffering
and privations of the people resulting from the crisis are in
some measure responsible for the dangerous upheavals of
which we are the witness. In such periods discontent breeds
hatred, and hatred leads to acts of violence and revolution,
and often even to war. Thus distress and evil produce new
distress and new evil. Again the leading statesmen are bur-
dened with tremendous responsibilities just the same as

twenty years ago. May they succeed through timely agreement to establish a condition of unity and clarity of international obligations in Europe, so that for every State a warlike adventure must appear as utterly hopeless. But the work of statesmen can succeed only if they are backed by the serious and determined will of the people.

We are concerned not merely with the technical problem of securing and maintaining peace, but also with the important task of education and enlightenment. If we want to resist the powers which threaten to suppress intellectual and individual freedom we must keep clearly before us what is at stake, and what we owe to that freedom which our ancestors have won for us after hard struggles.

Without such freedom there would have been no Shakespeare, no Goethe, no Newton, no Faraday, no Pasteur and no Lister. There would be no comfortable houses for the mass of the people, no railway, no wireless, no protection against epidemics, no cheap books, no culture and no enjoyment of art for all. There would be no machines to relieve the people from the arduous labor needed for the production of the essential necessities of life. Most people would lead a dull life of slavery just as under the ancient despotisms of Asia. It is only men who are free, who create the inventions and intellectual works which to us moderns make life worth while.

Without doubt the present economic difficulties will eventually bring us to the point where the balance between supply of labor and demand of labor, between production and consumption, will be enforced by law. But even this problem we shall solve as free men and we shall not allow ourselves for its sake to be driven into a slavery, which ultimately would bring with it stagnation of every healthy development.

In this connection I should like to give expression to an idea which has occurred to me recently. I lived in solitude in the country and noticed how the monotony of a quiet life stimulates the creative mind. There are certain callings in our modern organization which entail such an isolated life without making a great claim on bodily and intellectual effort. I think of such occupations as the service in lighthouses and lightships. Would it not be possible to fill such places with young people who wish to think out scientific problems, especially of a mathematical or philosophical nature? Very few of such people have the opportunity during the most productive period of their lives to devote themselves undisturbed for any length of time to scientific problems. Even if a young person is lucky enough to obtain a scholarship for a short period he must endeavor to arrive as quickly as possible at definite conclusions. That cannot be of advantage in the pursuit of pure science. The young scientist who carries on an ordinary practical profession which maintains him is in a much better position—assuming of course that this profession leaves him with sufficient spare time and energy. In this way perhaps a greater number of creative individuals could be given an opportunity for mental development than is possible at present. In these times of economic depression and political upheaval such considerations seem to be worth attention.

Shall we worry over the fact that we are living in a time of danger and want? I think not. Man like every other animal is by nature indolent. If nothing spurs him on, then he will hardly think, and will behave from habit like an automaton. I am no longer young and can, therefore, say that as a child and as a young man I experienced that phase—when a young man thinks only about the trivialities of personal existence, and talks like his fellows and behaves like them. Only with difficulty can one see what is really behind such a conventional mask. For owing to habit and speech his real personality is, as it were wrapped in cotton wool.

How different it is today! In the lightning flashes of our tempestuous times one sees human beings and things in their nakedness. Every nation and every human being reveal clearly their aims, powers and weaknesses, and also their passions. Routine becomes of no avail under the swift change of conditions; conventions fall away like dry husks.

Men in their distress begin to think about the failure of economic practice and about the necessity of political combinations which are supernational. Only through perils and upheavals can Nations be brought to further developments. May the present upheavals lead to a better world.

Above and beyond this valuation of our time we have this further duty, the care for what is eternal and highest amongst our possessions, that which gives to life its import and which we wish to hand on to our children purer and richer than we received it from our forebears.

25

A MESSAGE
TO INTELLECTUALS *

WE MEET TODAY, as intellectuals and scholars of many nationalities, with a deep and historic responsibility placed
upon us. We have every reason to be grateful to our French
and Polish colleagues whose initiative has assembled us here
for a momentous objective: to use the influence of wise men
in promoting peace and security throughout the world. This
is the age-old problem with which Plato, as one of the first,
struggled so hard: to apply reason and prudence to the solution of man's problems instead of yielding to atavist instincts
and passions.

By painful experience we have learnt that rational thinking
does not suffice to solve the problems of our social life. Penetrating research and keen scientific work have often had
tragic implications for mankind, producing, on the one hand,
inventions which liberated man from exhausting physical
labor, making his life easier and richer; but on the other
hand, introducing a grave restlessness into his life, making
him a slave to his technological environment, and—most
catastrophic of all—creating the means for his own mass
destruction. This, indeed, is a tragedy of overwhelming
poignancy!

However poignant that tragedy is, it is perhaps even more
tragic that, while mankind has produced many scholars so

* The following address was objected to by the Organizing Committee of
the Intellectuals' Conference for Peace. The message was subsequently released to the press on August 29, 1948.

extremely successful in the field of science and technology, we have been for a long time so inefficient in finding adequate solutions to the many political conflicts and economic tensions which beset us. No doubt, the antagonism of economic interests within and among nations is largely responsible to a great extent for the dangerous and threatening condition in the world today. Man has not succeeded in developing political and economic forms of organization which would guarantee the peaceful coexistence of the nations of the world. He has not succeeded in building the kind of system which would eliminate the possibility of war and banish forever the murderous instruments of mass destruction.

We scientists, whose tragic destination has been to help in making the methods of annihilation more gruesome and more effective, must consider it our solemn and transcendent duty to do all in our power in preventing these weapons from being used for the brutal purpose for which they were invented. What task could possibly be more important for us? What social aim could be closer to our hearts? That is why this Congress has such a vital mission. We are here to take counsel with each other. We must build spiritual and scientific bridges linking the nations of the world. We must overcome the horrible obstacles of national frontiers.

In the smaller entities of community life, man has made some progress toward breaking down anti-social sovereignties. This is true, for example, of life within cities and, to a certain degree, even of society within individual states. In such communities tradition and education have had a moderating influence and have brought about tolerable relations among the peoples living within those confines. But in relations among separate states complete anarchy still prevails. I do not believe that we have made any genuine advance in this area during the last few thousand years. All too frequently conflicts among nations are still being decided by brutal power, by war. The unlimited desire for ever greater power seeks to become active and aggressive wherever and whenever the physical possibility offers itself.

Throughout the ages, this state of anarchy in international affairs has inflicted indescribable suffering and destruction upon mankind; again and again it has depraved the development of men, their souls and their well-being. For given time it has almost annihilated whole areas.

However, the desire of nations to be constantly prepared for warfare has, however, still other repercussions upon the lives of men. The power of every state over its citizens has grown steadily during the last few hundred years, no less in countries where the power of the state has been exercised wisely, than in those where it has been used for brutal tyranny. The function of the state to maintain peaceful and ordered relations among and between its citizens has become increasingly complicated and extensive largely because of the concentration and centralization of the modern industrial apparatus. In order to protect its citizens from attacks from without a modern state requires a formidable, expanding military establishment. In addition, the state considers it necessary to educate its citizens for the possibilities of war, an "education" not only corrupting to the soul and spirit of the young, but also adversely affecting the mentality of adults. No country can avoid this corruption. It pervades the citizenry even in countries which do not harbor outspoken aggressive tendencies. The state has thus become a modern idol whose suggestive power few men are able to escape.

Education for war, however, is a delusion. The technological developments of the last few years have created a completely new military situation. Horrible weapons have been invented, capable of destroying in a few seconds huge masses of human beings and tremendous areas of territory. Since science has not yet found protection from these weapons, the modern state is no longer in a position to prepare adequately for the safety of its citizens.

How, then, shall we be saved?

Mankind can only gain protection against the danger of unimaginable destruction and wanton annihilation if a supranational organization has alone the authority to produce or possess these weapons. It is unthinkable, however, that nations under existing conditions would hand over such authority to a supranational organization unless the organization would have the legal right and duty to solve all the conflicts which in the past have led to war. The functions of individual states would be to concentrate more or less upon internal affairs; in their relation with other states they would deal only with issues and problems which are in no way conducive to endangering international security.

Unfortunately, there are no indications that governments yet realize that the situation in which mankind finds itself makes the adoption of revolutionary measures a compelling necessity. Our situation is not comparable to anything in the past. It is impossible, therefore, to apply methods and measures which at an earlier age might have been sufficient. We must revolutionize our thinking, revolutionize our actions, and must have the courage to revolutionize relations among the nations of the world. Clichés of yesterday will no longer do today, and will, no doubt, be hopelessly out of date tomorrow. To bring this home to men all over the world is the most important and most fateful social function intellectuals have ever had to shoulder. Will they have enough courage to overcome their own national ties to the extent that is necessary to induce the peoples of the world to change their deep-rooted national traditions in a most radical fashion?

A tremendous effort is indispensable. If it fails now, the supranational organization will be built later, but then it will have to be built upon the ruins of a large part of the now existing world. Let us hope that the abolition of the existing international anarchy will not need to be bought by a self-inflicted world catastrophe the dimensions of which none of us can possibly imagine. The time is terribly short. We must act now if we are to act at all.

26

OPEN LETTER TO THE GENERAL ASSEMBLY OF THE UNITED NATIONS

WE ARE CAUGHT IN A SITUATION in which every citizen of every country, his children, and his life's work, are threatened by the terrible insecurity which reigns in our world today. The progress of technological development has not increased the stability and the welfare of humanity. Because of our inability to solve the problem of international organization, it has actually contributed to the dangers which threaten peace and the very existence of mankind.

The delegates of fifty-five governments, meeting in the second General Assembly of the United Nations, undoubtedly will be aware of the fact that during the last two years—since the victory over the Axis powers—no appreciable progress has been made either toward the prevention of war or toward agreement in specific fields such as control of atomic energy and economic cooperation in the reconstruction of war-devastated areas.

The UN cannot be blamed for these failures. No international organization can be stronger than the constitutional powers given it, or than its component parts want it to be. As a matter of fact, the United Nations is an extremely important and useful institution *provided* the peoples and governments of the world realize that it is merely a transitional system toward the final goal, which is the establishment of a supranational authority vested with sufficient legislative and executive powers to keep the peace. The present impasse lies in the fact that there is no sufficient, reliable supranational authority. Thus the responsible leaders of all governments are obliged to act on the assumption of eventual war. Every step motivated by that assumption contributes to the general fear and distrust and hastens the final catastrophe. However strong national armaments may be, they do not create military security for any nation nor do they guarantee the maintenance of peace.

There can never be complete agreement on international control and the administration of atomic energy or on general disarmament until there is a modification of the traditional concept of national sovereignty. For as long as atomic energy and armaments are considered a vital part of national security no nation will give more than lip service to international treaties. Security is indivisible. It can be reached only when necessary guarantees of law and enforcement obtain everywhere, so that military security is no longer the problem of any single state. There is no compromise possible between preparation for war, on the one hand, and preparation of a world society based on law and order on the other.

Every citizen must make up his mind. If he accepts the premise of war, he must reconcile himself to the maintenance of troops in strategic areas like Austria and Korea; to the sending of troops to Greece and Bulgaria; to the accumulation of stockpiles of uranium by whatever means; to universal military training, to the progressive limitation of civil liberties. Above all, he must endure the consequences of military secrecy which is one of the worst scourges of our time and one of the greatest obstacles to cultural betterment.

If on the other hand every citizen realizes that the only guarantee for security and peace in this atomic age is the constant development of a supranational government, then he will do everything in his power to strengthen the United Nations. It seems to me that every reasonable and responsible citizen in the world must know where his choice lies.

Yet the world at large finds itself in a vicious circle since the UN powers seem to be incapable of making up their minds on this score. The Eastern and Western blocs each attempt frantically to strengthen their respective power positions. Universal military training, Russian troops in Eastern Europe, United States control over the Pacific Islands, even the stiffening colonial policies of the Netherlands, Great Britain and France, atomic and military secrecy—are all part of the old familiar jockeying for position.

The time has come for the UN to strengthen its moral authority by bold decisions. First, the authority of the General Assembly must be increased so that the Security Council as well as all other bodies of the UN will be subordinated to it. As long as there is a conflict of authority between the Assembly and the Security Council, the effectiveness of the whole institution will remain necessarily impaired.

Second, the method of representation at the UN should be considerably modified. The present method of selection by government appointment does not leave any real freedom to the appointee. Furthermore, selection by governments cannot give the peoples of the world the feeling of being fairly and proportionately represented. The moral authority of the UN would be considerably enhanced if the delegates were elected directly by the people. Were they responsible to an electorate, they would have much more freedom to follow their consciences. Thus we could hope for more statesmen and fewer diplomats.

Third, the General Assembly should remain in session throughout the critical period of transition. By staying constantly on the job, the Assembly could fulfill two major tasks: first, it could take the initiative toward the establishment of a supranational order; second, it could take quick and effective steps in all those danger areas (such as currently exist on the Greek border) where peace is threatened.

The Assembly, in view of these high tasks, should not delegate its powers to the Security Council, especially while that body is paralyzed by the shortcomings of the veto provisions. As the only body competent to take the initiative boldly and resolutely, the UN must act with utmost speed to create the necessary conditions for international security by laying the foundations for a real world government.

Of course there will be opposition. It is by no means certain that the U.S.S.R.—which is often represented as the main antagonist to the idea of world government—would maintain its opposition if an equitable offer providing for real security were made. Even assuming that Russia is now opposed to the idea of world government, once she becomes convinced that world government is nonetheless in the making her whole attitude may change. She may then insist on only the necessary guarantees of equality before the law so as to avoid finding herself in perennial minority as in the present Security Council.

Nevertheless, we must assume that despite all efforts Russia and her allies may still find it advisable to stay out of such a world government. In that case—and only after all efforts have been made in utmost sincerity to obtain the cooperation of Russia and her allies—the other countries would have to proceed alone. It is of the utmost importance that this partial world government be very strong, comprising at least two-thirds of the major industrial and economic areas of the world. Such strength in itself would make it possible for the partial world government to abandon military secrecy and all the other practices born of insecurity.

Such a partial world government should make it clear from the beginning that its doors remain wide open to any non-member—particularly Russia—for participation on the basis of complete equality. In my opinion, the partial world government should accept the presence of observers from non-member governments at all its meetings and constitutional conventions.

In order to achieve the final aim—which is one world, and not two hostile worlds—such a partial world government must never act as an alliance against the rest of the world. The only real step toward world government is world government itself.

In a world government the ideological differences between the various component parts are of no grave consequence. I am convinced that the present difficulties between the U.S.A. and the U.S.S.R. are not due primarily to ideological differences. Of course, these ideological differences are a contributing element in an already serious tension. But I am convinced that even if the U.S.A. and Russia were both capitalist countries—or communist, or monarchist, for that matter —their rivalries, conflicting interests, and jealousies would result in strains similar to those existing between the two countries today.

The UN now and world government eventually must serve one single goal—the guarantee of the security, tranquillity, and the welfare of all mankind.

27

DR. EINSTEIN'S MISTAKEN NOTIONS

An Open Letter from Sergei Vavilov, A. N. Frumkin, A. F. Joffe, and N. N. Semyonov *

THE CELEBRATED PHYSICIST, Albert Einstein, is famed not only for his scientific discoveries; of late years he has paid much attention to social and political problems. He speaks over the radio and writes in the press. He is associated with a number of public organizations. Time and again he raised his voice in protest against the Nazi barbarians. He is an advocate of enduring peace, and has spoken against the threat of a new war, and against the ambition of the militarists to bring American science completely under their control.

Soviet scientists, and the Soviet people in general, are appreciative of the humanitarian spirit which prompts these activities of the scientist, although his position has not always been as consistent and clear-cut as might be desired. However, in some of Einstein's more recent utterances there have been aspects which seem to us not only mistaken, but positively prejudicial to the cause of peace which Einstein so warmly espouses.

* Biographical Note: Sergei Vavilov, a physicist specializing in the field of fluorescence, is President of the Academy of Sciences of the USSR. A. N. Frumkin, a colloid chemist of note, is Director of the Colloid-Electrochemical Institute of the Academy of Sciences in Moscow. A. F. Joffe is well known for his work on the behavior of crystals under water, and is Director of the Physico-Chemical Institute of the Academy in Leningrad. N. N. Semyonov, an authority on chemical kinetics, is Director of the Institute of Chemical Physics of the Academy in Moscow.

We feel it our duty to draw attention to this, in order to clarify so important a question as to how most effectively to work for peace. It is from this point of view that the idea of a "world government" which Dr. Einstein has of late been sponsoring must be considered.

In the motley company of proponents of this idea, besides out-and-out imperialists who are using it as a screen for unlimited expansion, there are quite a number of intellectuals in the capitalist countries who are captivated by the plausibility of the idea, and who do not realize its actual implications. These pacifist and liberal-minded individuals believe that a "world government" would be an effective panacea against the world's evils and a guardian of enduring peace.

The advocates of a "world government" make wide use of the seemingly radical argument that in this atomic age state sovereignty is a relic of the past, that it is, as Spaak, the Belgian delegate, said in the UN General Assembly, an "old-fashioned" and even "reactionary" idea. It would be hard to imagine an allegation that is farther from the truth.

In the first place, the idea of a "world government" and "superstate" are by no means products of the atomic age. They are much older than that. They were mooted, for instance, at the time the League of Nations was formed.

Further, these ideas have never been progressive in these modern times. They are a reflection of the fact that the capitalist monopolies, which dominate the major industrial countries, find their own national boundaries too narrow. They need a world-wide market, world-wide sources of raw materials, and world-wide spheres of capital investment. Thanks to their domination in political and administrative affairs, the monopoly interests of the big powers are in a position to utilize the machinery of government in their struggle for spheres of influence and their efforts economically and politically to subjugate other countries, to play the master in these countries as freely as in their own.

We know this very well from the past experience of our own country. Under tsarism, Russia, with her reactionary regime, which was servilely accommodating to the interests of capital, with her low-paid labor and vast natural resources, was an alluring morsel to foreign capitalists. French, British, Belgian and German firms battened on our country like birds of prey, earning profits which would have been inconceivable in their own countries. They chained tsarist Russia to the capitalist West with extortionate loans. Supported by funds obtained from foreign banks, the tsarist government brutally repressed the revolutionary movement, retarded the development of Russian science and culture, and instigated Jewish pogroms.

The Great October Socialist Revolution smashed the chains of economic and political dependence that bound our country to the world capitalist monopolies. The Soviet Government made our country for the first time a really free and independent state, promoted the progress of our Socialist economy, technology, science and culture at a speed hitherto unwitnessed in history, and turned our country into a reliable bulwark of international peace and security. Our people upheld their country's independence in the civil war, in the struggle against the intervention of a bloc of imperialist states, and in the great battles of the war against the Nazi invaders.

And now the proponents of a "world super-state" are asking us voluntarily to surrender this independence for the sake of a "world government," which is nothing but a flamboyant signboard for the world supremacy of the capitalist monopolies.

It is obviously preposterous to ask of us anything like that. And it is not only with regard to the Soviet Union that such a demand is absurd. After World War II, a number of countries succeeded in breaking away from the imperialist system of oppression and slavery. The peoples of these countries are working to consolidate their economic and political independence, debarring alien interference in their domestic affairs. Further, the rapid spread of the movement for national independence in the colonies and dependencies has awakened the national consciousness of hundreds of millions of people, who do not desire to remain in the status of slaves any longer.

The monopolies of the imperialist countries, having lost a number of profitable spheres of exploitation, and running the risk of losing more, are doing their utmost to deprive the nations that have escaped from their mastery of the state independence which they, the monopolies, find so irksome, and to prevent the genuine liberation of the colonies. With this purpose, the imperialists are resorting to the most diverse methods of military, political, economic and ideological warfare.

It is in accordance with this social behest that the ideologians of imperialism are endeavoring to discredit the very idea of national sovereignty. One of the methods they resort to is the advocacy of pretentious plans for a "world state," which will allegedly do away with imperialism, wars and national enmity, ensure the triumph of universal law, and so on.

The predatory appetites of the imperialist forces that are striving for world supremacy are thus disguised under the garb of a pseudo-progressive idea which appeals to certain intellectuals—scientists, writers and others—in the capitalist countries.

In an open letter which he addressed last September to the United Nations delegations, Dr. Einstein suggested a new scheme for limiting national sovereignty. He recommends that the General Assembly be reconstructed and converted into a permanently functioning world parliament endowed with greater authority than the Security Council, which, Einstein declares (repeating what the henchmen of American diplomacy are asserting day in and day out), is paralyzed by the veto right. The General Assembly, reconstructed in accordance with Dr. Einstein's plan, is to have final powers of decision, and the principle of the unanimity of the Great Powers is to be abandoned.

Einstein suggests that the delegates to the United Nations should be chosen by popular election and not appointed by their governments, as at present. At a first glance, this proposal may seem progressive and even radical. Actually, it will in no way improve the existing situation.

Let us picture to ourselves what elections to such a "world parliament" would mean in practice.

A large part of humanity still lives in colonial and dependent countries dominated by the governors, the troops, and the financial and industrial monopolies of a few imperialist powers. "Popular election" in such countries would in practice mean the appointment of delegates by the colonial administration or the military authorities. One does not have to go far for examples; one need only recall the parody of a referendum in Greece, which was carried out by her royalist-fascist rulers under the protection of British bayonets.

But things would be not much better in the countries where universal suffrage formally exists. In the bourgeois-democratic countries, where capital dominates, the latter resorts to thousands of tricks and devices to turn universal suffrage and freedom of ballot into a farce. Einstein surely knows that in the last Congressional elections in the United States only 39 per cent of the electorate went to the polls; he surely knows that millions of Negroes in the Southern states are virtually deprived of the franchise, or are forced, not infrequently under threat of lynching, to vote for their bitterest enemies, such as the late arch-reactionary and Negrophobe, Senator Bilbo.

Poll taxes, special tests and other devices are employed to rob millions of immigrants, migrant workers and poor farmers of the vote. We will not mention the widespread practice of purchasing votes, the role of the reactionary press, that powerful instrument for influencing the masses wielded by millionaire newspaper proprietors, and so forth.

All this shows what popular elections to a world parliament, as suggested by Einstein, would amount to under existing conditions in the capitalist world. Its composition would be no better than the present composition of the General Assembly. It would be a distorted reflection of the real sentiments of the masses, of their desire and hope for lasting peace.

As we know, in the General Assembly and the UN committees, the American delegation has a regular voting machine at its disposal, thanks to the fact that the overwhelming majority of the members of the UN are dependent on the United States and are compelled to adapt their foreign policy to the requirements of Washington. A number of Latin-American countries, for instance, countries with single-crop agricultural systems, are bound hand and foot to the American monopolies, which determine the prices of their produce. Such being the case, it is not surprising that, under pressure of the American delegation, a mechanical majority has arisen in the General Assembly which votes in obedience to the orders of its virtual masters.

There are cases when American diplomacy finds it preferable to realize certain measures, not through the State Department, but under the flag of the United Nations. Witness the notorious Balkan committee or the commission appointed to observe the elections in Korea. It is with the object of converting the UN into a branch of the State Department that the American delegation is forcing through the project for a "Little Assembly," which would in practice replace the Security Council, with its principle of unanimity of the Great Powers that is proving such an obstacle to the realization of imperialist schemes.

Einstein's suggestion would lead to the same result, and thus, far from promoting lasting peace and international co-operation, would only serve as a screen for an offensive against nations which have established regimes that prevent foreign capital from extorting its customary profits. It would further the unbridled expansion of American imperialism, and ideologically disarm the nations which insist upon maintaining their independence.

By the irony of fate, Einstein has virtually become a supporter of the schemes and ambitions of the bitterest foes of peace and international cooperation. He has gone so far in this direction as to declare in advance in his open letter that if the Soviet Union refuses to join his newfangled organization, other countries would have every right to go ahead without it, while leaving the door open for eventual Soviet participation in the organization as a member or as an "observer."

Essentially this proposal differs very little from the suggestions of frank advocates of American imperialism, however remote Dr. Einstein may be from them in reality. The sum and substance of these suggestions is that if UN cannot be converted into a weapon of United States policy, into a screen for imperialist schemes and designs, that organization should be wrecked and a new "international" organization formed in its place, without the Soviet Union and the new democracies.

Does Einstein not realize how fatal such plans would be to international security and international cooperation?

We believe that Dr. Einstein has entered a false and dangerous path; he is chasing the mirage of a "world state" in a world where different social, political and economic systems exist. Of course there is no reason why states with different social and economic structures should not cooperate economically and politically, provided that these differences are soberly faced. But Einstein is sponsoring a political fad which plays into the hands of the sworn enemies of sincere international cooperation and enduring peace. The course he is inviting the member states of the United Nations to adopt would lead not to greater international security, but to new international complications. It would benefit only the capitalist monopolies, for whom new international complications hold out the promise of more war contracts and more profits.

It is because we so highly esteem Einstein as an eminent scientist and as a man of public spirit who is striving to the best of his ability to promote the cause of peace, that we consider it our duty to speak with utter frankness and without diplomatic adornment.

A REPLY TO THE SOVIET
SCIENTISTS

FOUR OF MY RUSSIAN COLLEAGUES have published a benevolent attack upon me in an open letter carried by the *New Times*. I appreciate the effort they have made and I appreciate even more the fact that they have expressed their point of view so candidly and straightforwardly. To act intelligently in human affairs is only possible if an attempt is made to understand the thoughts, motives, and apprehensions of one's opponent so fully that one can see the world through his eyes. All well-meaning people should try to contribute as much as possible to improving such mutual understanding. It is in this spirit that I should like to ask my Russian colleagues and any other reader to accept the following answer to their letter. It is the reply of a man who anxiously tries to find a feasible solution without having the illusion that he himself knows "the truth" or "the right path" to follow. If in the following I shall express my views somewhat dogmatically, I do it only for the sake of clarity and simplicity.

Although your letter, in the main, is clothed in an attack upon the non-socialistic foreign countries, particularly the United States, I believe that behind the aggressive front there lies a defensive mental attitude which is nothing else but the trend towards an almost unlimited isolationism. The escape into isolationism is not difficult to understand if one realizes what Russia has suffered at the hands of foreign countries during the last three decades—the German invasions with planned mass murder of the civilian population, foreign interventions during the civil war, the systematic campaign of calumnies in the western press, the support of Hitler as an alleged tool to fight Russia. However understandable this desire for isolation may be, it remains no less disastrous to Russia and to all other nations; I shall say more about it later on.

The chief object of your attack against me concerns my support of "world government." I should like to discuss this important problem only after having said a few words about the antagonism between socialism and capitalism; for your attitude on the significance of this antagonism seems to dominate completely your views on international problems. If the socio-economic problem is considered objectively, it appears as follows: technological development has led to increasing centralization of the economic mechanism. It is this development which is also responsible for the fact that economic power in all widely industrialized countries has become concentrated in the hands of relatively few. These people, in capitalist countries, do not need to account for their actions to the public as a whole; they must do so in socialist countries in which they are civil servants similar to those who exercise political power.

I share your view that a socialist economy possesses advantages which definitely counterbalance its disadvantages whenever the management lives up, at least to some extent, to adequate standards. No doubt, the day will come when all nations (as far as such nations still exist) will be grateful to Russia for having demonstrated, for the first time, by vigorous action the practical possibility of planned economy in spite of exceedingly great difficulties. I also believe that capitalism, or, we should say, the system of free enterprise, will prove unable to check unemployment, which will become increasingly chronic because of technological progress, and unable to maintain a healthy balance between production and the purchasing power of the people.

On the other hand we should not make the mistake of

blaming capitalism for all existing social and political evils, and of assuming that the very establishment of socialism would be able to cure all the social and political ills of humanity. The danger of such a belief lies, first, in the fact that it encourages fanatical intolerance on the part of all the "faithful" by making a possible social method into a type of church which brands all those who do not belong to it as traitors or as nasty evildoers. Once this stage has been reached, the ability to understand the convictions and actions of the "unfaithful" vanishes completely. You know, I am sure, from history how much unnecessary suffering such rigid beliefs have inflicted upon mankind.

Any government is in itself an evil insofar as it carries within it the tendency to deteriorate into tyranny. However, except for a very small number of anarchists, everyone of us is convinced that civilized society cannot exist without a government. In a healthy nation there is a kind of dynamic balance between the will of the people and the government, which prevents its degeneration into tyranny. It is obvious that the danger of such deterioration is more acute in a country in which the government has authority not only over the armed forces but also over all the channels of education and information as well as over the economic existence of every single citizen. I say this merely to indicate that socialism as such cannot be considered the solution to all social problems but merely as a framework within which such a solution is possible.

What has surprised me most in your general attitude, expressed in your letter, is the following aspect: You are such passionate opponents of anarchy in the economic sphere, and yet equally passionate advocates of anarchy, e.g., unlimited sovereignty, in the sphere of international politics. The proposition to curtail the sovereignty of individual states appears to you in itself reprehensible, as a kind of violation of a natural right. In addition, you try to prove that behind the idea of curtailing sovereignty the United States is hiding her intention of economic domination and exploitation of the rest of the world without going to war. You attempt to justify this indictment by analyzing in your fashion the individual actions of this government since the end of the last war. You attempt to show that the Assembly of the United Nations is a mere puppet show controlled by the United States and hence the American capitalists.

Such arguments impress me as a kind of mythology; they are not convincing. They make obvious, however, the deep estrangement among the intellectuals of our two countries which is the result of a regrettable and artificial mutual isolation. If a free personal exchange of views should be made possible and should be encouraged, the intellectuals, possibly more than anyone else, could help to create an atmosphere of mutual understanding between the two nations and their problems. Such an atmosphere is a necessary prerequisite for the fruitful development of political cooperation. However, since for the time being we depend upon the cumbersome method of "open letters" I shall want to indicate briefly my reaction to your arguments.

Nobody would want to deny that the influence of the economic oligarchy upon all branches of our public life is very powerful. This influence, however, should not be overestimated. Franklin Delano Roosevelt was elected president in spite of desperate opposition by these very powerful groups and was reelected three times; and this took place at a time when decisions of great consequence had to be made.

Concerning the policies of the American Government since the end of the war, I am neither willing, nor able, nor entitled to justify or explain them. It cannot be denied, however, that the suggestions of the American Government with regard to atomic weapons represented at least an attempt towards the creation of a supranational security organization. If they were not acceptable, they could at least have served as a basis of discussion for a real solution of the problems of international security. It is, indeed, the attitude of the Soviet Government, that was partly negative and partly dilatory, which has made it so difficult for well-meaning people in this country to use their political influence as they would have wanted, and to oppose the "war mongers." With regard to the influence of the United States upon the United Nations Assembly, I wish to say that, in my opinion, it stems not only from the economic and military power of the United States but also from the efforts of the United States and the United Nations to lead toward a genuine solution of the security problem.

Concerning the controversial veto power, I believe that the efforts to eliminate it or to make it ineffective have their primary cause less in specific intentions of the United States than in the manner in which the veto privilege has been abused.

Let me come now to your suggestion that the policy of the United States seeks to obtain economic domination and exploitation of other nations. It is a precarious undertaking to say anything reliable about aims and intentions. Let us rather examine the objective factors involved. The United States is fortunate in producing all the important industrial products and foods in her own country, in sufficient quantities. The country also possesses almost all important raw materials. Because of her tenacious belief in "free enterprise" she cannot succeed in keeping the purchasing power of the people in balance with the productive capacity of the country. For these very same reasons there is a constant danger that unemployment will reach threatening dimensions.

Because of these circumstances the United States is compelled to emphasize her export trade. Without it, she could not permanently keep her total productive machinery fully utilized. These conditions would not be harmful if the exports were balanced by imports of about the same value. Exploitation of foreign nations would then consist in the fact that the labor value of imports would considerably exceed that of exports. However, every effort is being made to avoid this, since almost every import would make a part of the productive machinery idle.

This is why foreign countries are not able to pay for the export commodities of the United States, payment which, in the long run, would indeed be possible only through imports by the latter. This explains why a large portion of all the gold has come to the United States. On the whole, this gold cannot be utilized except for the purchase of foreign commodities, which because of the reasons already stated, is not practicable. There it lies, this gold, carefully protected against theft, a monument to governmental wisdom and to economic science! The reasons which I have just indicated make it difficult for me to take the alleged exploitation of the world by the United States very seriously.

However, the situation just described has a serious political facet. The United States, for the reasons indicated, is compelled to ship part of its production to foreign countries. These exports are financed through loans which the United States is granting foreign countries. It is, indeed, difficult to imagine how these loans will ever be repaid. For all practical purposes, therefore, these loans must be considered gifts which may be used as weapons in the arena of power politics. In view of the existing conditions and in view of the general characteristics of human beings, this, I frankly admit, represents a real danger. Is it not true, however, that we have stumbled into a state of international affairs which tends to make every invention of our minds and every material good into a weapon and, consequently, into a danger for mankind?

This question brings us to the most important matter, in comparison to which everything else appears insignificant indeed. We all know that power politics, sooner or later, necessarily leads to war, and that war, under present circumstances, would mean a mass destruction of human beings and material goods, the dimensions of which are much, much greater than anything that has ever before happened in history.

Is it really unavoidable that, because of our passions and our inherited customs, we should be condemned to annihilate each other so thoroughly that nothing would be left over which would deserve to be conserved? Is it not true that all the controversies and differences of opinion which we have touched upon in our strange exchange of letters are insignificant pettinesses compared to the danger in which we all find ourselves? Should we not do everything in our power to eliminate the danger which threatens all nations alike?

If we hold fast to the concept and practice of unlimited sovereignty of nations it only means that each country reserves the right for itself of pursuing its objectives through warlike means. Under the circumstances, every nation must be prepared for that possibility; this means it must try with all its might to be superior to anyone else. This objective will dominate more and more our entire public life and will poison our youth long before the catastrophe is itself actually upon us. We must not tolerate this, however, as long as we still retain a tiny bit of calm reasoning and human feelings.

This alone is on my mind in supporting the idea of "World Government," without any regard to what other people may have in mind when working for the same objective. I advocate world government because I am convinced that there is no other possible way of eliminating the most terrible danger in which man has ever found himself. The objective of avoiding total destruction must have priority over any other objective.

I am sure you are convinced that this letter is written with all the seriousness and honesty at my command; I trust you will accept it in the same spirit.

Science and Life

28

FOR AN ORGANIZATION OF INTELLECTUAL WORKERS

I CONSIDER IT IMPORTANT, indeed urgently necessary, for intellectual workers to get together, both to protect their own economic status and also, generally speaking, to secure their influence in the political field.

On the first-mentioned, the economic side, the working class may serve us as a model: they have succeeded, at least to some extent, in protecting their economic interests. We can learn from them too how this problem can be solved by the method of organization. And also, we can learn from them what is our gravest danger, which we ourselves must seek to avoid: the weakening through inner dissensions, which, when things reach that point, make cooperation difficult and result in quarrels between the constituent groups.

But again, we can also learn from the workers that limitation to immediate economic aims, to the exclusion of all political goals and effective action will not suffice either. In this respect, the working classes in this country have only begun their development. It is inevitable, considering the progressive centralization of production, that the economic and the political struggle should become more and more closely interwoven, the political factor continually growing in significance in the process. In the meantime the intellectual worker, due to his lack of organization, is less well protected against arbitrariness and exploitation than a member of any other calling.

179

But intellectual workers should unite, not only in their own interest but also and no less importantly in the interest of society as a whole. For division among intellectuals has been partly to blame for the fact that the special parts and the experience which are the birthright of these groups have so seldom been made available for political aims. In their room political ambition and desire for profit almost exclusively determine events, instead of professional knowledge and judgment based upon objective thinking.

An organization of intellectual workers can have the greatest significance for society as a whole by influencing public opinion through publicity and education. Indeed it is its proper task to defend academic freedom, without which a healthy development of democracy is impossible.

An outstandingly important task for an organization of intellectual workers at the present moment is to fight for the establishment of a supranational political force as a protection against fresh wars of aggression. It seems to me that the working out with a view to selection of a particular plan for an international government should not, at the present moment, be our chief aim. For if there existed, among the majority of citizens, the firm intention of establishing international security, the technique of giving shape to such an instrument would not present an all-too-difficult problem. What is lacking in the majority is the conviction, founded on clear thinking, that there is no other means of permanently avoiding catastrophes like the present one. In the organization and promotion of enlightenment on this subject, I see the most important service which an organization of intellectual workers can perform at this historic moment. Only by means of setting energetically about such a task can an organization like the one here planned achieve inward strength and outward influence.

29

"WAS EUROPE A SUCCESS?"

THE HUMANITARIAN IDEAL of Europe appears indeed to be unalterably bound up with the free expression of opinion, to some extent with the free-will of the individual, with the effort toward objectivity in thought without consideration of mere utility, and with the encouragement of differences in the realm of mind and taste. These requirements and ideals comprise the nature of the European spirit. One cannot establish with reason the worth of these values and maxims, for they are matters of fundamental principle in the approach to life and are points of departure which can only be affirmed or denied by emotion. I only know that I affirm them with my whole soul, and would find it intolerable to belong to a society which consistently denied them.

I do not share the pessimism of those who believe that full intellectual growth is dependent on the foundation of open or concealed slavery. That may be true for eras of primitive technical development, where the production of the necessaries of life requires physical work by a majority of the people to the point of total exhaustion. In our time of high technical development, with a reasonably equitable division of labor and adequate provisions for all, the individual would have both time and strength to participate receptively and productively in the finest intellectual and artistic efforts his abilities and inclinations allowed. Unfortunately nothing approaching such conditions exist in our society. But everyone devoted to the specific European ideals will do his utmost to achieve aims of whose desirability and practicability an increasing number of right-minded persons are convinced.

Is it justifiable to set aside for a time the principles of individual freedom in deference to the high endeavor to improve economic organization? A fine and shrewd Russian scholar very skilfully defended this point of view to me in comparing the success of compulsion and terror—at least at the outset—in a functioning Russian Communism with the failure of German Social Democracy after the war. He did not convince me. No purpose is so high that unworthy methods in achieving it can be justified in my eyes. Violence sometimes may have cleared away obstructions quickly, but it never has proved itself creative.

30

AT A GATHERING FOR
FREEDOM OF OPINION

WE HAVE COME HERE TODAY to defend the freedom of opinion guaranteed by the Constitution of the United States, and also in defense of the freedom of teaching. By the same token we wish to draw the attention of intellectual workers to the great danger that now menaces these liberties.

How is such a thing possible? Why is the danger more menacing than in years gone by? The centralization of production has brought about a concentration of productive capital in the hands of a relatively small number of the citizens of the land. This small group exerts an overwhelming domination over the institutions for the education of our youth as well as over the great newspapers of the country. At the same time it wields enormous influences on the government. This in itself is already sufficient to constitute a serious menace to the intellectual freedom of the nation. But there is the additional fact that this process of economic concentration has given birth to a problem previously unknown—permanent unemployment for part of those who are able to work. The federal government is endeavoring to solve this problem by systematic control over economic processes—that is to say, by a limitation of the so-called free interplay of the fundamental economic forces of supply and demand.

But circumstances are stronger than men. The dominant economic minority, heretofore autonomous and responsible to no one, has placed itself in opposition to this limitation of its freedom of action, demanded for the good of the whole people. For its defense this minority is resorting to every known legal method at its disposal. We need not, therefore, be surprised that they are using their preponderant influence on the schools and the press to prevent youth from being enlightened on this problem which is so vital to the sound and peaceful development of life in this country.

It is for this reason that of late we have had to witness repeatedly the dismissal of worthy university teachers against the will of their colleagues, actions of which the press has informed the public but inadequately. It is also to the pressure of this economically dominant minority that we owe the unhappy institution of the teacher's oath, which is meant to diminish the freedom of teaching. I need not dwell on the point that freedom of teaching and of opinion in book or press is the foundation for the sound and natural development of any people. The lessons of history—especially the very latest chapters—are all too plain on this score. It is the bounden duty of everyone to stand with every ounce of energy for the preservation and enhancement of these liberties and to exert all possible influence in keeping public opinion aware of the existing danger.

These difficulties can be solved only when our great economic problem is solved in a democratic manner; but the groundwork for such a solution must be prepared by preserving freedom of expression. This, moreover, is also the only method by which the worst damage can be prevented.

Let all of us therefore summon our strength. Let us be tirelessly on guard, lest it be said later of the intellectual elite of this land: Timidly and without a struggle they surrendered the heritage handed down to them by their forefathers—a heritage of which they were not worthy.

31

ATOMIC WAR OR PEACE

I

THE RELEASE OF ATOMIC ENERGY has not created a new problem. It has merely made more urgent the necessity of solving an existing one. One could say that it has affected us quantitatively, not qualitatively. As long as there are sovereign nations possessing great power, war is inevitable. That is not an attempt to say when it will come, but only that it is sure to come. That was true before the atomic bomb was made. What has been changed is the destructiveness of war.

I do not believe that civilization will be wiped out in a war fought with the atomic bomb. Perhaps two-thirds of the people of the earth might be killed. But enough men capable of thinking, and enough books, would be left to start again, and civilization could be restored.

I do not believe that the secret of the bomb should be given to the United Nations Organization. I do not believe it should be given to the Soviet Union. Either course would be like a man with capital, and wishing another man to work with him on some enterprise, starting out by simply giving that man half of his money. The other man might choose to start a rival enterprise, when what is wanted is his cooperation. The secret of the bomb should be committed to a world government, and the United States should immediately announce its readiness to give it to a world government. This government should be founded by the United States, the Soviet Union and Great Britain, the only three powers with great military strength. All three of them should commit to this world government all of their military strength. The fact that there are only three nations with great military power should make it easier, rather than harder, to establish such a government.

Since the United States and Great Britain have the secret of the atomic bomb and the Soviet Union does not, they should invite the Soviet Union to prepare and present the first draft of a constitution of the proposed world government. That will help dispel the distrust of the Russians, which they already feel because the bomb is being kept a secret chiefly to prevent their having it. Obviously the first draft would not be the final one, but the Russians should be made to feel that the world government will assure them their security.

It would be wise if this constitution were to be negotiated by a single American, a single Briton and a single Russian. They would have to have advisers, but these advisers should only advise when asked. I believe three men can succeed in writing a workable constitution acceptable to them all. Six or seven men, or more, probably would fail. After the three great powers have drafted a constitution and adopted it, the smaller nations should be invited to join the world government. They should be free to stay out, and though they should feel perfectly secure in staying out, I am sure they would wish to join. Naturally they should be entitled to propose changes in the constitution as drafted by the Big Three. But the Big Three should go ahead and organize the world government, whether the smaller nations join or not.

The power of this world government would be over all military matters, and there need be only one further power. That is to interfere in countries where a minority is oppressing a majority, and so is creating the kind of instability that leads to war. Conditions such as exist in Argentina and Spain should be dealt with. There must be an end to the concept of non-intervention, for to end it is part of keeping the peace.

The establishment of this world government must not have to wait until the same conditions of freedom are to be found in all three of the great powers. While it is true that in the Soviet Union the minority rules, I do not consider that internal conditions there are of themselves a threat to world peace. One must bear in mind that the people in Russia did not have a long political education, and changes to improve Russian conditions had to be carried through by a minority for the reason that there was no majority capable of doing it. If I had been born a Russian, I believe I could have adjusted myself to this situation.

It should not be necessary, in establishing a world government with a monopoly of military authority, to change the structure of the three great powers. It would be for the three individuals who draft the constitution to devise ways for their different structures to be fitted together for collaboration.

Do I fear the tyranny of a world government? Of course I do. But I fear still more the coming of another war or wars. Any government is certain to be evil to some extent. But a world government is preferable to the far greater evil of wars, particularly with their intensified destructiveness. If such a world government is not established by a process of agreement, I believe it will come anyway, and in a much more dangerous form. For war or wars will end in one power being supreme and dominating the rest of the world by its overwhelming military strength.

Now we have the atomic secret, we must not lose it, and that is what we should risk doing, if we give it to the United Nations Organization or to the Soviet Union. But we must make it clear as quickly as possible that we are not keeping the bomb a secret for the sake of our power, but in the hope of establishing peace through a world government, and we will do our utmost to bring this world government into being.

I appreciate that there are persons who favor a gradual

approach to world government, even though they approve of it as the ultimate objective. The trouble with taking little steps, one at a time, in the hope of reaching the ultimate goal, is that while they are being taken, we continue to keep the bomb without making our reason convincing to those who do not have it. That of itself creates fear and suspicion, with the consequence that the relations of rival sovereignties deteriorate dangerously. So while persons who take only a step at a time may think they are approaching world peace, they actually are contributing by their slow pace to the coming of war. We have no time to spend in this way. If war is to be averted, it must be done quickly.

We shall not have the secret very long. I know it is argued that no other country has money enough to spend on the development of the atomic bomb, which assures us the secret for a long time. It is a mistake often made in this country to measure things by the amount of money they cost. But other countries which have the materials and the men and care to apply them to the work of developing atomic power can do so, for men and materials and the decision to use them, and not money, are all that are needed.

I do not consider myself the father of the release of atomic energy. My part in it was quite indirect. I did not, in fact, foresee that it would be released in my time. I believed only that it was theoretically possible. It became practical through the accidental discovery of chain reaction, and this was not something I could have predicted. It was discovered by Hahn in Berlin, and he himself misinterpreted what he discovered. It was Lize Meitner who provided the correct interpretation, and escaped from Germany to place the information in the hands of Niels Bohr.

I do not believe that a great era of atomic science is to be assured by organizing science, in the way large corporations are organized. One can organize to apply a discovery already made, but not to make one. Only a free individual can make a discovery. There can be a kind of organizing by which scientists are assured their freedom and proper conditions of work. Professors of science in American universities, for instance, should be relieved of some of their teaching so as to have time for more research. Can you imagine an organization of scientists making the discoveries of Charles Darwin?

Nor do I believe that the vast private corporations of the United States are suitable to the needs of these times. If a visitor should come to this country from another planet, would he not find it strange that in this country so much power is permitted to private corporations without their having commensurate responsibility? I say this to stress that the American government must keep the control of atomic energy, not because socialism is necessarily desirable, but because atomic energy was developed by the government, and it would be unthinkable to turn over this property of the people to any individuals or groups of individuals. As to socialism, unless it is international to the extent of producing world government which controls all military power, it might more easily lead to wars than capitalism, because it represents a still greater concentration of power.

To give any estimate when atomic energy can be applied to constructive purposes is impossible. What now is known is only how to use a fairly large quantity of uranium. The use of small quantities, sufficient, say, to operate a car or an airplane, so far is impossible, and one cannot predict when it will be achieved. No doubt, it will be achieved, but nobody can say when. Nor can one predict when materials more common than uranium can be used to supply atomic energy. Presumably all materials used for this purpose will be among the heavier elements of high atomic weight. Those elements are relatively scarce due to their lesser stability. Most of these materials may have already disappeared by radio-active disintegration. So though the release of atomic energy can be, and no doubt will be, a great boon to mankind, that may not be for some time.

I myself do not have the gift of explanation with which I am able to persuade large numbers of people of the urgency of the problems the human race now faces. Hence I should like to commend someone who has this gift of explanation, Emery Reves, whose book, *The Anatomy of the Peace,* is intelligent, clear, brief, and, if I may use the abused term, dynamic on the topic of war and need for world government.

Since I do not foresee that atomic energy is to be a great boon for a long time, I have to say that for the present it is a menace. Perhaps it is well that it should be. It may intimidate the human race to bring order into its international affairs, which, without the pressure of fear, it undoubtedly would not do.

II

Since the completion of the first atomic bomb nothing has been accomplished to make the world more safe from war, while much has been done to increase the destructiveness of war. I am not able to speak from any firsthand knowledge about the development of the atomic bomb, since I do not work in this field. But enough has been said by those who do to indicate that the bomb has been made more effective. Certainly the possibility can be envisaged of building a bomb of far greater size, capable of producing destruction over a larger area. It also is credible that an extensive use could be made of radioactivated gases which would spread over a wide region, causing heavy loss of life without damage to buildings.

I do not believe it is necessary to go on beyond these possibilities to contemplate a vast extension of bacteriological warfare. I am skeptical that this form presents dangers comparable with those of atomic warfare. Nor do I take into account a danger of starting a chain reaction of a scope great enough to destroy part or all of this planet. I dismiss this on the ground that if it could happen from a man-made atomic explosion it would already have happened from the action of the cosmic rays which are continually reaching the earth's surface.

But it is not necessary to imagine the earth being destroyed like a nova by a stellar explosion to understand vividly the growing scope of atomic war and to recognize that unless another war is prevented it is likely to bring destruction on a scale never before held possible and even now hardly conceived, and that little civilization would survive it.

In the first two years of the atomic era another phenomenon is to be noted. The public, having been warned of the horrible nature of atomic warfare, has done nothing about it, and to a large extent has dismissed the warning from its consciousness. A danger that cannot be averted had perhaps better be forgotten; or a danger against which every possible precaution has been taken also had probably better be forgotten. That is, if the United States had dispersed its industries and decentralized its cities, it might be reasonable for people to forget the peril they face.

I should say parenthetically that it is well that this country has not taken these precautions, for to have done so would make atomic war still more probable, since it would convince the rest of the world that we are resigned to it and are preparing for it. But nothing has been done to avert war, while much has been done to make atomic war more horrible; so there is no excuse for ignoring the danger.

I say that nothing has been done to avert war since the completion of the atomic bomb, despite the proposal for supranational control of atomic energy put forward by the United States in the United Nations. This country has made only a conditional proposal, and on conditions which the Soviet Union is now determined not to accept. This makes it possible to blame the failure on the Russians.

But in blaming the Russians the Americans should not ignore the fact that they themselves have not voluntarily renounced the use of the bomb as an ordinary weapon in the time before the achievement of supranational control, or if supranational control is not achieved. Thus they have fed the fear of other countries that they consider the bomb a legitimate part of their arsenal so long as other countries decline to accept their terms for supranational control.

Americans may be convinced of their determination not to launch an aggressive or preventive war. So they may believe it is superfluous to announce publicly that they will not a second time be the first to use the atomic bomb. But this country has been solemnly invited to renounce the use of the bomb—that is, to outlaw it—and has declined to do so unless its terms for supranational control are accepted.

I believe this policy is a mistake. I see a certain military gain from not renouncing the use of the bomb in that this may be deemed to restrain another country from starting a war in which the United States might use it. But what is gained in one way is lost in another. For an understanding over the supranational control of atomic energy has been made more remote. That may be no military drawback so long as the United States has the exclusive use of the bomb. But the moment another country is able to make it in substantial quantities, the United States loses greatly through the absence of an international agreement, because of the vulnerability of its concentrated industries and its highly developed urban life.

In refusing to outlaw the bomb while having the monopoly of it, this country suffers in another respect, in that it fails to return publicly to the ethical standards of warfare formally accepted previous to the last war. It should not be forgotten that the atomic bomb was made in this country as a preventive measure; it was to head off its use by the Germans, if they discovered it. The bombing of civilian centers was initiated by the Germans and adopted by the Japanese. To it the

Allies responded in kind—as it turned out, with greater effectiveness—and they were morally justified in doing so. But now, without any provocation, and without the justification of reprisal or retaliation, a refusal to outlaw the use of the bomb save in reprisal is making a political purpose of its possession. This is hardly pardonable.

I am not saying that the United States should not manufacture and stockpile the bomb, for I believe that it must do so; it must be able to deter another nation from making an atomic attack when it also has the bomb. But deterrence should be the only purpose of the stockpile of bombs. In the same way I believe that the United Nations should have the atomic bomb when it is supplied with its own armed forces and weapons. But it too should have the bomb for the sole purpose of deterring an aggressor or rebellious nations from making an atomic attack. It should not use the atomic bomb on its own initiative any more than the United States or any other power should do so. To keep a stockpile of atomic bombs without promising not to initiate its use is exploiting the possession of the bombs for political ends. It may be that the United States hopes in this way to frighten the Soviet Union into accepting supranational control of atomic energy. But the creation of fear only heightens antagonism and increases the danger of war. I am of the opinion that this policy has detracted from the very real virtue in the offer of supranational control of atomic energy.

We have emerged from a war in which we had to accept the degradingly low ethical standards of the enemy. But instead of feeling liberated from his standards, and set free to restore the sanctity of human life and the safety of noncombatants, we are in effect making the low standards of the enemy in the last war our own for the present. Thus we are starting toward another war degraded by our own choice.

It may be that the public is not fully aware that in another war atomic bombs will be available in large quantities. It may measure the dangers in the terms of the three bombs exploded before the end of the last war. The public also may not appreciate that, in relation to the damage inflicted, atomic bombs already have become the most economical form of destruction that can be used on the offensive. In another war the bombs will be plentiful and they will be comparatively cheap. Unless there is a determination not to use them that is far stronger than can be noted today among American political and military leaders, and on the part of the public itself, atomic warfare will be hard to avoid. Unless Americans come to recognize that they are not stronger in the world because they have the bomb, but weaker because of their vulnerability to atomic attack, they are not likely to conduct their policy at Lake Success or in their relations with Russia in a spirit that furthers the arrival at an understanding.

But I do not suggest that the American failure to outlaw the use of the bomb except in retaliation is the only cause of the absence of an agreement with the Soviet Union over atomic control. The Russians have made it clear that they will do everything in their power to prevent a supranational regime from coming into existence. They not only reject it in the range of atomic energy: they reject it sharply on principle, and thus have spurned in advance any overture to join a limited world government.

Mr. Gromyko has rightly said that the essence of the American atomic proposal is that national sovereignty is not compatible with the atomic era. He declares that the Soviet Union cannot accept this thesis. The reasons he gives are obscure, for they quite obviously are pretexts. But what seems to be true is that the Soviet leaders believe they cannot preserve the social structure of the Soviet state in a supranational regime. The Soviet government is determined to maintain its present social structure, and the leaders of Russia, who hold their great power through the nature of that structure, will spare no effort to prevent a supranational regime from coming into existence, to control atomic energy or anything else.

The Russians may be partly right about the difficulty of retaining their present social structure in a supranational regime, though in time they may be brought to see that this is a far lesser loss than remaining isolated from a world of law. But at present they appear to be guided by their fears, and one must admit that the United States has made ample contributions to these fears, not only as to atomic energy but in many other respects. Indeed this country has conducted its Russian policy as though it were convinced that fear is the greatest of all diplomatic instruments.

That the Russians are striving to prevent the formation of a supranational security system is no reason why the rest of the world should not work to create one. It has been pointed out that the Russians have a way of resisting with all their arts what they do not wish to have happen; but once it happens, they can be flexible and accommodate themselves to it. So it would be well for the United States and other powers not to permit the Russians to veto an attempt to create supranational security. They can proceed with some hope that once the Russians see they cannot prevent such a regime they may join it.

So far the United States has shown no interest in preserving the security of the Soviet Union. It has been interested in its own security, which is characteristic of the competition which marks the conflict for power between sovereign states. But one cannot know in advance what would be the effect on Russian fears if the American people forced their leaders to pursue a policy of substituting law for the present anarchy of international relations. In a world of law, Russian security would be equal to our own, and for the American people to espouse this wholeheartedly, something that should be possible under the workings of democracy, might work a kind of miracle in Russian thinking.

At present the Russians have no evidence to convince them that the American people are not contentedly supporting a policy of military preparedness which they regard as a policy of deliberate intimidation. If they had evidences of a passionate desire by Americans to preserve peace in the one way it can be maintained, by a supranational regime of law, this would upset Russian calculations about the peril to Russian security in current trends of American thought. Not until a genuine, convincing offer is made to the Soviet Union, backed by an aroused American public, will one be entitled to say what the Russian response would be.

It may be that the first response would be to reject the world of law. But if from that moment it began to be clear to the Russians that such a world was coming into existence without them, and that their own security was being increased, their ideas necessarily would change.

I am in favor of inviting the Russians to join a world government authorized to provide security, and if they are unwilling to join, to proceed to establish supranational security without them. Let me admit quickly that I see great peril in such a course. If it is adopted it must be done in a way to make it utterly clear that the new regime is not a combination of power against Russia. It must be a combination that by its composite nature will greatly reduce the chances of war. It will be more diverse in its interests than any single state, thus less likely to resort to aggressive or preventive war. It will be larger, hence stronger than any single nation. It will be geographically much more extensive, and thus more difficult to defeat by military means. It will be dedicated to supranational security, and thus escape the emphasis on national supremacy which is so strong a factor in war.

If a supranational regime is set up without Russia, its service to peace will depend on the skill and sincerity with which it is done. Emphasis should always be apparent on the desire to have Russia take part. It must be clear to Russia, and no less so to the nations comprising the organization, that no penalty is incurred or implied because a nation declines to join. If the Russians do not join at the outset, they must be sure of a welcome when they do decide to join. Those who create the organization must understand that they are building with the final objective of obtaining Russian adherence.

These are abstractions, and it is not easy to outline the specific lines a partial world government must follow to induce the Russians to join. But two conditions are clear to me: the new organization must have no military secrets; and the Russians must be free to have observers at every session of the organization, where its new laws are drafted, discussed, and adopted, and where its policies are decided. That would destroy the great factory of secrecy where so many of the world's suspicions are manufactured.

It may affront the military-minded person to suggest a regime that does not maintain any military secrets. He has been taught to believe that secrets thus divulged would enable a war-minded nation to seek to conquer the earth. (As to the so-called secret of the atomic bomb, I am assuming the Russians will have this through their own efforts within a short time.) I grant there is a risk in not maintaining military secrets. If a sufficient number of nations have pooled their strength they can take this risk, for their security will be greatly increased. And it can be done with greater assurance because of the decrease of fear, suspicion, and distrust that will result. The tensions of the increasing likelihood of war in a world based on sovereignty would be replaced by the relaxation of the growing confidence in peace. In time this might so allure the Russian people that their leaders would mellow in their attitude toward the West.

Membership in a supranational security system should not, in my opinion, be based on any arbitrary democratic standards. The one requirement from all should be that the representatives to supranational organization—assembly and council—must be elected by the people in each member country through a secret ballot. These representatives must represent the people rather than any government—which would enhance the pacific nature of the organization.

To require that other democratic criteria be met is, I believe, inadvisable. Democratic institutions and standards are the result of historic developments to an extent not always appreciated in the lands which enjoy them. Setting arbitrary standards sharpens the ideological differences between the Western and Soviet systems.

But it is not the ideological differences which now are pushing the world in the direction of war. Indeed, if all the Western nations were to adopt socialism, while maintaining their national sovereignty, it is quite likely that the conflict for power between East and West would continue. The passion expressed over the economic systems of the present seems to me quite irrational. Whether the economic life of America should be dominated by relatively few individuals, as it is, or these individuals should be controlled by the state, may be important, but it is not important enough to justify all the feelings that are stirred up over it.

I should wish to see all the nations forming the supranational state pool all their military forces, keeping for themselves only local police. Then I should like to see these forces commingled and distributed as were the regiments of the former Austro-Hungarian Empire. There it was appreciated that the men and officers of one region would serve the purposes of empire better by not being stationed exclusively in their own provinces, subject to local and racial pulls.

I should like to see the authority of the supranational regime restricted altogether to the field of security. Whether this would be possible I am not sure. Experience may point to the desirability of adding some authority over economic matters, since under modern conditions these are capable of causing national upsets that have in them the seeds of violent conflict. But I should prefer to see the function of the organization altogether limited to the tasks of security. I also should like to see this regime established through the strengthening of the United Nations, so as not to sacrifice continuity in the search for peace.

I do not hide from myself the great difficulties of establishing a world government, either a beginning without Russia or one with Russia. I am aware of the risks. Since I should not wish it to be permissible for any country that has joined the supranational organization to secede, one of these risks is a possible civil war. But I also believe that world government is certain to come in time, and that the question is how much it is to be permitted to cost. It will come, I believe, even if there is another world war, though after such a war, if it is won, it would be world government established by the victor, resting on the victor's military power, and thus to be maintained permanently only through the permanent militarization of the human race.

But I also believe it can come through agreement and through the force of persuasion alone, hence at low cost. But if it is to come in this way it will not be enough to appeal to reason. One strength of the communist system of the East is that it has some of the character of a religion and inspires the emotions of a religion. Unless the cause of peace based on law gathers behind it the force and zeal of a religion, it hardly can hope to succeed. Those to whom the moral teaching of the human race is entrusted surely have a great duty and a great opportunity. The atomic scientists, I think, have become convinced that they cannot arouse the American people to the truths of the atomic era by logic alone. There must be added that deep power of emotion which is a basic ingredient of religion. It is to be hoped that not only the churches but the schools, the colleges, and the leading organs of opinion will acquit themselves well of their unique responsibility in this regard.

32

THE WAR IS WON BUT
PEACE IS NOT

PHYSICISTS FIND THEMSELVES in a position not unlike that of Alfred Nobel. Alfred Nobel invented the most powerful explosive ever known up to his time, a means of destruction par excellence. In order to atone for this, in order to relieve his human conscience he instituted his awards for the promotion of peace and for achievements of peace. Today, the physicists who participated in forging the most formidable and dangerous weapon of all times are harassed by an equal feeling of responsibility, not to say guilt. And we cannot desist from warning, and warning again, we cannot and should not slacken in our efforts to make the nations of the world, and especially their governments, aware of the unspeakable disaster they are certain to provoke unless they change their attitude toward each other and toward the task of shaping the future. We helped in creating this new weapon in order to prevent the enemies of mankind from achieving it ahead of us, which, given the mentality of the Nazis, would have meant inconceivable destruction and the enslavement of the rest of the world. We delivered this weapon into the hands of the American and the British people as trustees of the whole of mankind, as fighters for peace and liberty. But so far we fail to see any guarantee of peace, we do not see any guarantee of the freedoms that were promised to the nations in the Atlantic Charter. The war is won, but the peace is not. The great powers, united in fighting, are now divided over the peace settlements. The world was promised freedom from fear, but in fact fear has increased tremendously since the termination of the war. The world was promised freedom from want, but large parts of the world are faced with starvation while others are living in abundance. The nations were promised liberation and justice. But we have witnessed, and are witnessing even now, the sad spectacle of "liberating" armies firing into populations who want their independence and social equality, and supporting in those countries, by force of arms, such parties and personalities as appear to be most suited to serve vested interests. Territorial questions and arguments of power, obsolete though they are, still prevail over the essential demands of common welfare and justice. Allow me to be more specific about just one case, which is but a symptom of the general situation: the case of my own people, the Jewish people.

As long as Nazi violence was unleashed only, or mainly, against the Jews the rest of the world looked on passively, and even treaties and agreements were made with the patently criminal government of the Third Reich. Later, when Hitler was on the point of taking over Rumania and Hungary, at the time when Maidanek and Oswiecim were in Allied hands, and the methods of the gas chambers were well known all over the world, all attempts to rescue the Rumanian and Hungarian Jews came to naught because the doors of Palestine were closed to Jewish immigrants by the British government, and no country could be found that would admit those forsaken people. They were left to perish like their brothers and sisters in the occupied countries.

We shall never forget the heroic efforts of the small countries, of the Scandinavian, the Dutch, the Swiss nations, and of individuals in the occupied parts of Europe who did all in their power to protect Jewish lives. We do not forget the humane attitude of the Soviet Union who was the only one among the big powers to open her doors to hundreds of thousands of Jews when the Nazi armies were advancing in Poland. But after all that has happened, and was not prevented from happening, how is it today? While in Europe territories are being distributed without any qualms about the wishes of the people concerned, the remainders of European Jewry, one fifth of its pre-war population, are again denied access to their haven in Palestine and left to hunger and cold and persisting hostility. There is no country, even today, that would be willing or able to offer them a place where they could live in peace and security. And the fact that many of them are still kept in the degrading conditions of concentration camps by the Allies gives sufficient evidence of the shamefulness and hopelessness of the situation. These people are forbidden to enter Palestine with reference to the principle of democracy, but actually the Western powers, in upholding the ban of the White Paper, are yielding to the threats and the external pressure of five vast and underpopulated Arab States. It is sheer irony when the British Foreign Minister tells the poor lot of European Jews they should remain in Europe because their genius is needed there, and, on the other hand, advises them not to try to get at the head of the queue lest they might incur new hatred and persecution. Well, I am afraid, they cannot help it; with their six million dead they have been pushed at the head of the queue, of the queue of Nazi victims, much against their will.

The picture of our postwar world is not bright. As far as we, the physicists, are concerned, we are no politicians and it has never been our wish to meddle in politics. But we know a few things that the politicians do not know. And we feel the duty to speak up and to remind those responsible that there is no escape into easy comforts, there is no distance ahead for proceeding little by little and delaying the necessary changes into an indefinite future, there is no time left for petty bargaining. The situation calls for a courageous effort, for a radical change in our whole attitude, in the entire political concept. May the spirit that prompted Alfred Nobel to create his great institution, the spirit of trust and confidence, of generosity and brotherhood among men, prevail in the minds of those upon whose decisions our destiny rests. Otherwise human civilization will be doomed.

33

THE MENACE OF MASS
DESTRUCTION

Everyone is aware of the difficult and menacing situation
in which human society—shrunk into one community with a
common fate—finds itself, but only a few act accordingly.
Most people go on living their every-day life: half frightened,
half indifferent, they behold the ghostly tragi-comedy that is
being performed on the international stage before the eyes
and ears of the world. But on that stage, on which the actors
under the floodlights play their ordained parts, our fate of
tomorrow, life or death of the nations, is being decided.

It would be different if the problem were not one of things
made by Man himself, such as the atomic bomb and other
means of mass destruction equally menacing all peoples. It
would be different, for instance, if an epidemic of bubonic
plague were threatening the entire world. In such a case conscientious and expert persons would be brought together and
they would work out an intelligent plan to combat the plague.
After having reached agreement upon the right ways and
means, they would submit their plan to the governments.
Those would hardly raise serious objections but rather agree
speedily on the measures to be taken. They certainly would
never think of trying to handle the matter in such a way that
their own nation would be spared whereas the next one
would be decimated.

But could not our situation be compared to one of a

menacing epidemic? People are unable to view this situation in its true light, for their eyes are blinded by passion. General fear and anxiety create hatred and aggressiveness. The adaptation to warlike aims and activities has corrupted the mentality of man; as a result, intelligent, objective and humane thinking has hardly any effect and is even suspected and persecuted as unpatriotic.

There are, no doubt, in the opposite camps enough people of sound judgment and sense of justice who would be capable and eager to work out together a solution for the factual difficulties. But the efforts of such people are hampered by the fact that it is made impossible for them to come together for informal discussions. I am thinking of persons who are accustomed to the objective approach to a problem and who will not be confused by exaggerated nationalism or other passions. This forced separation of the people of both camps I consider one of the major obstacles to the achievement of an acceptable solution of the burning problem of international security.

As long as contact between the two camps is limited to the official negotiations I can see little prospect for an intelligent agreement being reached, especially since considerations of national prestige as well as the attempt to talk out of the window for the benefit of the masses are bound to make reasonable progress almost impossible. What one party suggests officially is for that reason alone suspected and even made unacceptable to the other. Also behind all official negotiations stands—though veiled—the threat of naked power. The official method can lead to success only after spade-work of an informal nature has prepared the ground; the conviction that a mutually satisfactory solution can be reached must be gained first; then the actual negotiations can get under way with a fair promise of success.

We scientists believe that what we and our fellow-men do or fail to do within the next few years will determine the fate of our civilization. And we consider it our task untiringly to explain this truth, to help people realize all that is at stake, and to work, not for appeasement, but for understanding and ultimate agreement between peoples and nations of different views.

34

THE SCHOOLS AND THE
PROBLEM OF PEACE

B Y VIRTUE OF ITS GEOGRAPHIC situation the United States is
in the fortunate position of being able to teach a rational
pacifism in its schools, without having to fear for its security.
For there is no serious danger of a military attack from the
outside, and as a result no compulsion to educate youth in a
military spirit. On the other hand there is the danger of treat-
ing this problem purely from the emotional point of view. Yet
little is gained by mere wishful thinking, without a clear
grasp of the essential difficulties of the problem.

In the first place it ought to be made clear to youth that
the United States may be at any time drawn into military
involvements, even though a direct attack on the country
need scarcely be feared. Mere reference to America's participation in the last World War is sufficient proof of this. Even
Americans can hope for true security against being drawn
into military involvements only from a satisfactory solution
of the problem of peace in general. It is necessary to warn
against the view that political isolation of the United States
from the outside can result in adequate security for Americans. Instead a serious interest in an international solution
of the problem of peace must be awakened among young
people. In particular must youth be given a clear understanding of the grave responsibility which American politicians
have assumed by failing to support Wilson's grandly con-

ceived plans after peace was concluded, thus impairing the effectiveness of the League of Nations.

It must be pointed out that the mere demand for disarmament is futile, so long as there are great nations who are prepared to attain their future position in the world by means of military expansion. The reasonableness of the position represented by France, for example—namely that the security of the individual countries must be insured by international institutions—must be set forth. To achieve such security international treaties for common defense against those who break the peace are necessary but not sufficient. Instead, military defense resources must become internationalized by amalgamation and exchange of forces on a grand scale to such an extent that the military forces stationed in any one country cannot possibly be used exclusively for the purpose of pursuing the goals of that country.

To prepare the nations for such effective insurance of the peace, this vital problem should be clearly and sharply brought to the attention of young people. The spirit of international solidarity too should be strengthened and national chauvinism combatted as a harmful force impeding progress.

Schools ought to be intent on presenting history from the point of view of progress and the growth of human civilization, rather than using it as a means for fostering in the minds of the growing generation the ideals of outward power and military successes. In my opinion the use of H. G. Wells' *World History* should be highly recommended from this aspect.

It is of indirect yet nevertheless considerable importance, finally, that in the teaching of geography and history a sympathetic understanding be fostered for the characteristics of the different peoples of the world, especially for those whom we are in the habit of describing as "primitive."

35

ON MILITARY SERVICE

I STAND FIRMLY BY THE PRINCIPLE that a real solution of the problem of pacifism can be achieved only by the organization of a supranational court of arbitration, which, differing from the present League of Nations in Geneva, would have at its disposal the means of enforcing its decisions. In short, an international court of justice with a permanent military establishment, or better, police force. An excellent expression of this conviction of mine is contained in Lord Davies' book, *Force* (London, Ernst Benn, Ltd., 1934), the reading of which I strongly recommend to everyone who is seriously concerned with this fundamental problem of mankind.

Taking as starting point this fundamental conviction, I stand for every measure which appears to me capable of bringing mankind nearer to this goal. Up to a few years ago, the refusal to bear arms by courageous and self-sacrificing persons *was* such a measure; it is no longer—especially in Europe—a means to be recommended. When the great Powers had nearly equally democratic governments, and when none of these Powers founded its future plans on military aggression, the refusal to do military service on the part of a fairly large number of citizens might have induced the governments of these Powers to look favorably on international legal arbitration. Moreover, such refusals were apt to educate public opinion to real pacifism. The public came to consider as oppression any pressure brought by the State upon its citizens to force them to fulfil their military obligations, besides considering such pressure unethical from the moral standpoint.

Under these circumstances, such refusals worked for the highest good.

Today, however, we are brought face to face with the fact that powerful States make independent opinions in politics impossible for their citizens, and lead their own people into error through the systematic diffusion of false information. At the same time, these States become a menace to the rest of the world by creating military organizations which encompass their entire population. This false information is spread by a muzzled press, a centralized radio service, and school education ruled by an aggressive foreign policy. In States of that description, refusal to perform military service means martyrdom and death for those courageous enough to object. In those States in which citizens still cling to some of their political rights, refusal to do military service means weakening the power of resistance of the remaining sane portions of the civilized world.

Because of this, no reasonable human being would today favor the refusal to do military service, at least not in Europe, which is at present particularly beset with dangers.

I do not believe that under present circumstances passive resistance is an effective method, even if carried out in the most heroic manner. Other times, other means, even if the final aim remains the same.

The confirmed pacifist must therefore at present seek a plan of action different from that of former, more peaceful times. He must try to work for this aim: That those States which favor peaceful progress may come as close together as possible in order to diminish the likelihood that the warlike programs of political adventurers whose States are founded on violence and brigandage will be realized. I have in mind, in the first place, well-considered and permanent concerted action on the part of the United States and the British Empire, together with France and Russia when possible.

Perhaps the present danger will facilitate this *rapproche-*

ment and thus bring about a pacifistic solution of international problems. This would be the hopeful side to the present dark situation; here consistent action can contribute much toward influencing public opinion in the right direction.

36

MILITARY INTRUSION IN SCIENCE

THE MILITARY MENTALITY

IT SEEMS TO ME THAT the decisive point in the situation lies in the fact that the problem before us cannot be viewed as an isolated one. First of all, one may pose the following question: From now on institutions for learning and research will more and more have to be supported by grants from the state, since, for various reasons, private sources will not suffice. Is it at all reasonable that the distribution of the funds raised for these purposes from the taxpayer should be entrusted to the military? To this question every prudent person will certainly answer: "No!" For it is evident that the difficult task of the most beneficent distribution should be placed in the hands of people whose training and life's work give proof that they know something about science and scholarship.

If reasonable people, nevertheless, favor military agencies for the distribution of a major part of the available funds, the reason for this lies in the fact that they subordinate cultural concerns to their general political outlook. We must then focus our attention on these practical political viewpoints, their origins and their implications. In doing so we shall soon recognize that the problem here under discussion is but one of many, and can only be fully estimated and properly adjudged when placed in a broader framework.

The tendencies we have mentioned are something new for

America. They arose when, under the influence of the two World Wars and the consequent concentration of all forces on a military goal, a predominantly military mentality developed, which with the almost sudden victory became even more accentuated. The characteristic feature of this mentality is that people place the importance of what Bertrand Russell so tellingly terms "naked power" far above all other factors which affect the relations between peoples. The Germans, misled by Bismarck's successes in particular, underwent just such a transformation of their mentality—in consequence of which they were entirely ruined in less than a hundred years.

I must frankly confess that the foreign policy of the United States since the termination of hostilities has reminded me, sometimes irresistibly, of the attitude of Germany under Kaiser Wilhelm II, and I know that, independent of me, this analogy has most painfully occurred to others as well. It is characteristic of the military mentality that non-human factors (atom bombs, strategic bases, weapons of all sorts, the possession of raw materials, etc.) are held essential, while the human being, his desires and thoughts—in short, the psychological factors—are considered as unimportant and secondary. Herein lies a certain resemblance to Marxism, at least insofar as its theoretical side alone is kept in view. The individual is degraded to a mere instrument; he becomes "human materiel." The normal ends of human aspiration vanish with such a viewpoint. Instead, the military mentality raises "naked power" as a goal in itself—one of the strangest illusions to which men can succumb.

In our time the military mentality is still more dangerous than formerly because the offensive weapons have become much more powerful than the defensive ones. Therefore it leads, by necessity, to preventive war. The general insecurity that goes hand in hand with this results in the sacrifice of the citizen's civil rights to the supposed welfare of the state.

Political witch-hunting, controls of all sorts (e.g., control of teaching and research, of the press, and so forth) appear inevitable, and for this reason do not encounter that popular resistance, which, were it not for the military mentality, would provide a protection. A reappraisal of all values gradually takes place insofar as everything that does not clearly serve the utopian ends is regarded and treated as inferior.

I see no other way out of prevailing conditions than a farseeing, honest and courageous policy with the aim of establishing security on supranational foundations. Let us hope that men will be found, sufficient in number and moral force, to guide the nation on this path so long as a leading role is imposed on her by external circumstances. Then problems such as have been discussed here will cease to exist.

37

INTERNATIONAL SECURITY

GEOGRAPHICALLY THE AMERICANS are without doubt in an especially favorable position, and menace to this country through military attack need not necessarily be given serious consideration. Nevertheless they manifest a real interest in the building up an international court of arbitration for the purpose of settling peaceably all international disputes or disagreements and with power to guarantee indemnities. The World War has shown the fate of the nations to be closely interwoven, and the world-wide economic crisis teaches us all the same.

Therefore it is essential that the American youth direct their energies to the end that the United States shall take active part in all efforts toward making international order a reality. It is obvious that the war and the post-war period have been a source of great concern to many Americans. It also follows that the continued policy of aloofness would not only injure all mankind, but harm the United States as well.

Personalities

38

ISAAC NEWTON

Reason, of course, is weak, when measured against its never-ending task. Weak, indeed, compared with the follies and passions of mankind, which, we must admit, almost entirely control our human destinies, in great things and small. Yet the works of the understanding outlast the noisy bustling generations and spread light and warmth across the centuries. Consoled by this thought let us turn, in these unquiet days, to the memory of Newton, who three hundred years ago was given to mankind.

To think of him is to think of his work. For such a man can be understood only by thinking of him as a scene on which the struggle for eternal truth took place. Long before Newton there had been virile minds who conceived that it ought to be possible, by purely logical deduction from simple physical hypotheses, to make cogent explanations of phenomena perceptible to the senses. But Newton was the first to succeed in finding a clearly formulated basis from which he could deduce a wide field of phenomena by means of mathematical thinking, logically, quantitatively and in harmony with experience. Indeed, he might well hope that the fundamental basis of his mechanics would come in time to furnish the key to the understanding of all phenomena. So thought his pupils—with more assurance than he himself—and so his successors, up till the end of the eighteenth century. How did this miracle come to birth in his brain? Forgive me, reader, the illogical question. For if by reason we could deal with the problem of the "how," then there could be no question of a miracle in the proper sense of the word. It is the goal of every activity of the intellect to convert a "miracle" into something which it has grasped. If in this case the miracle permits itself to be converted, our admiration for the mind of Newton becomes only the greater thereby.

Galileo, by ingenious interpretation of the simplest facts of experience, had established the proposition: a body upon which no external force is at work permanently maintains its original velocity (and direction); if it alters its velocity (or the direction of its movement) the change must be referred to an external cause.

To utilize this knowledge quantitatively the conceptions velocity and rate of change of velocity—that is, acceleration in the case of any given motion of a body conceived as dimensionless (material point)—must first be interpreted with mathematical exactness. The task led Newton to invent the basis of differential and integral calculus.

This in itself was a creative achievement of the first order. But for Newton, as a physicist, it was simply the invention of a new kind of conceptual language which he needed in order to formulate the general laws of motion. For a given body he had now to put forward the hypothesis that his precisely formulated acceleration both in magnitude and direction was proportional to the force directed upon it. The coefficient of proportionality which characterizes the body with reference to its power of acceleration completely describes the (dimensionless) body with reference to its mechanical quality; thus was discovered the fundamental conception of mass.

All the foregoing might be described—though in the extremely modest manner of speaking—as an exact formulation of something the essence of which had already been recognized by Galileo. But it by no means succeeded in solving the main problem. In other words, the law of motion yields the movement of a body, only when the direction and magnitude of the force exerted upon it are known for all times.

Thus the problem reduced itself to another problem: how to find out the operative forces. To a mind any less bold than Newton's it must have seemed hopeless, considering the immeasurable multifarity of the effects which the bodies of a universe seem to produce upon each other. Moreover, the bodies whose motions we perceive are by no means dimensionless points—that is to say, perceptible as material points. How was Newton to deal with such chaos?

If we push a cart moving without friction on a horizontal plane it follows that the force we exert upon it is given directly. That is the ideal case from which the law of motion is derived. That we are not here dealing with a dimensionless point appears unessential.

How does it stand then with a falling body in space? A freely falling body behaves almost as simply as the dimensionless point, if one regards its movement as a whole. It is accelerated downwards. The acceleration, according to Galileo, is independent of its nature and its velocity. The earth, of course, must be decisive for the existence of this acceleration. It seemed, then, that the earth by its mere presence exerted a force upon the body. The earth consists of many parts. The idea seemed inevitable that each of these parts affects the falling body and that all these effects are combined. There seems then to be a force which bodies by their very presence exert upon each other through space. These forces seem to be independent of velocities, dependent only upon the relative position and quantitative property of the various bodies exerting them. This quantitative property might be conditioned by its mass, for the mass seems to characterize the body from the mechanical point of view. This strange effect of things at a distance may be called gravitation.

Now to gain precise knowledge of this effect, one has only to find out how strong is the force exerted upon each other by two bodies of given mass from a given distance. As for their direction, it would probably be no other than the line connecting them. Finally then, what remains unknown is only the dependence of this force upon the distance between the two bodies. But this one cannot know *a priori*. Here, only experience could be of use.

Such experience, however, was available to Newton. The acceleration of the moon was known from its orbit and could be compared with the acceleration of the freely falling body on the surface of the earth. Furthermore, the movements of the planets about the sun had been determined by Kepler with great exactness and comprehended in simple empirical laws. So it was possible to ascertain how the effects of gravitation coming from the earth and those coming from the sun depended on the factor of distance. Newton found that everything was explainable by a force which was inversely proportional to the square of the distance. And with that the goal was reached, the science of celestial mechanics was born, confirmed a thousand times over by Newton himself and those who came after him. But how about the rest of physics? Gravitation and the law of motion could not explain everything. What determined the equilibrium of the parts of a solid body? How was light to be explained, how electrical phenomena? By introducing material points and forces of various kinds acting at a distance, everything seemed in a fair way to be derivable from the law of motion.

That hope has not been fulfilled, and no one any longer believes in the solution of all our problems on this basis. Nevertheless, the thinking of physicists today is conditioned to a high degree by Newton's fundamental conceptions. It has so far not been possible to substitute for the Newtonian unified conception of the universe a similarly unified comprehensive conception. But what we have gained up till now would have been impossible without Newton's clear system.

From observation of the stars have chiefly come the intellectual tools indispensable to the development of modern technique. For the abuse of the latter in our time creative intellects like Newton's are as little responsible as the stars themselves, contemplating which their thoughts took wing. It is necessary to say this, because in our time esteem for intellectual values for their own sake is no longer so lively as it was in the centuries of the intellectual renascence.

39

JOHANNES KEPLER

In kepler's letters we find ourselves confronted with a sensitive personality, passionately devoted to the quest for deeper insight into the character of natural processes—a man who reached the exalted goal he set himself in spite of all internal and external difficulties. Kepler's life was devoted to the solution of a dual problem. The sun and the planets change their apparent position with reference to their background of fixed stars in a complex manner open to immediate observation. In other words, all the observations and records compiled with such care dealt not actually with the movements of the planets in space but with temporal shifts undergone by the direction earth-planet in the course of time.

Once Copernicus had convinced the small group capable of grasping it that in this process the sun must be regarded as being at rest, with the planets, including the earth, revolving about the sun, the first great problem proved to be this: to determine the true motions of the planets, including the earth, as they might be visible to an observer on the nearest fixed star who was equipped with a perfect stereoscopic double-telescope. This was Kepler's first great problem. The second problem was embodied in this question: What are the mathematical laws under which these motions proceed? It is plain that the solution of the second problem, if at all within reach of the human mind, was predicated on the solution of the first. Before a theory explaining a certain process can be tested, that process must first be known.

Kepler's solution of the first problem is based on a truly

inspired notion that made possible the determination of the true orbit of the earth. To construct that orbit, a second fixed point in planetary space, in addition to the sun, is required. When such a second point is available, it and the sun may both be used as points of reference for angular measurements, and the earth's true orbit can be determined by the same methods of triangulation that customarily serve in surveying and cartography.

But where was such a second fixed point to be found, since all visible objects, except the sun, themselves execute motions that are not known in detail? This was Kepler's answer: The apparent motions of the planet Mars are known with great accuracy, including the time of its revolution about the sun (the "Martian year"). It is probable that at the end of each Martian year Mars is at the same spot in (planetary) space. If we limit ourselves for the time being to these points in time, then the planet Mars represents for them a fixed point in planetary space, a point that may be used in triangulation.

Employing this principle, Kepler first of all determined the true motion of the earth in planetary space. Since the earth itself may be used as a point for triangulation at any time, he was also able to determine the true motions of the other planets from his observations.

This is how Kepler gained the basis for formulating the three fundamental laws with which his name will remain associated for all time to come. Today, after the fact, no one can fully appreciate how much ingenuity, how much hard and tireless work was required to discover these laws and ascertain them with such precision.

The reader ought to know this as he learns from the letters under what hardships Kepler accomplished this gigantic work. He refused to be paralyzed or discouraged either by poverty or by the lack of comprehension among those of his contemporaries who had the power to shape his life and work. Yet he was dealing with a subject that offered immediate danger to him who professed the truth. But Kepler was one of the few who are simply incapable of doing anything but stand up openly for their convictions in every field. At the same time he was not one who took undiluted pleasure in personal controversy, as was plainly the case with Galileo, whose inspired barbs delight the informed reader even today. Kepler was a devout Protestant, but he made no secret of the fact that he did not approve of all decisions by the Church. He was, accordingly, regarded as a kind of moderate heretic and treated as such.

This brings me to the inner difficulties Kepler had to overcome—difficulties at which I have already hinted. They are not as readily perceived as the outward difficulties. Kepler's lifework was possible only once he succeeded in freeing himself to a great extent of the intellectual traditions into which he was born. This meant not merely the religious tradition, based on the authority of the Church, but general concepts on the nature and limitations of action within the universe and the human sphere, as well as notions of the relative importance of thought and experience in science.

He had to rid himself of the animist approach in research, a mode of thought oriented toward ulterior ends. He first had to recognize that even the most lucidly logical mathematical theory was of itself no guarantee of truth, becoming meaningless unless it was checked against the most exacting observations in natural science. But for this philosophical orientation Kepler's work would not have been possible. He does not speak of it, but the inner struggle is reflected in his letters. Let the reader watch out for remarks concerning astrology. They show that the vanquished inner foe had been rendered harmless, even though he was not yet altogether dead.

40

MARIE CURIE IN MEMORIAM

At a time when a towering personality like Mme. Curie has come to the end of her life, let us not merely rest content with recalling what she has given to mankind in the fruits of her work. It is the moral qualities of its leading personalities that are perhaps of even greater significance for a generation and for the course of history than purely intellectual accomplishments. Even these latter are, to a far greater degree than is commonly credited, dependent on the stature of character.

It was my good fortune to be linked with Mme. Curie through twenty years of sublime and unclouded friendship. I came to admire her human grandeur to an ever growing degree. Her strength, her purity of will, her austerity toward herself, her objectivity, her incorruptible judgment—all these were of a kind seldom found joined in a single individual. She felt herself at every moment to be a servant of society and her profound modesty never left any room for complacency. She was oppressed by an abiding sense for the asperities and inequities of society. This is what gave her that severe outward aspect, so easily misinterpreted by those who were not close to her—a curious severity unrelieved by any artistic strain. Once she had recognized a certain way as the right one, she pursued it without compromise and with extreme tenacity.

The greatest scientific deed of her life—proving the existence of radioactive elements and isolating them—owes its accomplishment not merely to bold intuition but to a devotion and tenacity in execution under the most extreme hardships imaginable, such as the history of experimental science has not often witnessed.

If but a small part of Mme. Curie's strength of character and devotion were alive in Europe's intellectuals, Europe would face a brighter future.

41

MAX PLANCK IN MEMORIAM

A MAN TO WHOM IT HAS been given to bless the world with a great creative idea has no need for the praise of posterity. His very achievement has already conferred a higher boon upon him.

Yet it is good—indeed, it is indispensable—that representatives of all who strive for truth and knowledge should be gathered here today from the four corners of the globe. They are here to bear witness that even in these times of ours, when political passion and brute force hang like swords over the anguished and fearful heads of men, the standard of our ideal search for truth is being held aloft undimmed. This ideal, a bond forever uniting scientists of all times and in all places, was embodied with rare completeness in Max Planck.

Even the Greeks had already conceived the atomistic nature of matter and the concept was raised to a high degree of probability by the scientists of the nineteenth century. But it was Planck's law of radiation that yielded the first exact determination—independent of other assumptions—of the absolute magnitudes of atoms. More than that, he showed convincingly that in addition to the atomistic structure of matter there is a kind of atomistic structure to energy, governed by the universal constant h, which was introduced by Planck.

This discovery became the basis of all twentieth-century research in physics and has almost entirely conditioned its development ever since. Without this discovery it would not have been possible to establish a workable theory of molecules and atoms and the energy processes that govern their transformations. Moreover, it has shattered the whole framework of classical mechanics and electrodynamics and set science a fresh task: that of finding a new conceptual basis for all physics. Despite remarkable partial gains, the problem is still far from a satisfactory solution.

In paying homage to this man the American National Academy of Sciences expresses its hope that free research, for the sake of pure knowledge, may remain unhampered and unimpaired.

42

PAUL LANGEVIN IN
MEMORIAM

THE NEWS OF PAUL LANGEVIN'S DEATH dealt me a greater
blow than most of the events of these fateful years, so fraught
with disappointment. Why should this have been the case?
Was his not a long life, crowded with fruitful creative work—
the life of a man in harmony with himself? Was he not widely
revered for his keen insight into intellectual problems, universally beloved for his devotion to every good cause, for his
understanding kindness toward all creatures? Is there not a
certain satisfaction in the fact that natural limits are set to
the life of the individual, so that at its conclusion it may
appear as a work of art?

The sorrow brought on by Paul Langevin's passing has
been so particularly poignant because it has given me a feeling of being left utterly alone and desolate. There are so very
few in any one generation, in whom clear insight into the
nature of things is joined with an intense feeling for the
challenge of true humanity and the capacity for militant
action. When such a man departs, he leaves a gap that seems
unbearable to his survivors.

Langevin was endowed with unusual clarity and agility in
scientific thought, together with a sure intuitive vision for
the essential points. It was as a result of these qualities that
his lectures exerted a crucial influence on more than one generation of French theoretical physicists. But Langevin also
knew a great deal about experimental technique and his criticism and constructive suggestions always carried a fruitful

effect. His own original researches, moreover, decisively influenced the development of science, mainly in the fields of magnetism and ion theory. Yet the burden of responsibility which he was always ready to assume circumscribed his own research work, so that the fruits of his labors emerge in the publications of other scientists to a greater extent than in his own.

It appears to me as a foregone conclusion that he would have developed the Special Theory of Relativity, had that not been done elsewhere; for he had clearly perceived its essential aspects. Another admirable thing is that he fully appreciated the significance of De Broglie's ideas—from which Schrödinger subsequently developed the methods of wave mechanics—even before these ideas had become consolidated into a consistent theory. I vividly recall the pleasure and warmth with which he told me about it—and I also remember that I followed his remarks but hesitantly and doubtfully.

All his life Langevin suffered from an awareness of the deficiencies and inequities of our social and economic institutions. Yet he believed firmly in the power of reason and knowledge. So pure in heart was he that he was convinced all men should be ready for complete personal renunciation, once they had seen the light of reason and justice. Reason was his creed—a creed that was to bring not only light but also salvation. His desire to promote the happier life for all men was perhaps even stronger than his craving for pure intellectual enlightenment. Thus it was that he devoted much of his time and vital energy to political enlightenment. No one who appealed to his social conscience ever went away from him empty-handed. Thus it was too that the very moral grandeur of his personality earned him the bitter enmity of many of the more humdrum intellectuals. He in turn understood them all and in his kindness never harbored resentment against anyone.

I can only give expression to my gratitude for having personally known this man of purity and illumination.

43

WALTHER NERNST IN MEMORIAM

WALTHER NERNST, who died recently, was one of the most characteristic and most interesting scholars with whom I have been closely connected during my life. He did not miss any of the conferences on physics in Berlin, and his brief remarks gave evidence of a truly amazing scientific instinct combined both with a sovereign knowledge of an enormous volume of factual materials, which was always at his command, and with a rare mastery of the experimental methods and tricks in which he excelled. Although sometimes good-naturedly smiling at his childlike vanity and self-complacency, we all had for him not only a sincere admiration, but also a personal affection. So long as his egocentric weakness did not enter the picture, he exhibited an objectivity very rarely found, an infallible sense for the essential, and a genuine passion for knowledge of the deep interrelations of nature. But for such a passion his singularly creative productivity and his important influence on the scientific life of the first third of this century would not have been possible.

He ascended from Arrhenius, Ostwald and Van't Hoff, as the last of a dynasty which based their investigations on thermodynamics, osmotic pressure and ionic theory. Up to 1905 his work was essentially restricted to that range of ideas. His theoretical equipment was somewhat elementary, but he mastered it with a rare ingenuity. I refer, for instance, to the theory of electromotive powers in solutions of locally variable concentration, the theory of diminution of the solubility by adding a dissolved substance. During this period he invented the witty null-method of determining the dielectric constant of electrically conducting bodies by means of Wheatstone's Bridge (alternating current, telephone as indicator, compensating capacity in comparison-bridge branches).

This first productive period is largely concerned with improving the methodology and completing the exploration of a field the principles of which had already been known before Nernst. This work led him gradually to a general problem which is characterized by the question: Is it possible to compute from the known energy of the conditions of a system, the useful work which is to be gained by its transition from one state into another? Nernst realized that a theoretical determination of the transition work A from the energy-difference U by means of equations of thermodynamics alone is not possible. There could be inferred from thermodynamics that, at absolute zero, the temperature of the quantities A and U must be equal. But one could not derive A from U for any arbitrary temperatures, even if the energy-values or differences in U were known for all conditions. This computation was not possible until there was introduced, with regard to the reaction of these quantities under low temperatures, an assumption which appeared obvious because of its simplicity. This assumption is simply that A becomes temperature-independent under low temperatures. The introduction of this assumption as a hypothesis (third main principle of the theory of heat) is Nernst's greatest contribution to theoretical science. Planck found later a solution which is theoretically more satisfactory; namely, the entropy disappears at absolute zero temperature.

From the standpoint of the older ideas on heat, this third main principle required very strange reactions of bodies under low temperatures. To pass upon the correctness of this principle, the methods of calorimetry under low temperatures had to be greatly improved. The calorimetry of high temperatures also owes to Nernst considerable progress. Through all these investigations, as well as through many stimulating suggestions with which his untiring inventive genius supplied experimenters in his field, he promoted the research work of his generation most effectively. The beginnings of the quantum theory were assisted by the important results of those caloric investigations, and this especially before Bohr's theory of the atom made spectroscopy the most important experimental field. Nernst's standard work, "Theoretical Chemistry," offers, not only to the student but also to the scholar, an abundance of stimulating ideas; it is theoretically elementary, but clever, vivid and full of intimations of manifold interrelations. It truly reflects his intellectual characteristics.

Nernst was not a one-sided scholar. His sound common sense engaged successfully in all fields of practical life, and every conversation with him brought something interesting to light. What distinguished him from almost all his fellow-countrymen was his remarkable freedom from prejudices. He was neither a nationalist nor a militarist. He judged things and people almost exclusively by their direct success, not by a social or ethical ideal. This was a consequence of his freedom from prejudices. At the same time he was interested in literature and had such a sense of humor as is very seldom found with men who carry so heavy a load of work. He was an original personality; I have never met any one who resembled him in any essential way.

44

PAUL EHRENFEST IN
MEMORIAM

IT HAPPENS SO OFTEN NOWADAYS that men of high qualities depart this life of their own free will that we no longer feel such a conclusion to be unusual. Yet the decision to take leave generally stems from an incapacity—or at least an unwillingness—to resign oneself to new and more difficult *outward* conditions of life. To refuse to live out one's natural life because of *inner* conflicts that are felt to be intolerable—that is even today in persons of sound mind a rare occurrence, possible only in the case of the noblest and morally most exalted personalities. It is to such a tragic inner conflict that our friend Paul Ehrenfest has succumbed. Those who knew him well, as was vouchsafed to me, know that this unblemished personality in the main fell victim to a conflict of conscience that in some form or other is spared no university teacher who has passed, say, his fiftieth year.

I came to know him twenty-two years ago. He visited me in Prague, coming straight from Russia where he as a Jew was debarred from teaching at institutions of higher learning. He was looking for a sphere of work in central or western Europe. But we talked little of that, for it was the state of science at the time that took up almost all of our interest. Both of us realized that classical mechanics and the theory of the electric field had failed in the face of the phenomena of heat radiation and molecular processes (the statistical theory of heat), but there seemed to be no feasible way out of this dilemma. The logical gap in Planck's Theory of Radiation—which we both, nevertheless, greatly admired—was apparent to us. We also discussed the Theory of Relativity, to which he responded with a certain skepticism but with the critical judgment peculiar to him. Within a few hours we were true friends—as though our dreams and aspirations were meant for each other. We remained joined in close friendship until he departed this life.

His stature lay in his unusually well developed faculty to grasp the essence of a theoretical notion, to strip a theory of its mathematical accouterments until the simple basic idea emerged with clarity. This capacity made him a peerless teacher. It was on its account that he was invited to scientific congresses; for he always brought clarity and acuteness into any discussion. He fought against fuzziness and circumlocution, when necessary employing his sharp wit and even downright discourtesy. Some of his utterances could have been interpreted almost as arrogant, yet his tragedy lay precisely in an almost morbid lack of self-confidence. He suffered incessantly from the fact that his critical faculties transcended his constructive capacities. In a manner of speaking, his critical sense robbed him of his love for the offspring of his own mind even before they were born.

Shortly after our first encounter there occurred the great turning-point in Ehrenfest's outward career. Our revered master, Lorentz, anxious to retire from regular university teaching, had recognized Ehrenfest for the inspired teacher that he was and recommended him as his successor. A marvelous sphere of activity opened up to the still youthful man. He was not merely the best teacher in our profession whom I have ever known; he was also passionately preoccupied with the development and destiny of men, especially his students. To understand others, to gain their friendship and trust, to aid anyone embroiled in outer or inner struggles, to encourage youthful talent—all this was his real element, almost more than immersion in scientific problems. His students and colleagues in Leyden loved and esteemed him. They knew his utter devotion, his nature so wholly attuned to service and help. Should he not have been a happy man?

In truth he felt unhappier than anyone else who was close to me. The reason was that he did not feel equal to the lofty task that confronted him. Of what use was it that everyone held him in esteem? His sense of inadequacy, objectively unjustified, plagued him incessantly, often robbing him of the peace of mind necessary for tranquil research. So greatly did he suffer that he was compelled to seek solace in distraction. His frequent aimless travels, his preoccupation with the radio, and many other features of his restless life stemmed not from a need for composure and harmless hobbies but rather from a curious urge for escape caused by the psychic conflict at which I have hinted.

In the last few years this situation was aggravated by the strangely turbulent development which theoretical physics has recently undergone. To learn and to teach things that one cannot fully accept in one's heart is always a difficult matter, doubly difficult for a mind of fanatical honesty, a mind to which clarity means everything. Added to this was the increasing difficulty of adaptation to new thoughts which always confronts the man past fifty. I do not know how many readers of these lines will be capable of fully grasping that tragedy. Yet it was this that primarily occasioned his escape from life.

It seems to me that the tendency toward exaggerated self-criticism is associated with experiences in boyhood. Humiliation and mental oppression by ignorant and selfish teachers wreak havoc in the youthful mind that can never be undone and often exert a baleful influence in later life. The intensity of such experiences in Ehrenfest's case may be judged from the fact that he refused to entrust his dearly beloved children to any school.

His relations with his friends played a far greater role in Ehrenfest's life than is the case with most men. He was virtually dominated by his sympathies and also by antipathies based on moral judgments. The strongest relationship in his life was that to his wife and fellow worker, an unusually strong and steadfast personality and his intellectual equal. Perhaps her mind was not quite as agile, versatile, and sensitive as his own, but her poise, her independence of others, her steadfastness in the face of all hardships, her integrity in thought, feeling, and action—all these were a blessing to him and he repaid her with a veneration and love such as I have not often witnessed in my life. A fateful partial estrangement from her was a frightful experience for him, one with which his already wounded soul was unable to cope.

We whose lives have been enriched by the power and integrity of his spirit, the kindness and warmth of his rich mind, and not least his irrepressible humor and trenchant wit—we know how much his departure has impoverished us. He will live on in his students and in all whose aspirations were guided by his personality.

45

MAHATMA GANDHI

A LEADER OF HIS PEOPLE, unsupported by any outward authority: a politician whose success rests not upon craft nor the mastery of technical devices, but simply on the convincing power of his personality; a victorious fighter who has always scorned the use of force; a man of wisdom and humility, armed with resolve and inflexible consistency, who has devoted all his strength to the uplifting of his people and the betterment of their lot; a man who has confronted the brutality of Europe with the dignity of the simple human being, and thus at all times risen superior.

Generations to come, it may be, will scarce believe that such a one as this ever in flesh and blood walked upon this earth.

46

CARL VON OSSIETZKY

ONLY ONE WHO SPENT the years following the First World War in Germany can fully understand how hard a battle it was that a man like Ossietzky had to fight. He knew that the tradition of his countrymen, bent on violence and war, had not lost its power. He knew how difficult, thankless and dangerous a task it was, to preach sanity and justice to his countrymen who had been hardened by a rough fate and the demoralizing influence of a long war. In their blindness they repaid him in hatred, persecution and slow destruction; to heed him and to act accordingly would have meant their salvation and would have been a true relief for the whole world.

It will be to the eternal fame of the Nobel Foundation that it bestowed its high honor on this humble martyr, and that it is resolved to keep alive his memory and the memory of his work. It is also wholesome for mankind today, since the fatal illusion against which he fought has not been removed by the outcome of the last war. The abstention from the solution of human problems by brute force—is the task today as it was then.

My People

47

WHY DO THEY HATE THE JEWS?

I SHOULD LIKE TO BEGIN by telling you an ancient fable, with a few minor changes—a fable that will serve to throw into bold relief the mainsprings of political anti-Semitism:

The shepherd boy said to the horse: "You are the noblest beast that treads the earth. You deserve to live in untroubled bliss; and indeed your happiness would be complete were it not for the treacherous stag. But he practiced from youth to excel you in fleetness of foot. His faster pace allows him to reach the water holes before you do. He and his tribe drink up the water far and wide, while you and your foal are left to thirst. Stay with me! My wisdom and guidance shall deliver you and your kind from a dismal and ignominious state."

Blinded by envy and hatred of the stag, the horse agreed. He yielded to the shepherd lad's bridle. He lost his freedom and became the shepherd's slave.

The horse in this fable represents a people, and the shepherd lad a class or clique aspiring to absolute rule over the people; the stag, on the other hand, represents the Jews.

I can hear you say: "A most unlikely tale! No creature would be as foolish as the horse in your fable." But let us give it a little more thought. The horse had been suffering the pangs of thirst, and his vanity was often pricked when he saw the nimble stag outrunning him. You, who have known no such pain and vexation, may find it difficult to understand that hatred and blindness should have driven the horse to act

with such ill-advised, gullible haste. The horse, however, fell
an easy victim to temptation because his earlier tribulations
had prepared him for such a blunder. For there is much truth
in the saying that it is easy to give just and wise counsel—to
others!—but hard to act justly and wisely for oneself. I say to
you with full conviction: We all have often played the tragic
role of the horse and we are in constant danger of yielding to
temptation again.

The situation illustrated in this fable happens again and
again in the life of individuals and nations. In brief, we may
call it the process by which dislike and hatred of a given person or group are diverted to another person or group incapable of effective defense. But why did the role of the stag
in the fable so often fall to the Jews? Why did the Jews so
often happen to draw the hatred of the masses? Primarily because there are Jews among almost all nations and because
they are everywhere too thinly scattered to defend themselves against violent attack.

A few examples from the recent past will prove the point:
Toward the end of the nineteenth century the Russian people
were chafing under the tyranny of their government. Stupid
blunders in foreign policy further strained their temper until
it reached the breaking point. In this extremity the rulers of
Russia sought to divert unrest by inciting the masses to hatred
and violence toward the Jews. These tactics were repeated
after the Russian government had drowned the dangerous
revolution of 1905 in blood—and this maneuver may well have
helped to keep the hated regime in power until near the end
of the World War.

When the Germans had lost the World War hatched by
their ruling class, immediate attempts were made to blame
the Jews, first for instigating the war and then for losing it.
In the course of time, success attended these efforts. The
hatred engendered against the Jews not only protected the
privileged classes, but enabled a small, unscrupulous and in-

solent group to place the German people in a state of complete bondage.

The crimes with which the Jews have been charged in the course of history—crimes which were to justify the atrocities perpetrated against them—have changed in rapid succession. They were supposed to have poisoned wells. They were said to have murdered children for ritual purposes. They were falsely charged with a systematic attempt at the economic domination and exploitation of all mankind. Pseudo-scientific books were written to brand them an inferior, dangerous race. They were reputed to foment wars and revolutions for their own selfish purposes. They were presented at once as dangerous innovators and as enemies of true progress. They were charged with falsifying the culture of nations by penetrating the national life under the guise of becoming assimilated. In the same breath they were accused of being so stubbornly inflexible that it was impossible for them to fit into any society.

Almost beyond imagination were the charges brought against them, charges known to their instigators to be untrue all the while, but which time and again influenced the masses. In times of unrest and turmoil the masses are inclined to hatred and cruelty, whereas in times of peace these traits of human nature emerge but stealthily.

Up to this point I have spoken only of violence and oppression against the Jews—not of anti-Semitism itself as a psychological and social phenomenon existing even in times and circumstances when no special action against the Jews is under way. In this sense, one may speak of latent anti-Semitism. What is its basis? I believe that in a certain sense one may actually regard it as a normal manifestation in the life of a people.

The members of any group existing in a nation are more closely bound to one another than they are to the remaining population. Hence a nation will never be free of friction while such groups continue to be distinguishable. In my belief, uniformity in a population would not be desirable, even if it were attainable. Common convictions and aims, similar interests, will in every society produce groups that, in a certain sense, act as units. There will always be friction between such groups—the same sort of aversion and rivalry that exists between individuals.

The need for such groupings is perhaps most easily seen in the field of politics, in the formation of political parties. Without parties the political interests of the citizens of any state are bound to languish. There would be no forum for the free exchange of opinions. The individual would be isolated and unable to assert his convictions. Political convictions, moreover, ripen and grow only through mutual stimulation and criticism offered by individuals of similar disposition and purpose; and politics is no different from any other field of our cultural existence. Thus it is recognized, for example, that in times of intense religious fervor different sects are likely to spring up whose rivalry stimulates religious life in general. It is well known, on the other hand, that centralization—that is, elimination of independent groups—leads to one-sidedness and barrenness in science and art because such centralization checks and even suppresses any rivalry of opinions and research trends.

Just What Is a Jew?

The formation of groups has an invigorating effect in all spheres of human striving, perhaps mostly due to the struggle between the convictions and aims represented by the different groups. The Jews too form such a group with a definite character of its own, and anti-Semitism is nothing but the antagonistic attitude produced in the non-Jews by the Jewish group. This is a normal social reaction. But for the political abuse resulting from it, it might never have been designated by a special name.

What are the characteristics of the Jewish group? What, in

the first place, is a Jew? There are no quick answers to this question. The most obvious answer would be the following: A Jew is a person professing the Jewish faith. The superficial character of this answer is easily recognized by means of a simple parallel. Let us ask the question: What is a snail? An answer similar in kind to the one given above might be: A snail is an animal inhabiting a snail shell. This answer is not altogether incorrect; nor, to be sure, is it exhaustive; for the snail shell happens to be but one of the material products of the snail. Similarly, the Jewish faith is but one of the characteristic products of the Jewish community. It is, furthermore, known that a snail can shed its shell without thereby ceasing to be a snail. The Jew who abandons his faith (in the formal sense of the word) is in a similar position. He remains a Jew.

Difficulties of this kind appear whenever one seeks to explain the essential character of a group.

The bond that has united the Jews for thousands of years and that unites them today is, above all, the democratic ideal of social justice, coupled with the ideal of mutual aid and tolerance among all men. Even the most ancient religious scriptures of the Jews are steeped in these social ideals, which have powerfully affected Christianity and Mohammedanism and have had a benign influence upon the social structure of a great part of mankind. The introduction of a weekly day of rest should be remembered here—a profound blessing to all mankind. Personalities such as Moses, Spinoza and Karl Marx, dissimilar as they may be, all lived and sacrificed themselves for the ideal of social justice; and it was the tradition of their forefathers that led them on this thorny path. The unique accomplishments of the Jews in the field of philanthropy spring from the same source.

The second characteristic trait of Jewish tradition is the high regard in which it holds every form of intellectual aspiration and spiritual effort. I am convinced that this great respect for intellectual striving is solely responsible for the contributions that the Jews have made toward the progress of knowledge, in the broadest sense of the term. In view of their relatively small number and the considerable external obstacles constantly placed in their way on all sides, the extent of those contributions deserves the admiration of all sincere men. I am convinced that this is not due to any special wealth of endowment, but to the fact that the esteem in which intellectual accomplishment is held among the Jews creates an atmosphere particularly favorable to the development of any talents that may exist. At the same time a strong critical spirit prevents blind obeisance to any mortal authority.

I have confined myself here to these two traditional traits, which seem to me the most basic. These standards and ideals find expression in small things as in large. They are transmitted from parents to children; they color conversation and judgment among friends; they fill the religious scriptures; and they give to the community life of the group its characteristic stamp. It is in these distinctive ideals that I see the essence of Jewish nature. That these ideals are but imperfectly realized in the group—in its actual everyday life—is only natural. However, if one seeks to give brief expression to the essential character of a group, the approach must always be by the way of the ideal.

WHERE OPPRESSION IS A STIMULUS

In the foregoing I have conceived of Judaism as a community of tradition. Both friend and foe, on the other hand, have often asserted that the Jews represent a race; that their characteristic behavior is the result of innate qualities transmitted by *heredity* from one generation to the next. This opinion gains weight from the fact that the Jews for thousands of years have predominantly married within their own group. Such a custom may indeed *preserve* a homogeneous race—if it existed originally; it cannot *produce* uniformity of the race—if there was originally a racial intermixture. The Jews, however, are beyond doubt a mixed race, just as are all other groups of our civilization. Sincere anthropologists are agreed on this point; assertions to the contrary all belong to the field of political propaganda and must be rated accordingly.

Perhaps even more than on its own tradition, the Jewish group has thrived on oppression and on the antagonism it has forever met in the world. Here undoubtedly lies one of the main reasons for its continued existence through so many thousands of years.

The Jewish group, which we have briefly characterized in the foregoing, embraces about sixteen million people—less than one per cent of mankind, or about half as many as the population of present-day Poland. Their significance as a political factor is negligible. They are scattered over almost the entire earth and are in no way organized as a whole—which means that they are incapable of concerted action of any kind.

Were anyone to form a picture of the Jews solely from the utterances of their enemies, he would have to reach the conclusion that they represent a world power. At first sight that seems downright absurd; and yet, in my view, there is a certain meaning behind it. The Jews as a group may be powerless, but the sum of the achievements of their individual members is everywhere considerable and telling, even though these achievements were made in the face of obstacles. The forces dormant in the individual are mobilized, and the individual himself is stimulated to self-sacrificing effort, by the spirit that is alive in the group.

Hence the hatred of the Jews by those who have reason to shun popular enlightenment. More than anything else in the world, they fear the influence of men of intellectual independence. I see in this the essential cause for the savage hatred of Jews raging in present-day Germany. To the Nazi group the Jews are not merely a means for turning the resentment of the people away from themselves, the oppressors; they see the Jews as a nonassimilable element that cannot be driven into uncritical acceptance of dogma, and that, therefore—as long as it exists at all—threatens their authority because of its insistence on popular enlightenment of the masses.

Proof that this conception goes to the heart of the matter is convincingly furnished by the solemn ceremony of the burning of the books staged by the Nazi regime shortly after its seizure of power. This act, senseless from a political point of view, can only be understood as a spontaneous emotional outburst. For that reason it seems to me more revealing than many acts of greater purpose and practical importance.

In the field of politics and social science there has grown up a justified distrust of generalizations pushed too far. When thought is too greatly dominated by such generalizations, misinterpretations of specific sequences of cause and effect readily occur, doing injustice to the actual multiplicity of events. Abandonment of generalization, on the other hand, means to relinquish understanding altogether. For that reason I believe one may and must risk generalization, as long as one remains aware of its uncertainty. It is in this spirit that I wish to present in all modesty my conception of anti-Semitism, considered from a general point of view.

In political life I see two opposed tendencies at work, locked in constant struggle with each other. The first, optimistic, trend proceeds from the belief that the free unfolding of the productive forces of individuals and groups essentially leads to a satisfactory state of society. It recognizes the need for a central power, placed above groups and individuals, but concedes to such power only organizational and regulatory functions. The second, pessimistic, trend assumes that free interplay of individuals and groups leads to the destruction of society; it thus seeks to base society exclusively upon authority, blind obedience and coercion. Actually this trend is pessimistic only to a limited extent: for it is optimistic in regard to those who are, and desire to be, the bearers of power and authority. The adherents of this second trend are the enemies of the free groups and of education for independent thought. They are, moreover, the carriers of political anti-Semitism.

Here in America all pay lip service to the first, optimistic, tendency. Nevertheless, the second group is strongly represented. It appears on the scene everywhere, though for the most part it hides its true nature. Its aim is political and spiritual dominion over the people by a minority, by the circuitous route of control over the means of production. Its proponents have already tried to utilize the weapon of anti-Semitism as well as of hostility to various other groups. They will repeat the attempt in times to come. So far all such tendencies have failed because of the people's sound political instinct.

And so it will remain in the future, if we cling to the rule: Beware of flatterers, especially when they come preaching hatred.

48

THE DISPERSAL OF EUROPEAN
JEWRY

THE HISTORY OF THE PERSECUTIONS which the Jewish people
have had to suffer is almost inconceivably long. Yet the war
that is being waged against us in Central Europe today [1] falls
into a special category of its own. In the past we were persecuted *despite* the fact that we were the people of the Bible;
today, however, it is just *because* we are the people of the
Book that we are persecuted. The aim is to exterminate not
only ourselves but to destroy, together with us, that spirit
expressed in the Bible and in Christianity which made possible the rise of civilization in Central and Northern Europe.
If this aim is achieved Europe will become a barren waste.
For human community life cannot long endure on a basis of
crude force, brutality, terror, and hate.

Only understanding for our neighbors, justice in our deal-
ings, and willingness to help our fellow men can give human
society permanence and assure security for the individual.
Neither intelligence nor inventions nor institutions can serve
as substitutes for these most vital parts of education.

Many Jewish communities have been uprooted in the wake
of the present upheaval in Europe. Hundreds of thousands of
men, women, and children have been driven from their homes
and made to wander in despair over the highways of the
world. The tragedy of the Jewish people today is a tragedy

[1] Spoken in 1939.

which reflects a challenge to the fundamental structure of modern civilization.

One of the most tragic aspects of the oppression of Jews and other groups has been the creation of a refugee class. Many distinguished men in science, art, and literature have been driven from the lands which they enriched with their talents. In a period of economic decline these exiles have within them the possibilities for reviving economic and cultural effort; many of these refugees are highly skilled experts in industry and science. They have a valuable contribution to make to the progress of the world. They are in a position to repay hospitality with new economic development and the opening up of new opportunities of employment for native populations. I am told that in England the admission of refugees was directly responsible for giving jobs to 15,000 unemployed.

As one of the former citizens of Germany who have been fortunate enough to leave that country, I know I can speak for my fellow refugees, both here and in other countries, when I give thanks to the democracies of the world for the splendid manner in which they have received us. We, all of us, owe a debt of gratitude to our new countries, and each and every one of us is doing the utmost to show our gratitude by the quality of our contributions to the economic, social, and cultural work of the countries in which we reside.

It is, however, a source of gravest concern that the ranks of the refugees are being constantly increased. The developments of the past week have added several hundred thousand potential refugees from Czechoslovakia. Again we are confronted with a major tragedy for a Jewish community which had a noble tradition of democracy and communal service.

The power of resistance which has enabled the Jewish people to survive for thousands of years is a direct outgrowth of Jewish adherence to the Biblical doctrines on the relationships among men. In these years of affliction our readiness to help one another is being put to an especially severe test. Each of us must personally face this test, that we may stand it as well as our fathers did before us. We have no other means of self-defense than our solidarity and our knowledge that the cause for which we are suffering is a momentous and sacred cause.

49

LET'S NOT FORGET

IF WE AS JEWS CAN LEARN anything from these politically sad times, it is the fact that destiny has bound us together, a fact which in times of quiet and security, we often so easily and gladly forget. We are accustomed to lay too much emphasis on the differences that divide the Jews of different lands and different religious views. And we forget often that it is the concern of every Jew, when anywhere the Jew is hated and treated unjustly, when politicians with flexible consciences set into motion against us the old prejudices, originally religious, in order to concoct political schemes at our expense. It concerns every one of us because such diseases and psychotic disturbances of the folk-soul are not estopped by oceans and national borders, but act precisely like economic crises and epidemics.

50

UNPUBLISHED PREFACE
TO A BLACKBOOK

THIS BOOK IS A COLLECTION of documentary material on the systematic work of destruction by which the German Government murdered a great proportion of the Jewish people. Responsibility for the truth of the facts set forth is borne by the Jewish organizations that have joined to create the present work and present it to the public.

The purpose of this publication is manifest. It is to convince the reader that an international organization for safeguarding the sanctity of life can effectively fulfill its purpose only if it does not limit itself to protecting countries against military attack but also extends its protection to national minorities within the individual countries. For in the last reckoning it is the individual who must be protected against annihilation and inhuman treatment.

It is true that this goal can be attained only if the principle of non-intervention, which has played such a fateful role in the last decades, is cast overboard. Yet today no one can doubt the need for this far-reaching step any longer. For even those who envision only the attainment of protection against military attack from the outside must today realize that the disasters of war are preceded by certain internal developments in the various countries, and not merely by military and armaments preparations.

Not until the creation and maintenance of decent conditions of life for all men are recognized and accepted as a common obligation of all men and all countries—not until then shall we, with a certain degree of justification, be able to speak of mankind as civilized.

Percentagewise the Jewish people have lost more than any other people affected by the disasters of recent years. If a truly just settlement is to be striven for, the Jewish people must be given special consideration in the organization of the peace. The fact that the Jews, in the formal political sense, cannot be regarded as a nation, insofar as they possess no country and no government, ought to be no impediment. For the Jews have been treated as a uniform group, as though they were a nation. Their status as a uniform political group is proved to be a fact by the behavior of their enemies. Hence in striving toward a stabilization of the international situation they should be considered as though they were a nation in the customary sense of the word.

Another factor must be emphasized in this connection. In parts of Europe Jewish life will probably be impossible for years to come. In decades of hard work and voluntary financial aid the Jews have restored the soil of Palestine to fertility. All these sacrifices were made because of trust in the officially sanctioned promise given by the governments in question after the last war, namely that the Jewish people were to be given a secure home in their ancient Palestinian country. To put it mildly, the fulfillment of this promise has been but hesitant and partial. Now that the Jews—especially the Jews in Palestine—have in this war too rendered a valuable contribution, the promise must be forcibly called to mind. The demand must be put forward that Palestine, within the limits of its economic capacity, be thrown open to Jewish immigration. If supranational institutions are to win that confidence that must form the most important buttress for their endurance, then it must be shown above all that those who, trusting to these institutions, have made the heaviest sacrifices are not defrauded.

51

THE GOAL OF
HUMAN EXISTENCE

Our age is proud of the progress it has made in man's intellectual development. The search and striving for truth and knowledge is one of the highest of man's qualities—though often the pride is most loudly voiced by those who strive the least. And certainly we should take care not to make the intellect our god; it has, of course, powerful muscles, but no personality. It cannot lead, it can only serve; and it is not fastidious in its choice of a leader. This characteristic is reflected in the qualities of its priests, the intellectuals. The intellect has a sharp eye for methods and tools, but is blind to ends and values. So it is no wonder that this fatal blindness is handed on from old to young and today involves a whole generation.

Our Jewish forbears, the prophets and the old Chinese sages understood and proclaimed that the most important factor in giving shape to our human existence is the setting up and establishment of a goal; the goal being a community of free and happy human beings who by constant inward endeavor strive to liberate themselves from the inheritance of anti-social and destructive instincts. In this effort the intellect can be the most powerful aid. The fruits of intellectual effort, together with the striving itself, in cooperation with the creative activity of the artist, lend content and meaning to life.

But today the rude passions of man reign in our world,

more unrestrained than ever before. Our Jewish people, a small minority everywhere, with no means of defending themselves by force, are exposed to the cruelest suffering, even to complete annihilation, to a far greater degree than any other people in the world. The hatred raging against us is grounded in the fact that we have upheld the ideal of harmonious partnership and given it expression in word and deed among the best of our people.

52

OUR DEBT TO ZIONISM

Rarely since the conquest of Jerusalem by Titus has the Jewish community experienced a period of greater oppression than prevails at the present time. In some respects, indeed, our own time is even more troubled, for man's possibilities of emigration are more limited today than they were then.

Yet we shall survive this period too, no matter how much sorrow, no matter how heavy a loss in life it may bring. A community like ours, which is a community purely by reason of tradition, can only be strengthened by pressure from without. For today every Jew feels that to be a Jew means to bear a serious responsibility not only to his own community, but also toward humanity. To be a Jew, after all, means first of all, to acknowledge and follow in practice those fundamentals in humaneness laid down in the Bible—fundamentals without which no sound and happy community of men can exist.

We meet today because of our concern for the development of Palestine. In this hour one thing, above all, must be emphasized: Judaism owes a great debt of gratitude to Zionism. The Zionist movement has revived among Jews the sense of community. It has performed productive work surpassing all the expectations any one could entertain. This productive work in Palestine, to which self-sacrificing Jews throughout the world have contributed, has saved a large number of our brethren from direst need. In particular, it has been possible to lead a not inconsiderable part of our youth toward a life of joyous and creative work.

Now the fateful disease of our time—exaggerated nationalism, borne up by blind hatred—has brought our work in Palestine to a most difficult stage. Fields cultivated by day must have armed protection at night against fanatical Arab outlaws. All economic life suffers from insecurity. The spirit of enterprise languishes and a certain measure of unemployment (modest when measured by American standards) has made its appearance.

The solidarity and confidence with which our brethren in Palestine face these difficulties deserve our admiration. Voluntary contributions by those still employed keep the unemployed above water. Spirits remain high, in the conviction that reason and calm will ultimately reassert themselves. Everyone knows that the riots are artificially fomented by those directly interested in embarrassing not only ourselves but especially England. Everyone knows that banditry would cease if foreign subsidies were withdrawn.

Our brethren in other countries, however, are in no way behind those in Palestine. They, too, will not lose heart but will resolutely and firmly stand behind the common work. This goes without saying.

Just one more personal word on the question of partition. I should much rather see reasonable agreement with the Arabs on the basis of living together in peace than the creation of a Jewish state. Apart from practical consideration, my awareness of the essential nature of Judaism resists the idea of a Jewish state with borders, an army, and a measure of temporal power no matter how modest. I am afraid of the inner damage Judaism will sustain—especially from the development of a narrow nationalism within our own ranks, against which we have already had to fight strongly, even without a Jewish state. We are no longer the Jews of the Maccabee period. A return to a nation in the political sense of the word would be equivalent to turning away from the spiritualization of our community which we owe to the genius of our prophets. If external necessity should after all compel us to assume this burden, let us bear it with tact and patience.

One more word on the present psychological attitude of the world at large, upon which our Jewish destiny also depends. Anti-Semitism has always been the cheapest means employed by selfish minorities for deceiving the people. A tyranny based on such deception and maintained by terror must inevitably perish from the poison it generates within itself. For the pressure of accumulated injustice strengthens those moral forces in man which lead to a liberation and purification of public life. May our community through its suffering and its work contribute toward the release of those liberating forces.

53

TO THE HEROES OF THE BATTLE OF THE WARSAW GHETTO

THEY FOUGHT AND DIED as members of the Jewish nation, in the struggle against organized bands of German murderers. To us these sacrifices are a strengthening of the bond between us, the Jews of all the countries. We strive to be one in suffering and in the effort to achieve a better human society, that society which our prophets have so clearly and forcibly set before us as a goal.

The Germans as an entire people are responsible for these mass murders and must be punished as a people if there is justice in the world and if the consciousness of collective responsibility in the nations is not to perish from the earth entirely. Behind the Nazi party stands the German people, who elected Hitler after he had in his book and in his speeches made his shameful intentions clear beyond the possibility of misunderstanding. The Germans are the only people who have not made any serious attempt of counter-action leading to the protection of the innocently persecuted. When they are entirely defeated and begin to lament over their fate, we must not let ourselves be deceived again, but keep in mind that they deliberately used the humanity of others to make preparation for their last and most grievous crime against humanity.

54

BEFORE THE MONUMENT TO THE MARTYRED JEWS OF THE WARSAW GHETTO

THE MONUMENT BEFORE WHICH you have gathered today was built to stand as a concrete symbol of our grief over the irreparable loss our martyred Jewish nation has suffered. It shall also serve as a reminder for us who have survived to remain loyal to our people and to the moral principles cherished by our fathers. Only through such loyalty may we hope to survive this age of moral decay.

The more cruel the wrong that men commit against an individual or a people, the deeper their hatred and contempt for their victim. Conceit and false pride on the part of a nation prevent the rise of remorse for its crime. Those who have had no part in the crime, however, have no sympathy for the sufferings of the innocent victims of persecution and no awareness of human solidarity. That is why the remnants of European Jewry are languishing in concentration camps and the sparsely populated lands of this earth close their gates against them. Even our right, so solemnly pledged, to a national homeland in Palestine is being betrayed. In this era of moral degradation in which we live the voice of justice no longer has any power over men.

Let us clearly recognize and never forget this: That mutual cooperation and the furtherance of living ties between the Jews of all lands is our sole physical and moral protection in the present situation. But for the future our hope lies in overcoming the general moral abasement which today gravely menaces the very existence of mankind. Let us labor with all our powers, however feeble, to the end that mankind recover from its present moral degradation and gain a new vitality and a new strength in its striving for right and justice as well as for a harmonious society.

55

THE CALLING OF THE JEWS

THIS IS A TIME when there seems to be a particular need for men of philosophical persuasion—that is to say, friends of wisdom and truth—to join together. For while it is true that our time has accumulated more knowledge than any earlier age, that love of truth and insight which lent wings to the spirit of the Renaissance has grown cold, giving way to sober specialization rooted in the material spheres of society rather than in the spiritual. But groups such as this one are devoted solely to spiritual aims.

In centuries past Judaism clung exclusively to its moral and spiritual tradition. Its teachers were its only leaders. But with adaptation to a larger social whole this spiritual orientation has receded into the background, though even today the Jewish people owe to it their apparently indestructible vigor. If we are to preserve that vigor for the benefit of mankind, we must hold to that spiritual orientation toward life.

The Dance about the Golden Calf was not merely a legendary episode in the history of our forefathers—an episode that seems to me in its simplicity more innocent than that total adherence to material and selfish goals threatening Judaism in our own days. At this time a union of those who rally to the spiritual heritage of our people has supreme justification. This is all the more true for a group that is free of all historical and national narrowness. We Jews should be and remain the carriers and patrons of spiritual values. But we should also always be aware of the fact that these spiritual values are and always have been the common goal of all mankind.

56

MOSES MAIMONIDES

THERE IS SOMETHING SUBLIME in the spectacle of men join-
ing together in a spirit of harmony to honor the memory of a
man whose life and work lie seven centuries in the past. This
feeling is accentuated all the more sharply at a time in which
passion and strife tend more than usually to obscure the influence of reasoned thought and balanced justice. In the bustle
of everyday life our view grows clouded with desire and
passion, and the voice of reason and justice is almost inaudible
in the hubbub of the struggle of all against all. But the fer-
ment of those times long past has long since been stilled, and
scarcely more is left of it than the memory of those few who
exerted a crucial and fruitful influence on their contemporaries and thus on later generations as well. Such a man was
Maimonides.

Once the Teutonic barbarians had destroyed Europe's
ancient culture, a new and finer cultural life slowly began to
flow from two sources that had somehow escaped being altogether buried in the general havoc—the Jewish Bible and
Greek philosophy and art. The union of these two sources, so
different one from the other, marks the beginning of our
present cultural epoch, and from that union, directly or indirectly, has sprung all that makes up the true values of our
present-day life.

Maimonides was one of those strong personalities who by
their writings and their human endeavors helped to bring
about that synthesis, thus paving the way for later developments. Just how this happened will be related to us tonight

by friends whose studies have come closer than I to the heart of Maimonides' lifework and the history of the European mind.

May this hour of grateful remembrance serve to strengthen within us the love and esteem in which we hold the treasures of our culture, gained in such bitter struggle. Our fight to preserve those treasures against the present powers of darkness and barbarism cannot then but carry the day.

57

STEPHEN WISE

Among all those whom I have personally met who have labored in the cause of justice and in the interest of the hard-pressed Jewish people, only a few were at all times selfless—but there was no one who gave his love and energy with such consuming devotion as Stephen Wise. All his life he has been a fighter for the cause of Zionism to which the memory of his ceaseless activities will be bound for ever. He has walked the thorny paths of the true prophet, at all times disdaining sordid compromise and never bending the knee to those in power. By relentlessly exposing the weakness and imperfections both in our own ranks and in the larger political arena of the non-Jewish world, he has made great and lasting contributions wherever he has gone. There are those who do not love him, but there is no one who has ever denied him recognition and respect, for everybody knows that behind the enormous labors of this man there has always been the passionate desire to make mankind better and happier.

58

TO THE UNIVERSITY OF JERUSALEM

THE LITTLE THAT I COULD DO, in a long life favored by external circumstances to deepen our physical knowledge, has brought me so much praise that for a long time I have felt rather more embarrassed than elated. But from you there comes a token of esteem that fills me with pure joy—joy about the great deeds that our Jewish people have accomplished within a few generations, under exceptionally difficult conditions, by itself alone, through boundless courage and immeasurable sacrifices. The University which twenty-seven years ago was nothing but a dream and a faint hope, this University is today a living thing, a home of free learning and teaching and happy brotherly work. There it is, on the soil that our people have liberated under great hardships; there it is, a spiritual center of a flourishing and buoyant community whose accomplishments have finally met with the universal recognition they deserved.

In this last period of the fulfilment of our dreams there was but one thing that weighed heavily upon me: the fact that we were compelled by the adversities of our situation to assert our rights through force of arms; it was the only way to avert complete annihilation. The wisdom and moderation the leaders of the new state have shown gives me confidence, however, that gradually relations will be established with the Arab people which are based on fruitful cooperation and mutual respect and trust. For this is the only means through which both peoples can attain true independence from the outside world.

59

THE AMERICAN COUNCIL
FOR JUDAISM

I AM VERY HAPPY INDEED to hear that the platform for which
the American Council for Judaism stands is meeting with
strong opposition. This organization appears to me to be
nothing more than a pitiable attempt to obtain favor and
toleration from our enemies by betraying true Jewish ideals
and by mimicking those who claim to stand for 100 per cent
Americanism. I believe this method to be both undignified
and ineffective. Our opponents are bound to view it with dis-
dain and even with contempt, and in my opinion justly. He
who is untrue to his own cause cannot command the respect
of others. Apart from these considerations, the movement in
question is a fairly exact copy of the Zentralverein Deutscher
Staatsbürger Jüdischen Glaubens ("Central Association of
German Citizens of Jewish Faith") of unhappy memory,
which in the days of our crucial need showed itself utterly
impotent and corroded the Jewish group by undermining that
inner certitude by which alone our Jewish people could have
overcome the trials of this difficult age.

60

THE JEWS OF ISRAEL

THERE IS NO PROBLEM of such overwhelming importance to us Jews as consolidating that which has been accomplished in Israel with amazing energy and an unequalled willingness for sacrifice. May the joy and admiration that fill us when we think of all that this small group of energetic and thoughtful people has achieved give us the strength to accept the great responsibility which the present situation has placed upon us.

When appraising the achievement, however, let us not lose sight of the cause to be served by this achievement: rescue of our endangered brethren, dispersed in many lands, by uniting them in Israel; creation of a community which conforms as closely as possible to the ethical ideals of our people as they have been formed in the course of a long history.

One of these ideals is peace, based on understanding and self-restraint, and not on violence. If we are imbued with this ideal, our joy becomes somewhat mingled with sadness, because our relations with the Arabs are far from this ideal at the present time. It may well be that we would have reached this ideal, had we been permitted to work out, undisturbed by others, our relations with our neighbors, for we *want* peace and we realize that our future development depends on peace.

It was much less our own fault or that of our neighbors than of the Mandatory Power, that we did not achieve an undivided Palestine in which Jews and Arabs would live as equals, free, in peace. If one nation dominates other nations, as was the case in the British Mandate over Palestine, she can hardly avoid following the notorious device of Divide et Impera. In plain language this means: create discord among the governed people so they will not unite in order to shake off the yoke imposed upon them. Well, the yoke has been removed, but the seed of dissension has borne fruit and may still do harm for some time to come—let us hope not for too long.

The Jews of Palestine did not fight for political independence for its own sake, but they fought to achieve free immigration for the Jews of many countries where their very existence was in danger; free immigration also for all those who were longing for a life among their own. It is no exaggeration to say that they fought to make possible a sacrifice perhaps unique in history.

I do not speak of the loss in lives and property fighting an opponent who was numerically far superior, nor do I mean the exhausting toil which is the pioneer's lot in a neglected arid country. I am thinking of the additional sacrifice that a population living under such conditions has to make in order to receive, in the course of eighteen months, an influx of immigrants which comprise more than one third of the total Jewish population of the country. In order to realize what this means you have only to visualize a comparable feat of the American Jews. Let us assume there were no laws limiting the immigration into the United States; imagine that the Jews of this country volunteered to receive more than one million Jews from other countries in the course of one year and a half, to take care of them, and to integrate them into the economy of this country. This would be a tremendous achievement, but still very far from the achievement of our brethren in Israel. For the United States is a big, fertile country, sparsely populated with a high living standard and a highly developed productive capacity, not to compare with small Jewish Palestine whose inhabitants, even without the additional burden of mass immigration, lead a hard and frugal life, still threatened by enemy attacks. Think of the privations and personal sacrifices which this voluntary act of brotherly love means for the Jews of Israel.

The economic means of the Jewish Community in Israel do not suffice to bring this tremendous enterprise to a successful end. For a hundred thousand out of more than three hundred thousand persons who immigrated to Israel since May 1948 no homes or work could be made available. They had to be concentrated in improvised camps under conditions which are a disgrace to all of us.

It must not happen that this magnificent work breaks down because the Jews of this country do not help sufficiently or quickly enough. Here, to my mind, is a precious gift with which all Jews have been presented: the opportunity to take an active part in this wonderful task.

ACKNOWLEDGMENTS

ARTICLE

2. From *Portraits and Self-Portraits* by George Schreiber; Houghton, Mifflin Co., Boston, 1936.
3. From *I Believe*, edited by Clifton Fadiman; copyright by Simon & Schuster, Inc., New York, 1939.
4. From a message on Founder's Day of the Young Men's Christian Association, October 11, 1937.
5. From the Time Capsule statement at the New York World's Fair, dated August 10, 1938.
6. From *Freedom, Its Meaning*, edited by Ruth Nanda Anshen; Harcourt Brace and Co., New York, 1940. (Translation prepared by James Gutmann, Professor of Philosophy, Columbia University.)
7. From an address at the commencement exercises of Swarthmore College, 1938.
8. I. From an address at Princeton Theological Seminary before the Northeastern Regional Conference of the American Association of Theological Schools, May 19, 1939.
   II. From *Science, Philosophy and Religion*, a Symposium; published by the Conference on Science, Philosophy and Religion in Their Relation to the Democratic Way of Life, Inc., New York, 1941.
9. From an address at the Seventy-second Convocation of the University of the State of New York in Chancellors Hall of the State Education Building at Albany, New York, in celebration of the Tercentenary of Higher Education in America, October 15, 1936. (Translation prepared by Lina Arronet.)
10. From *The American People's Encyclopedia*, copyright by the Spencer Press, Inc., Chicago, 1949.
11. From *Science Illustrated*: New York, April, 1946.
12. Originally published in the *London Times*, November 28, 1919.
13. From *The Journal of the Franklin Institute*, Vol. 221, No. 3; March, 1936.
14. From *Science*; Washington, D. C., May 24, 1940.
15. A broadcast recording for the Science Conference; London, September 28, 1941, and published in *Advancement of Science*; London, Vol. 2, no. 5.

16. From *Relativity—A Richer Truth* by Philipp Frank; published by the Beacon Press, Boston, 1950.

17. From *Technion Journal*; New York, 1946.

18. From *Monthly Review*; New York, May, 1949.

19. From *Pageant*; New York, January, 1946.

20. From *Science*; Washington, D. C., Winter issue, 1935–36. (Translation prepared by Heinz and Ruth Norden.)

21. From a broadcast over ABC to the Rally of Students for Federal World Government; Chicago, May 24, 1946.

22. From *One World or None*, edited by Katherine Way and Dexter Masters; Whittlesey House, New York, 1946.

23. From the address delivered at Carnegie Hall, New York, upon receiving the One World Award, April 27, 1948.

24. From a speech delivered in Albert Hall, London, October, 1933.

25. From the message to the Peace Congress of Intellectuals in Wroclav. (This message was never delivered, but was released to the press on August 29, 1948.)

26. From *United Nations World*; New York, October, 1947.

27. From Moscow *New Times*, November 26, 1947; and from *Bulletin of the Atomic Scientists*; Chicago, February, 1948.

28. From a statement to the National Wartime Conference, 1944.

29. From *The Nation*; New York, October 3, 1934.

30. Written in 1936 for a gathering of university teachers which never took place.

31. From *Atlantic Monthly*; Boston, November, 1945 and November, 1947. As told to Raymond Swing.

32. From an address at the Fifth Nobel Anniversary Dinner at the Hotel Astor, New York, December 10, 1945.

33. From an address at the second annual dinner given by the Foreign Press Association to the General Assembly and Security Council of the United Nations, at the Waldorf-Astoria Hotel, New York, November 11, 1947.

34. From an address delivered at the Conference of the Progressive Education Association, November 23, 1934.

35. From *Policy*; Chicago, November 27, 1934.

36. From *The American Scholar*; New York, Summer, 1947.

37. From an address to the students of the California Institute of Technology, January 22, 1933.

38. From *The Manchester Guardian*; Manchester, England, Christmas 1942

39. Preface to *Johannes Kepler's Letters* edited by Mrs. David Baumgardt .

40. Statement on the occasion of the Curie Memorial Celebration at the Roerich Museum, New York, November 23, 1935.

41. Statement read at the Memorial Services for Max Planck, April, 1948.

42. From *La Pensee*; Paris, February–March, 1947.

43. From *The Scientific Monthly*; Washington, D. C., Vol. LIV, February, 1942.

44. From *Almanak van het Leidsche Studentencorps* published by S. C. Doesburg Verlag, Leiden, Holland; 1934.

45. Statement on the occasion of Mahatma Gandhi's 75th birthday, 1944.

46. Statement read at the Nobel Foundation Dinner, December 10, 1946.

47. From *Collier's*; New York, November 26, 1938.

48. From an address over the Columbia Broadcasting System for the United Jewish Appeal, March 22, 1939.

49. Written in 1934.

50. Unpublished preface to a Black Book. Written in 1945.

51. From a broadcast for the United Jewish Appeal, April 11, 1943.

52. From an address delivered at the "Third Seder" celebration of the National Labor Committee for Palestine, at the Commodore Hotel, New York, April 17, 1938, and published in *New Palestine*; Washington, D. C., April 29, 1938.

53. From *Bulletin of the Society of Polish Jews*; New York, 1944.

54. From a statement read at the unveiling of the Memorial for the Battle of the Warsaw Ghetto; Warsaw, April 19, 1948.

55. From an address to the Jewish Academy of Sciences and Arts; March 22, 1936.

56. From a statement read at the Maimonides Jubilee Celebration, New York, April, 1935. (Translation prepared by Heinz and Ruth Norden.)

57. From *Opinion*; New York, March, 1949.

58. Statement to the Hebrew University in Jerusalem, Israel, on March 15, 1949.

59. From a letter to the Committee on Unity for Palestine, New York, 1945.

60. From a broadcast for the United Jewish Appeal, over the National Broadcasting Company, November 27. 1949.